A LAYMAN'S GUIDE TO THE UNIVERSE

THE EARTH,
LIFE ON EARTH,
AND THE MIGRATIONS OF HUMANKIND

by

Roger Hilsman

PublishingWorks
2003

Published by PublishingWorks
    4 Franklin Street
    Exeter, New Hampshire 03833
    800/333-9883
    www.publishingworks.com

Cover Design by: Traci Wasson

ISBN: 0-9744803-1-2

"The universe we observe has precisely the properties we should expect if there is, at bottom, no design, no purpose, no evil and no good, nothing but blind, pitiless, indifference." —Richard Darkin, biologist, *River Out of Eden*.

"The more the universe seems comprehensible, the more it also seems pointless." — Dr. Steven Weinberg, Nobel Laureate, 1979.

"There are more things in heaven and earth, Horatio, than are dreamt of in your philosophy." —William Shakespeare, *Hamlet*.

AKNOWLEDGMENTS

The title is intended not only to describe the book for what it is, a guide for laymen written by a layman. But it is also intended to honor the memory of Bernard Brodie whose *A Layman's Guide to Naval Strategy* was published in the early days of World War II. Although Alfred T. Mahan was the first American to write extensively on strategy, it was Brodie who pioneered the subject as a legitimate concern of university teaching and policy-oriented research.

CONTENTS

Part Five: Circles of Stone, Religions, Myths, and Legends

Part Six: Conclusion, How Will It End?

PREFACE

This book had its origins in an attempt to understand the flood of new discoveries in such fields as string theory, the origin of the moon, continental drift, the descent of man, the "punctuated equilibrium" revision of Darwinism, the implications of anthropology of DNA, the consequences of the recent discoveries about the Black Sea Flood, the migrations of early man, and the techniques of seafaring developed by the Vikings and the Polynesians.

Many years ago, I developed a habit of jotting down in my own words what specialists in other fields were saying. Some of my children and their children got interested in these notes and asked questions that led me to expand the effort. Later, my daughter-in-law, Nelly Métayer Hilsman, suggested turning the notes into a book, arguing that it would be as interesting to others and their children and grandchildren as it was to mine.

Early drafts of the book tried to avoid giving dates in terms of B.C. and A.D. by saying that an event occurred a certain number of years before the present. Later drafts tried the device of BCE and ACE—Before the Current Era and After the Current Era. But almost everyone who read any of these drafts complained that both systems were hopelessly confusing and that even the Chinese understand what was meant when a date in Chinese history is given in terms of B.C. or A.D. So I succumbed.

Part One

The Cosmos

Chapter 1

In the Beginning

Some time about 14 billion years ago all matter, energy, and—believe it or not—*space* were so compressed they could fit on the head of a pin so small that beside it a grain of sand would look colossal. The temperature was so high that the basic forces of the universe were unified. For reasons not yet known, this pinpoint of space, energy, and matter suddenly began to expand. Humankind has learned a great deal of what happened in the microseconds after the universe began to expand, when the expansion was no older than a very, very tiny fraction of a second (10^{-43} seconds of age, to be exact). But no one has any idea about how long it existed in its earlier state before it began to expand. In fact, there are only two things that humankind thinks it knows about that earlier state. The first is that there is reason to believe that such a state would be highly unstable. The second is that tiny black holes probably formed, disappeared, formed again, and so on, very rapidly.

Under these extreme conditions, the structure of space-time was severely curved. Physical phenomena that we now describe partly by Einstein's theory of relativity and partly by quantum mechanics were indistinguishable in that early state of the universe. But it should be said that general relativity, which describes things that are very, very large, and quantum mechanics, which describes things that are very, very small, cannot both be right. String theory, described in Chapter 5, attempts to resolve this tension and argues that general relativity and quantum mechanics require each other.

The earlier theory propounded by Isaac Newton required that influences be transmitted over vast distances of space *instantaneously*. Einstein's theory posited that this is impossible, that *nothing, neither object nor influence* can travel faster than the speed of light. Einstein also showed not only that space and time are dependent on the observer's state of motion, but that space and time can warp and curve in response to the presence of matter and energy. It is not something moving from one place to another that transmits the force of gravity but these distortions of space and time. A very crude analogy would be that a star sits on an elastic net, so that a sphere, such as the Earth, anywhere on the net would roll toward the star.

As the universe continued to expand, gravity split from the other forces. Shortly afterwards, the strong nuclear force and the electro-weak force parted company. No one knows for sure, but this was apparently the cause of the next phase, the era of inflation. This was a very rapid expansion of the size of the universe (10^{30} times!) in a very short time. In fact, it expanded faster than the speed of light, which is a paradox since Einstein's theory holds that nothing can go any faster than light. The phenomenon is loosely similar to what happens when water freezes. A gram of water at zero degrees centigrade stores more energy than a gram of ice at the same temperature. So when water is transformed from a liquid to a solid it releases this latent energy. Something similar happened in the era of inflation. During this era, the universe rapidly expanded, stretching and smoothing matter and energy so that no region in the universe varied in density from another by more than one part in 100,000.

All the above is informed speculation, but from this point on, the story gains support from physics confirmed in the laboratory. Parenthetically, it should be noted that one of the reasons that so much progress has been made so recently in understanding how the universe evolved is due to the invention of the electronic computer, which can perform calculations in less than a second that would take more than 10,000 lifetimes of human calculation.

At this time, the universe was still hot enough for photons to convert their energy spontaneously into matter and anti-matter particles—which then annihilated each other to become photons again.

As the universe continued to cool, the electro-weak force split to become the electromagnetic force and the weak nuclear force. These two, along with gravity and the strong nuclear force, are the four distinct and familiar forces of nature.

Probably at the time of this second splitting of force the symmetry between matter and anti-matter disappeared, for reasons that are not yet understood. This led to a slight excess of matter over anti-matter. For every billion anti-matter particles there were now a billion-plus-one matter particles. As the temperature of the photon bath continued to drop, pairs of matter and anti-matter particles could no longer be created spontaneously from the available photons. All the remaining pairs of matter and anti-matter particles swiftly annihilated each other, leaving behind a universe with one particle of ordinary matter—and no anti-matter—for every billion photons.

During this period, the free-roving electrons scattered the photons to and fro, creating an opaque soup of matter and energy. If this asymmetry *had not* emerged, the universe would have forever consisted of light and nothing else.

When the universe cooled to one or two degrees Kelvin—about the temperature of fireplace embers—the loose electrons were moving slowly enough to get snatched by the loose nuclei to form complete atoms of hydrogen, helium, and lithium—the three lightest elements. The universe became transparent to visible light for the first time. These free-flying photons are seen today as the cosmic microwave background, which is 2.7 degrees Kelvin.

Over the following billion years, the universe continued to expand and cool while matter gravitated into the massive concentrations called galaxies. As many as one hundred *billion* galaxies formed, each containing hundreds of billions of stars. These stars are visible to us because of the light generated by the thermonuclear fusion in their cores.

Black Holes

Einstein predicted what have come to be known as *black holes*. He reasoned that when a very large star uses up its fuel, the nuclear reaction creating the pressure to resist gravity comes to an end, and the star collapses. A black hole is a concentration of so much matter so densely packed that its gravity prevents anything from escaping. John Wheeler later coined the name black hole—black, because at the time it was believed that light could not escape from it; hole, because anything getting too close to one of them would be sucked in, never to return. The name stuck.

A star not big enough to form a black hole ends up composed solely of neutrons. A neutron star is very, very dense. Its gravity is 10^{12} times that of Earth. Its surface is so smooth that a 1-millimeter bump would be a mountain, and the same energy would be required to climb that very tiny bump as to escape from Earth's gravity. A pin dropped from a table on a neutron star would release as much energy as a ton of high explosives. To escape from Earth, a rocket must speed at 11 km per second. On a neutron star, it would have to go much faster, 150,000 km per second, half the speed of light.

Neutron stars rotate once every 3 to 5 seconds. Those with magnetic fields emit streams of radio waves from their magnetic poles. When a neutron star is so oriented that these beams strike the Earth, it is called a pulsar.

Matter in a black hole was at first assumed to be locked in it forever, but Stephen Hawking recently theorized that over many billions upon billions of years black holes could release matter—a concept that he hopes may some day win him a Nobel Prize.

Also in 1999, some astronomers theorized that the mysterious bursts of gamma rays that are occasionally observed are a byproduct of the birth of black holes. Most black holes at birth are probably no more than 3 to 5 times the mass of the Sun, growing larger as they suck in more stars and as they collide with other black holes. Bursts of gamma rays occur in the cosmic deep on average about once a day and never in the same place twice. These are the largest known explosions in the universe, save only the Big Bang itself. The bursts last only a few seconds, but leave a longer-lived afterglow in x-ray, radio, and other wavelengths that can be studied.

It is thought that black holes can be created in one of two ways: One way would be a variation of what was originally thought, as above, that a very large giant star uses up its fuel, the nuclear reaction creating the pressure to resist gravity dies down, and the star collapses. The revised theory is that as the core grows denser, some of the matter in the outer layers is ejected into space, while the rest is sucked into the core.

Another way for a black hole to be formed is if two neutron stars orbiting each other spiral toward a collision and the stellar cores collide and fuse. Some part of the matter involved would remain orbiting the fused object. A black hole can also increase in size by capturing a neutron star, or two black holes can fuse. In all three cases, the dense cores are black holes around which the orbiting matter surrounding them forms a doughnut-shaped disk, a torus. A few minutes later, the torus is "swallowed" by the spinning black hole as matter spirals into the hole.

Waves of radiation and subatomic particles are propelled from the center of the torus and the black hole at varying speeds, some much faster than others. As the faster waves overtake the slower ones, shock waves are formed and intense bursts of gamma waves are released into space.

Elements Other Than Hydrogen, Helium, and Lithium

Stars with more than about ten times the mass of the Sun achieve sufficient pressure and temperature in their cores to manufacture elements heavier than hydrogen, helium, and lithium. This includes the elements that make up rocky planets such as ours, which in turn make life possible.

These elements would remain locked away in these stars forever except for the fact that in a relatively short time compared to the life of stars like the Sun such very big stars reach a stage at which they explode and scatter the elements they have manufactured throughout their galaxy. After seven or eight billion years stars began to be born that contained these elements. The Sun is such a star. Neither very large nor very small, it was born in an unremarkable region (the Orion Arm) of an unremarkable galaxy (the Milky Way), in an unremarkable part of the universe (the outskirts of the Virgo super cluster of stars).

The Hubble showed that two galaxies would collide. The Milky Way, our own galaxy, captured a number of smaller galaxies. The Milky Way is 10 billion years old and contains 400 billion visible stars. In other galaxies the black holes are several billion times the mass of the Sun. In the Milky Way the black hole is only 3 million times as large as the solar mass.

The Chinese first recorded the explosion of a star in 386 A.D., confirmed in 2000, in the constellation Sagittarius, about 15,000 light-years from Earth. The result was a pulsar, an extremely dense neutron star left after the explosion of a supernova. The first recorded sighting of such an exploding star was in 1054 A.D., by Chinese and Japanese astronomers. The discovery in 386 is different from that of 1054, which makes it highly significant, requiring additional study.

In Europe the discovery of 1054 was reported as "an orb of extraordinary brilliance." Shortly after the death of Pope Leo IX on April 19, 1054, the Church made Leo a saint, and named the new star after him! The remnant of the explosion is the Crab Nebula.

Chapter 2

The Growth of Science

Modern science dates from the time of Copernicus five hundred years ago and the one hundred-year struggle to prove that the Sun and not the Earth was the center of the solar system. It was Copernicus who laid down the fundamental principle of science that an observer should not assume that he or she occupies a privileged position such as living on a planet that is the center of the solar system! But the groundwork was laid even earlier. Two thousand years ago, the Athenians knew that the Earth was round, and one of them, Erastothenes, made a good estimate of the Earth's circumference. The concept of zero, of which Euclid was totally innocent, was formulated on the Indian subcontinent soon after the beginning of the modern era. Even the alchemists in their search for the philosopher's stone that would turn anything it touched to gold came to understand that chemical reactions can turn substances into things that not only look different but behave differently.

In the early 1700s, the boast was made that there had never been such a hundred-year period of scientific achievement since the resurgence of Greek science at Alexandria in the second century A.D. In Britain, Francis Bacon argued for experimentation, and William Harvey began dissecting animals and people for the first time since the Greek physician Galen had discovered the functions of the heart, arteries, and blood 1,200 years earlier. In France, René Descartes embarked on his study of the nature of the world.

He gave us the system of geometry based on algebra that is still called Cartesian geometry.

Galilei Galileo was the first to use the modern idiom of science and in that sense was the first scientist. He established that acceleration creates force. He saw that mass measured by its weight on Earth must be identical with the mass inferred when it collides with other objects anywhere in the universe (this is the *equivalence principle*). He was the first to use a telescope and discovered the satellites of Jupiter.

Isaac Newton identified gravity. He devised the differential calculus to calculate the orbits of planets and other trajectories. His book, *Principia Mathematica*, published in 1687, synthesized what was then known about the world. John Dalton established the idea that matter was made of atoms. Charles Darwin's theory of evolution by natural selection came in 1858. Louis Pasteur showed that bacteria accomplish the fermentation that turns milk into cheese and went on to demonstrate the germ theory of infectious disease. Heinrich Hertz generated invisible waves in the radio-frequency range. Then Guglielmo Marconi spanned the ocean with such waves as radio. W. K. Röntgen invented x-rays. Antoine Becquerel found that similar radiation is given off by uranium—that is, radioactivity. In England, J. L. Thompson proved the existence of negatively charged electricity—the electron.

James Clerk Maxwell developed one set of equations for both electricity and magnetism, in an attempt to explain the phenomenon of light. A ray of light does indeed behave like a wave, and the speed of light in empty space is related to the electrical and magnetic properties of empty space.

But this posed a problem. The flashes of light from an exploding star keep traveling outward long after their source has vanished. So light acted as if it was both corpuscular, that is, matter traveling through space and a wave motion, which is energy that requires something to travel through, just as a stone thrown in a pond generates ripples that move through the water. Maxwell posited "lumeniferous aether"—later called, simply, ether.

In a famous experiment in the latter part of the nineteenth century Albert A. Michelson and Edward W. Morley split a ray of light into two beams. One ray was bounced back and forth between mirrors in the direction of the Earth's travel. The other was bounced back and forth perpendicular to the Earth's travel. If there is such a thing as ether that has substance, the one perpendicular to the Earth's travel will be slowed by friction. But when the two rays were brought back together they meshed perfectly. There was no drag; hence, there could be no ether. So light could not be a wave motion, since a wave needs material through which to travel.

But light strikes a substance without any effect on the substance, except to warm it, so it is not like other corpuscular substances either. Hundreds of different theories were developed but none satisfactorily explained all this.

Then came Albert Einstein. In his theory of Special Relativity, he noted that in our low-speed world, a force applied to an object results in greater speed. But he argued that at the very high speeds approaching that of light, the increase in speed will be less. The increase would be in the mass of the object. The energy turns into mass, or substance.

Several conclusions follow that are counter-intuitive, i.e. that violate common sense:

1. Nothing can travel faster than the speed of light.

2. Energy can be converted into mass and mass into energy.

3. The Newtonian notions of absolute position and time are devoid of meaning. Only relative distances and times are meaningful. (In this respect, Einstein followed Ernst Mach who maintained that theories should refer only to quantities that are measurable.)

4. There can be no ether, for that would allow the determination of absolute speeds or distances.

5. We live in a four-dimensional world, because the three dimensions of ordinary space are conjoined with the extra dimension of time.

The reason that Einstein's theory runs against intuition is because our senses lack experience with objects moving near the speed of light.

The Michelson-Morley experiment showed that there was no ether or other substance that could serve as a means by which space and time can be given absolute meaning.

By the end of the nineteenth century it was established that all objects emit radiation spanning a spectrum of frequencies, and that the frequencies are higher as the temperature is increased.

In 1900, Max Planck proposed that radiation of a particular frequency existed only as *quanta*. The greater the frequency, the greater the energy of the quanta concerned. He had discovered that even energy itself consists of atoms. Then in 1905, Einstein proved the point (see below) by explaining why a certain minimum frequency (and thus energy) of light is required to extract electrons from metals or to make semiconductors carry an electrical current (now the basis of a photographer's light meter). In 1910, Ernest

Rutherford showed that all atoms are constructed of a positive nucleus embodying most of the mass, surrounded by electrons. Typically the dimensions of the nucleus are one ten-thousandth of the atom as a whole.

Studies of hydrogen showed that atoms emit radiation with precisely defined frequency—the so-called spectral lines. Then Niels Bohr came up with the essential clue—that electrons orbit the nucleus, just as planets orbit the Sun. But there is an enormous difference. Electrons are allowed only a restricted set of orbits, each with a well-defined energy. So each spectral line arises when an electron changes from one allowed orbit to another, and its frequency corresponds to the differences between the two energies.

Bohr had hit upon the conditions in which an electron can remain indefinitely in its orbit without losing energy. Radiation—light or heat—consists of indivisible quanta characterized by frequencies that may span a considerable range. This is why light is not a wave motion, but more like what Newton suggested, "corpuscles of different colors." When Einstein published his second paper on quantum mechanics, physicists had to accept that light was both a wave motion and corpuscular. The corpuscles were christened photons.

In 1926, it was shown that not only light but also electrons could be both wavelike and corpuscular.

Then came Werner Heisenberg and the uncertainty principle—that it is not possible to measure both the speed and the position of an electron at the same time. Then came Erwin Schrödinger (of cat fame, see below) who devised *wave mechanics*, which cast the properties of quantum mechanics in the language of mathematics. Then Paul Dirac showed that the two descriptions are equivalent to each other.

In 1929, Edwin T. Hubble established that the universe is expanding. Almost all the galaxies within range of his telescope were receding, and the speed of the recession increased with distance.

If all other galaxies are receding, doesn't this mean that our galaxy is the center? No, the galaxies are embedded in space, and it is space that is expanding—uniformly in all directions. Galaxies can move toward or away from each other within space, but space continues to expand as they do so.

So you can measure the distance of a galaxy from Earth by measuring the degree to which its light is reddened or red-shifted, and you can so infer its distance. And to get the age of the universe, you extrapolate the present motion backwards until all the galaxies were together to get the date when the universe began. Using this method in the 1960s, scientists came to prefer an age between 10 to 20 billion years.

However, age is estimated by brightness, and the dust in space makes the stars seem dimmer and hence older than they really are. But even more important, the speed of the expansion of the universe has been slowing all this time, because of the drag of gravity by the galaxies on each other. So to estimate the age you have to know how much matter there is in the universe. The more matter, the more the expansion has been slowed. Therefore, it is at least possible that the true age is only a third of 10 billion to 20 billion years.

In 1999, a galaxy was discovered 14.25 billion light years from Earth. It has a red shift of 6.68. This means that the expansion of the universe stretches the light it emits by a factor of 6.68. The light that we see left is its galaxy when the universe was only 5 percent of its present age. Two other galaxies have been found whose colors indicate that they may be even more distant. One has a red shift of 10 and lies 14.6 billion light years away. All three are unexpectedly bright, and when the light departed from them on its long journey they were manufacturing stars at a prodigious rate, equivalent to a few dozen Suns each year. This is at odds with current theory, which holds that the most distant, i.e. earliest, galaxies should be faint and make few stars.

In the spring of the year 2000, another galaxy was discovered by the Sloan Digital Sky Survey that had emitted its light only 1 billion years after the Big Bang, and still more discoveries are anticipated in the near future.

Also in 1999, a group of astronomers using the Hubble telescope in an eight-year project designed to determine the age of the universe concluded that the universe has been expanding for at least 12 billion years. The scientists, led by Dr. Wendy L. Freedman, used the Hubble to measure the distance to 800 stars of known brightness, the Cepheid Variables, in 18 different galaxies. But they also concluded that the age of the universe could be closer to 13.5 billion years or even 15 billion years, "depending on the uncertainty about the density of cosmic matter and the possible existence of a mysterious form of vacuum energy." The "mysterious form of vacuum energy" is the so-called "cosmological constant" that so bedeviled Einstein. If the universe is the latter age, 15 billion years, it is because of a "cosmological constant" that is a kind of anti-gravity force that acts to speed up cosmic expansion.

These scientists concluded that the Hubble constant, which is different from the cosmological constant, is 70, plus or minus 7. This means that a galaxy appears to be flying away at a rate of 70 kilometers per second per megaparsec, or 160,000 miles per hour for every 3.26 light years it is distant from Earth.

The Big Bang

George Gamow had the idea of the Big Bang. Before the Big Bang, as we said, all matter, energy, and space was the size of a very small pinhead. Outside the pinhead there was nothing, not even space. Inside the pinhead, the temperature was much greater than anything humankind has ever seen since, anywhere.

How can hot empty space spawn matter? At temperatures greater than absolute zero (minus 273 degrees centigrade) all empty space is filled with radiation. This is what Planck had learned in 1900. And the intensity of radiation increases rapidly with rising temperature. Double the temperature and the radiation increases sixteen fold. But radiation exerts pressure. So a tiny bubble of space, matter, and energy at a great temperature will generate huge radiation and pressure, and it will therefore expand. Hence the Big Bang.

If the tiny bubble is so highly unstable, how did it come to be? The instant it was created, it should have begun to expand. Maybe it did, no one knows.

So radiation can behave both as if it were wavelike and as if it were a collection of particles moving with the speed of light. And the particles, the photons, can create matter out of empty space if they have enough energy. By 1947 everyone knew that a single photon, if energetic enough, could create a pair of electrons out of empty space: a positive electron, i.e. a positron, and an ordinary electron. So why shouldn't the very high radiation of the Big Bang create not only electrons but also protons and neutrons, which are the ingredients of matter?

So there would have been a small fraction of a second as the infant universe cooled when the temperature (between 10 and 100 billion degrees) and the density of protons and neutrons would have both been great enough for protons and neutrons to form both helium and the nuclei of the heavy isotope of hydrogen (deuterium). Other materials, the rare isotope of helium called helium-3 and versions of the nuclei of lithium, would also be created. Certainly there is no way that these materials could be formed in stars, as such elements as carbon, oxygen, and iron are formed inside very large stars. Instead they would have been consumed.

The many tons of heavy water with which some types of nuclear reactors are filled are literally a chemical relic of the early stages of the Big Bang.

The Cosmic Wave Background

In 1966, researchers at the Bell Labs quite by accident found another relic of the Big Bang, its leftover radiation. This is the cosmic microwave background, which is now just 2.7 degrees Kelvin above absolute zero. It is a relic *not* of the early stages of the Big Bang, but of a later time when all the matter in the present universe had already come into being in the form of hydrogen mixed with helium and lithium. As the continued expansion of the universe caused the temperature to fall, intact hydrogen atoms began to form. Since the bath of radiation would no longer have been coupled to matter, the universe became transparent—more than 100,000 years after the initial expansion of the Big Bang. It is from this time that cosmic microwave background radiation dates.

Planck Time

To measure a very small time interval with precision we need to use Planck's quanta, which has a short wavelength and thus higher energy. Since light moves at a finite speed, this increasing amount of energy must be focused into smaller dimensions (smaller than the interval being measured times the speed of light). A limit is reached when the required energy is so high and tightly concentrated that it would collapse into a black hole. This point has been named the Planck time (10^{-43} seconds). At that point, space-time probably had a chaotic foam-like structure. Tiny black holes may have been continually appearing and disappearing. It has been speculated that this activity may have been violent enough to spawn new domains of space-time that evolved into separate universes, but this is only speculation.

Chapter 3

Problems, Puzzles, and the Proliferation of Particles

One of the ancients, Aristarchus of Samos about 310 to 230 B.C., measured the distance from the Earth to the Sun with remarkable accuracy. His calculation suggested that the Sun was much bigger than the Earth, and it seemed unlikely that the larger body would orbit the smaller. Then in the second century B.C. Eratosthenes, a Greek, made a significant discovery. (He lived in the town of Syene, present day Aswan, where there is now a huge dam on the Nile). There was a deep well where the Sun at midday on June 21 reflected off the water far down in the well, something that happened on no other day of the year. The point was that the Sun was exactly overhead at the time, and at no other time of the year. Eratosthenes also knew that the Sun was never vertically overhead in Alexandria. The closest it got was on June 21, when it was off by an angle he measured with a vertical stick at 7.2 degrees.

The distance from Alexandria to Syene was measured at 5,000 stades almost exactly due south. From this, and from the difference in the angle of the sunlight at midday on June 21, Eratosthenes was able to figure out how far it would be to go completely around the Earth.

We do not know exactly how far a stade was. If it was 500 feet, the estimate of the circumference of the Earth was 23,300 miles. If a stade was about 520 feet, which some scholars believe, the correct answer is about 25,000 miles, which is much closer.

In modern times, to get the longer base needed to measure the distance to a star, the method was to take a sighting on the star whose distance was to be measured when the Earth was on one side of its orbit and then to take it again six months later when the Earth was on the other side. Thus the diameter of the Earth's orbit provided the base of the triangle. This worked for nearby stars, but if the distances were really great the angles were still much too tiny.

To measure really great distances, such as to other galaxies, you need a "standard candle" whose intrinsic brightness is independently known. What are called Cepheid Variables was first recognized in our own galaxy over a century ago. These are stars like the Sun, but more massive that have consumed a substantial part of their original thermonuclear fuel. They are at least 1,000 times brighter than the Sun and highly unstable. Their output of light varies rhythmically over intervals ranging from a few days to a few months. What is important is that the speed of their pulsation is related directly to their average brightness. The brighter they are, the faster they pulsate. This relationship was established when Cepheid Variables were seen in the dwarf galaxies called the Magellanic Clouds. These clouds of stars are visible in the southern sky and are apparently in orbit around our own galaxy at a distance of 100,000 light years. The dwarf galaxies of the Magellanic Clouds provided a sample of Cepheids at roughly the same distance from the solar system, so these were used as a standard candle. The 100-inch telescope that Hubble was using allowed him to distinguish individual stars in distant galaxies, so he looked for Cepheid Variables and used them to measure the distances to those galaxies.

This method has been enormously useful. But the space telescope named after Hubble that orbits the Earth has enabled scientists to look even further out towards the edges of the universe and back in time, and for this task the Cepheid Variable candle is inadequate. Robert Kirshner of Harvard and others have developed a method for using Type II supernovas as a standard candle, and this lets them measure things out to 5 billion years. A very surprising preliminary finding is that although gravity slowed down the expansion of the universe for a time, recently the expansion has speeded up. If so, our universe may be much bigger than we thought. The light from some galaxies may not have had time to reach us and maybe never will.

The Hubble Constant

The Hubble constant is the rate at which the expansion speed increases with distance, usually written as H_0 and pronounced H nought. If the H_0 is 50 kilometers per second per megaparsec, which is 3.26 million light years, then for every 3.26 million light years that one looks into space, galaxies are receding another 50 kilometers per second faster. The *deceleration parameter* is the rate at which the expansion is slowing down due to the gravitational attraction the galaxies exert on each other. Astronomers combine the two into the quantity omega, which measures the cosmic mass density. If omega is 1 and the Hubble constant is 50, the universe is approximately 15 billion years old. A study of Cepheid Variables in distant galaxies in 1994 implied that the universe was younger than this, between 7.5 and 11.5 billion years old. On the other hand, a study of white dwarfs in the outer halo of our own galaxy suggested they might be 16 billion years old or older. It is conceivable that the older stars are relics of some older "universe," but it is also highly improbable. Most astrophysicists at the moment believe that an age of 14 billion years will probably be the one that is finally settled on.

The Quasar Puzzle

In 1963, objects were discovered that look like stars but were so reddened that they had to be thousands of millions of light years away. They also radiated matter from their poles in two narrow jets. They were named quasi-stellar objects or quasars. Finally, scientists realized that quasars are galaxies dating from the time when the universe was only 20 to 30 percent of its present age.

A black hole is at the center of a quasar, but why the radiation? Objects being sucked into the black hole will move rapidly around the hole in orbit. The result will be a disk-shaped object heated by collisions to a high temperature before disappearing into the black hole. If the black hole is also rotating, it may generate magnetic fields so strong that material is ejected in a narrow cone from the poles of rotation, which would explain the opposing jets of matter.

The Question of "Dark Matter"

The mass of a galaxy measured by its output of light is always less than the mass inferred from the speed of the galaxy's rotation. This has led to the conclusion that there must be a very large amount of so-called dark matter in the universe that can only be detected by its effect on galaxies that can be seen. The matter that can be seen is not enough to hold galaxies together. Without something like dark matter, they would fly apart. It is estimated that as much as eighty percent of all the mass in the universe may be dark matter. A certain "critical density" of the universe would bring the expansion of the universe to a halt. More than a critical density would eventually bring a reversal, a contracting universe rather than an expanding universe, leading eventually to the opposite of the Big Bang—a Big Crunch. Recent opinion is that the density is not enough to lead to a big crunch. The result may be a slowing expansion, finally to a snail's pace.

This view may change if enough dark matter is found. For example, there may be more brown dwarves than anyone imagined. A brown dwarf does not have enough mass to sustain full-scale nuclear fusion. But it is massive enough—0 to 70 times the mass of Jupiter—to burn deuterium, which gives it a gentle glow for the early part of its long life. This glow permits us to see a number of those that are close by, but not those at any distance. Most brown dwarves travel alone; only one is known to be orbiting a star. Six new brown dwarves have been discovered close by in our own galaxy, and all six contain methane, which means they are very cool. Our telescopes can see only the closest of these, so this suggests that the Milky Way is brimming with such objects. As many as 200 to 400 may lie within 30 light years of Earth. However, the number of brown dwarves needed to hold the universe together is so large that it seems doubtful that they can account for all that is needed. The dark matter required to hold the galaxies together seems so great and so utterly invisible that it may be very different from the ordinary matter of which the stars are made. It may be that this peculiar form of matter originated in the Big Bang and clumps around the visible parts of galaxies like a halo. But recently a revised version of superstring theory, described in Chapter 6, suggests still another explanation: that dark matter is a form of gravity seeping into our part of the universe from somewhere else. The director of the particle physics laboratory decided to shut down the CERN, the French acronym for a particle accelerator, even though the scientists using it begged that they were about to discover the particle that most scientists believe is the origin of all mass in the universe, the Higgs boson. He had granted extensions several times, but finally drew the line. His reason was that the present machine was being replaced by a new one, the Large Hadron Collider, that will almost certainly see the particle if it exists, but will not be finished until 2005. A result is that the Fermi National Laboratory that will begin operations in the spring of 2002 may well make the discovery.

As described in Chapter 5, the possibility of an entire family of very heavy particles called WIMPs or "weakly interacting massive particles," has been predicted by an advanced theory called supersymmetry that attempts to marry gravity and quantum mechanics. In February 2000, a group of physicists at the University of Rome announced that they believed they had identified WIMPs. The Sun orbits the Milky Way at a speed of 140 miles a second and presumably is moving through clouds of WIMPs. If so, a billion of them would be passing through your body each second. Although normally invisible, a WIMP should interact with matter on rare occasions, and the Rome group built a detector underground to protect it from cosmic rays and filled it with sodium iodide, which emits a tiny flash of light when particles collide with it. Because of the direction the Earth orbits the Sun and the Sun in turn orbits the galaxy, the "wind" of WIMPs should be slightly stronger in the summer than in the winter. The Rome group believes it detected a particle that weighs at least 50 times as much as a proton and yet would almost always pass through other matter without a trace because it has such a weak ability to interact with it.

A number of other physicists were quick to dispute these findings. A team of physicists from ten American universities that had built a detector at Stanford designed specifically to find dark matter said that they had experienced thirteen particle detections, about the same number. But they argued that these were not consistent with the WIMP hypothesis. So they had concluded that the detections were neutrons not WIMPs. But they also admitted that it was possible that two or three of the 13 detections could possibly be WIMPs.

Since both the Rome and the Stanford groups are exploring uncharted waters, the scientific community was justified in being highly skeptical. But skepticism was tempered by the fact that theory predicts something like WIMPs and that whoever discovers them for sure is a prime candidate for a Nobel Prize.

It is also possible that there are still other kinds of dark matter. One of the weirdest possibilities was discovered in 2001 when some scientists found some experimental evidence that certain very rare interactions of particles, called kaons, imply a distinction between the forward and backward directions of time. The idea is that when and if the universe stops expanding and begins to contract, time will reverse itself. If so, it is conceivable that some isolated star could survive through the switch from expansion to contraction with its time arrows intact and pointed in the opposite direction to the rest of the particular universe. Lawrence S. Schulman of Clarkson University in Potsdam, New York, suggested that if the idea is accepted that a Big Crunch will follow the Big Bang, it is conceivable that when the universe turns around and begins to collapse, time also turns around. If this is the case, suppose celestial bodies with reversed time originated in our distant future and had already experienced the turn around from Big Bang to Big Crunch. Because of their enormous age, these stars would no longer be luminous. Their presence could be detected only by gravity. So if all this supposition turned out to be true, they could be the missing dark matter.

The Formation of Galaxies

The current speculation is that the universe remained dark for about one billion years. At that stage the universe consisted of 75 percent hydrogen and 25 percent helium with a trace of lithium. Then atoms and molecules clumped together in aggregations that were both stable and compact. This state of affairs could arise from very slight fluctuations in the original density of matter following the Big Bang. Current opinion is that galaxies were the first to form and that at first they consisted of clouds of gas massive enough so that billions of stars would eventually be formed within them. The clouds would have continued to form at a majestic pace, so slow that the gravitational energy could be radiated away before further collapse was prevented by ignition of thermonuclear reactions inside them.

Matter

John Dalton posited atoms. The discovery of electrons followed, then Ernest Rutherford showed that at the center of atoms were nuclei with positive charge, and that the nuclei carried 99.9 percent of the mass of each atom. A hydrogen atom has one electron, helium two. But the helium nucleus is exactly four times as massive as the nucleus of the hydrogen atom, which is a proton.

Rutherford suggested neutrons, comparable in mass, but with no electrical charge. James Chadwick then found that radiation consists of electrically neutral particles with a mass identical to the protons. It was the collective works of J. J. Thomson, Ernest Rutherford, Niels Bohr, and James Chadwick that established that atoms are like a solar system, with a central nucleus containing protons and neutrons, surrounded by a swarm of orbiting electrons.

Then work at the Stanford Linear Accelerator Center found that protons and neutrons were not fundamental particles either. Each is composed of three smaller particles — whimsically given the name "quarks" from James Joyce's *Finnegan's Wake*. "Up," "down," and "strange" quarks were first identified, then "charm," "bottom," and "up." Composites of the six quarks, with or without their anti-particles, constitute the *hadrons*, the self-standing particles of nuclear matter. Particles with three quarks (which include the nucleons) are called *baryons*. Those with two are called mesons. It turned out that a proton consists of two up-quarks and one down-quark. A neutron consists of two down-quarks and an up-quark.

Quarks occur in pairs or in triplets. It is the strong nuclear force that holds quarks together in composite hadrons. The force comes from another quantum field called a *gluon field*. The idea is that some quarks are held together by the mutual exchange of novel particles of gluons, which stand in relation to the strong nuclear forces, as do photons to electromagnetic forces.

The attraction and repulsion of quarks is determined by "color" (whimsy again), which has three values—red, green, and blue. There are also anti-red, anti-green, and anti-blue. Baryons, made up of three quarks, are colorless if the color charges are red, green, and blue or the same combination of anti-colors. Mesons, with two quarks, are colorless if they are a combination of a particular color-charge with the corresponding anti-color (say red and anti-red). This scheme, called quantum chromodynamics, is the basis of the now-standard way of treating the strong nuclear forces that hold together the quarks.

Everything we see on Earth and in the heavens above appears to be made up of electrons, up-quarks, and down-quarks. There are also other ingredients in the universe that we cannot see. One is a *neutrino*. These are hard to find, because they rarely interact with matter. A neutrino can pass through many trillion miles of lead without the slightest effect on its motion. As you read this, billions of neutrinos ejected by the Sun are passing through both your body and the Earth.

In the 1930s, people studying cosmic rays discovered a new particle, the *muon*. It was identical to an electron except that it is 200 times heavier. There was nothing that necessitated the muon, no unsolved puzzle, and no tailor-made niche. With a notable lack of enthusiasm, I. I. Rabi commented, "Who ordered that?"

Physicists continued to slam bits of matter together with ever-increasing energy, creating for instant conditions like the Big Bang. They found another even heavier cousin of the electron, named a *tau*. They also found two other particles similar to the neutrino—the muon-neutrino and the tau-neutrino. (The neutrino was then renamed the electron-neutrino.)

Each particle has an anti-particle with an identical mass, but opposite in charge. For example, the anti-particle of an electron is a positron. It has the same mass as an electron but a positive charge of +1 while an electron has a charge of -1. Matter and anti-matter annihilate each other to produce pure energy, which is why there is extremely little naturally occurring anti-matter in the world around us.

The matter particles fall into three groups or families. The corresponding particle types across the three families have identical properties except for their mass (given in multiples of proton mass), which grows larger in each successive family. The table below is from Brian Greene, *The Elegant Universe*, page 9. The values of the neutrino masses are not known.

| Family I | | Family II | | Family III | |
Particle	Mass	Particle	Mass	Particle	Mass
Electron	.00054	Muon	.11	Tau	1.9
Electron-neutrino	$< 10^{-8}$	Muon-neutrino	$< .0003$	Tau-neutrino	$< .033$
Up quark	.047	Charm quark	1.6	Top quark	189
Down-quark	.0074	Strange quark	.16	Bottom quark	5.2

The upshot is that physicists have probed the structure of matter to scales of about a billionth of a billionth of a meter and shown that *everything* encountered so far, whether occurring naturally or created with atom smashers, consists of some combination of particles from these three families and their anti-matter partners.

As Brian Greene comments, why are there so many fundamental particles, especially since most things in the world around us need only electrons, up-quarks, and down-quarks? Why three families instead of one or four? Why such a random spread of masses? Why does the tau weigh 3,520 times as much as an electron? Why does the top-quark weigh 40,200 times?

Force

There are four forces: gravity, the electromagnetic force, the weak nuclear force, and the strong nuclear force. Gravity keeps the Earth orbiting around the Sun and our feet planted on the ground. The electromagnetic force runs modern civilization, from electric lights to computers. The weak nuclear and strong nuclear forces are less familiar because their strength diminishes rapidly over all but subatomic distance. The strong force keeps quarks "glued" together inside protons and neutrons and keeps protons and neutrons tightly crammed together inside atomic nuclei. The weak force is best known as the force responsible for radioactive decay of substances such as uranium.

At the microscopic level, all forces have an associated particle that can be thought of as being the smallest packet or bundle of the force. If you fire a laser beam, you are firing a stream of photons, the smallest bundles of the electromagnetic force. Similarly, the smallest constituents of weak and strong force fields are particles called *weak gauge bosons* and *gluons*. Physicists believe that the gravitational force also has an associated particle — the graviton — but its existence has yet to be confirmed experimentally.

The four forces of nature, together with their associated force particles and their masses in multiples of the proton mass are given in the table below, also from Brian Greene, (page 11). The weak force comes in varieties with two possible masses listed. Theoretical studies show that the graviton should be massless.

Force	Force Particle	Mass
Strong	Gluon	0
Electromagnetic	Photon	0
Weak	Weak gauge bosons	86, 97*
Gravity	Graviton	0

*(The weak force comes in two varieties; so two possible masses are listed)

31

Again, Greene asks, why four? Why not one or five? Why such a spread in strength? The electromagnetic repulsion is a million billion billion billion billion (10^{42}) times stronger than gravity. The reason electromagnetic compulsion does not overwhelm us is that most things are composed of an equal amount of positive and negative electric charges and cancel each other out. Gravity is always attractive and there are no similar cancellations.

Chapter 4

Einstein's Frustration

In Einstein's day, the strong and weak forces had not yet been discovered, but he found the existence of even two distinct forces—gravity and electromagnetism—deeply troubling. He did not accept that nature is founded on such an extravagant design. So he started on a thirty-year search for a unified field theory that he hoped would show that these two forces are really manifestations of one grand underlying principle. This quixotic quest isolated him from the mainstream of physics. As he wrote to a friend in the early 1940s, "I have become a lonely old chap who is mainly known because he doesn't wear socks and who is exhibited as a curiosity on special occasions." He was actually far ahead of his time.

Einstein maintained that acceleration is one thing, but force-free motion is relative. It has meaning only by comparison with other objects also undergoing force-free motion. There is simply no possibility of "absolute" constant-velocity motion. Only comparisons have any physical meaning. The conclusion is that the laws of physics must be absolutely identical for all observers undergoing constant-velocity motion. This is the first key ingredient of Einstein's special relativity.

The second key is that light travels at 186,000 miles per second regardless of the condition of the observer; i.e., regardless of benchmarks for comparison. If you run away from a beam of light, it will still travel toward you at the same speed. If you run toward it, it will still travel toward you at the same speed.

But speed is a notion of the distance that an object can travel in a given amount of time. So we are talking about space and time. The paradox is that time elapses more slowly for an individual in motion than for one who is stationary. In a laboratory, muons disintegrate in a process akin to radioactivity in two millionths of a second. But if their speed is boosted by a particle accelerator to 99.5 percent of the speed of light, the muon's lifetime is increased by a factor of 10. But the muons do not live longer—at that speed time passes more slowly. A person, say, can read 600 books in a lifetime, at 99.5 percent of the speed of light, he or she could still read only 600 books, because his or her rate of reading—and everything else—slows down as well. Einstein held that *all* objects in the universe *always* travel through *space–time* at one fixed speed, that of light. *But this is through all four dimensions, including time.* When an object moves through space, some of the motion through time must be diverted. The speed of an object through space is merely a reflection of how much its motion through time is diverted.

This is why there is a limit to how fast an object can move through space. The maximum speed of an object through space occurs if *all* of its motion through time is converted to motion through space. All of the motion of light is through space, so light does not get old. A photon emerging from the Big Bang is the same age today as it was then. There is no passage of time at light speed. So space and time are interwoven. Einstein also showed that energy and mass are also interwoven and can be converted one into the other. In the same equation, he showed the relationship of matter, energy, and the ultimate possible speed, that of light: $E = MC^2$, where E is energy, M is mass and C is the speed of light. So one percent of two pounds of uranium can produce the devastation of Hiroshima and the H of the H_2O in a few pounds of seawater could meet the energy needs of the entire world. It was mentioned above that an accelerator has pushed a muon to 99.5 percent of the speed of light. Why not push it to 99.999 percent of the speed of light? At 99.99999999 percent of the speed of light its mass would increase by a factor of more than 70,000. It would require an *infinite* amount of energy to push it to the speed of light. This is of course impossible, and this is why *nothing* can travel faster than the speed of light.

Newton's view of gravity was that absolutely everything exerts an attractive gravitational force on everything else. The force exerted by one object on another is proportional to the product of their masses and inversely proportional to the square of the distance between them. This was a marvelous insight that has permitted humankind to understand the motion of planets and to send rocket ships to the moon. Newton accepted the existence of gravity and developed equations to describe its effects, but he never offered any insight as to how gravity works.

But Newton's view of gravity and Einstein's theory of relativity are incompatible. According to Newton, if the Sun exploded, the result would instantly be felt on the Earth, 93 million miles away through the sudden change in gravitational force governing the Earth's motion. But according to Einstein's theory of relativity nothing travels faster than light and disturbances to the fabric of the universe travel at precisely the speed of light. Light takes 8 minutes to travel from the Sun to the Earth, and no effect could be transmitted faster. This incompatibility led Einstein to develop his general theory of relativity in which our understanding of both space and time underwent a revolution.

Einstein then had what he called his "happiest thought," that accelerated motion and gravity had equivalent effects—the *equivalence principle*. A person in a sealed box could not tell the difference between the effects of accelerating in space far removed from any gravitational effects and the effects of gravity. Einstein's happiest thought was that he realized that he would be able to use his understanding of accelerated motion, which is concrete and tangible, to help him understand gravity, which is elusive and ethereal. (An object accelerates if either its speed increases or the direction of its motion changes.) After an enormous amount of work, he forged the second link in the chain uniting gravity and accelerated motion, the curvature of space and time.

The gravitational tether holding the Earth in orbit around the Sun is not some mysterious instantaneous action of the Sun; rather, it is the warping of the spatial fabric caused by the Sun's presence. So the result is as if the Earth is rolling downhill toward the Sun.

Time

In the gravitational field of an ordinary star, like the Sun, the slowing of time, as you get closer to the Sun, is quite small. A clock stationed one billion miles from the Sun would be 99.9998 percent of what one at the surface is. At the surface of a neutron star of the same mass, but crushed to a density some million billion times that of solar density, the larger gravitational field would cause the clock to tick at about 76 percent of the rate a billion miles away. The much stronger gravitational field outside of a black hole would cause time to slow even further.

Just shy of the "event horizon" of a black hole (beyond which nothing can escape being drawn into the hole itself), time would be slowed so much that if someone spent a year at that spot, 10,000 years would pass on Earth.

Because a black hole swallows everything that gets as close as its event horizon, it must be studied indirectly, by the effect it has on nearby stars. Evidence of this kind indicates that at the center of our own galaxy there is a black hole 2 1/2 *million* times as massive as the Sun. Big as this is, quasars seem to have black holes at their center whose masses are *billions* of times as large the Sun!

Using the equations of Georg Bernhard Riemann, a nineteenth century mathematician, Einstein was able to describe the mutual evolution of space, time, and matter quantitatively. To his great surprise, when these were applied to the universe as a whole, the universe is either shrinking or expanding, but not staying the same. The equations of general relativity show this explicitly.

This was too much even for Einstein, who was ingrained as all humans are in the idea of a never-changing universe. So Einstein put a "cosmological constant" in his equations. Edwin Hubble then showed that the universe *was* expanding, and Einstein called the cosmological constant the biggest blunder of his life.

Planck's Constant (h bar)

Imagine a perfectly insulated oven with the air removed and set at 400 degrees. By heating the walls, you generate radiation—heat and light in the form of electromagnetic waves. In 1900, physicists calculated that at any chosen temperature, the energy is infinite—an obviously ridiculous conclusion.

When Maxwell's electromagnetic theory is applied, it turns out that the waves generated by the hot walls must have a *whole* number of peaks and valleys.

Nineteenth century thermodynamics held that each of these waves, *regardless of its wavelength,* carries the same amount of energy (the precise amount is determined by the temperature of the oven). But an infinite number of wavelengths are possible; thus, you have the same ridiculous conclusion.

Max Planck earned the Nobel Prize in 1918 by assuming that the energy carried by an electromagnetic wave comes in lumps and that the energy can be a whole number but not a fraction. The answer his theory gave to the temperature in the oven agreed spectacularly with experimental measurements. By adjusting what is called the proportionality factor, now known as Planck's constant and denoted "h bar," he could predict the energy for any given temperature. This one factor is about a billionth of a billionth of a billionth of an everyday unit. Thus, Planck solved the infinite energy paradox.

In 1905, Einstein found an explanation for why energy was lumpy and was awarded the 1921 Nobel Prize. When electromagnetic radiation, light, shines on certain metals, they emit electrons. In metals, some of their electrons are only loosely bound within atoms (which is why metals are such good conductors of electricity). When light strikes a metal surface it releases energy. Light also releases energy when it strikes your skin and so makes it feel warmer or, if you get too much, results in sunburn. This transferred energy can agitate electrons in the metal and some of the loosely bound ones can be knocked clear off the surface. You might think that the speed of the ejected electrons would increase with the brightness of the light, but this does *not* happen. But the speed does increase with the frequency of the light—an increase in frequency corresponds to a change in color from red to orange to yellow to green to blue. For some unknown reason the color of the light and not its total energy controls whether or not the electrons are ejected.

Planck's guess of lumpy energy actually reflects a fundamental feature of electromagnetic waves. They are composed of particles—photons—that are little bundles, or quanta, of light. A typical 100-watt bulb emits 100 billion billion (10^{20}) photons per second. The reason that the energy embodied by such waves is lumpy is because they are composed of lumps!

But the story is not as tidy as it might appear. Consider the double slit experiment, demonstrated in most high school physics courses. A beam of light is projected on a board in which there are two slits and behind this is a photographic plate. If light were a particle, as Newton thought, you would get two bars of light on the screen, one from each of the slits. If light is a wave, then there will be interference between the portions of the wave emerging from each slit and the result will be a series of vertical bars.

But Einstein resurrected Newton's particle theory by introducing photons. Suppose you turn down the intensity of the light beam until it fires individual photons, one every few minutes. Amazingly, the result will be an interference pattern! How can individual photons passing through the screen and hitting the photographic plate manage to arrange themselves to produce the bright and dark bands of an interference pattern? Photons passing through one slit should form a vertical band, and photons passing through the other should form another vertical band. But they don't. They form an interference pattern. The only possible answer is that light has both wave-like and particle-like qualities!

If anything is counter-intuitive this certainly is! How can individual photons passing through the screen one by one conspire to produce the bright and dark bands of interfering waves? Photons may be particles, but they embody wave-like features as well. The fact that a wave-like feature—frequency—determines the energy of these particles is the first clue that a strange union is occurring. The photoelectric effect shows that light has particle properties. The double-slit experiment shows that light manifests the interference properties of waves. *Together they show that light has both wave-like and particle properties*. Intuitively we understand that something is either a wave or a particle, but not both. But the experiments show that light *is* both.

In 1923, a young French nobleman, Louis de Broglie, suggested that the wave-particle duality applied not only to light but to matter as well. He reasoned that Einstein's $E = M C^2$ relates mass to energy, that Planck and Einstein had related energy to the frequency of waves and therefore by combining the two, mass should have a wave-like incarnation. Just as light is a wave motion that quantum theory shows to have an equally valid particle description, an electron might have an equally valid description in terms of waves. Einstein took to this theory at once as a natural outgrowth of his own contributions of relativity and photons.

Then Clinton Davisson and Lester Germer at the Bell Telephone Company began studying how a beam of electrons bounces off a chunk of nickel. The experiment is very much like the one with light and two slits. A very similar pattern emerged. The experiment showed that electrons exhibit interference phenomena, the telltale sign of *waves*. So you are forced to the conclusion that an electron embodies a wave-like character in conjunction with its more familiar depiction as a particle. Similar experiments showed that all matter has a wave-like character.

How can this be reconciled with the fact that matter looks and feels solid? As de Broglie showed, the wavelength is proportional to Planck's constant. The resulting wavelengths are similarly minuscule compared with everyday scales. This is why the wave-like character of matter becomes directly apparent only upon careful microscopic investigation. Just as the huge value of C, the speed of light, obscures much of the true nature of space and time, the smallness of the resulting wavelengths obscures the wave-like aspects of matter in the day-to-day world.

If you bounce only one photon off an object, you receive only enough information to determine the object's position within a margin of error equal to the wave's wavelength. So if you use high frequency (short wavelength) you can locate an electron with great precision. But high frequency photons are very energetic and therefore sharply disturb the electron's velocity. If you use low-frequency photons (long wavelength) you minimize the impact on the electron's motion, but you sacrifice precision in determining the electron's position. So the more precisely you know the position of the electron, the less you can know its velocity. This is Heisenberg's point. You cannot know both with complete precision.

The overall conclusion is that the idea that objects have definite positions and speeds and that they have definite energies at definite moments are mere artifacts of Planck's constant being so tiny in terms of the scales of the everyday world. When this quantum realization is applied to the fabric of space–time, it shows fatal imperfections in the "stitches of gravity" and leads us to the third and primary conflict physics has faced during the past century.

To understand most very big things you need general relativity. To understand most very small things you need quantum mechanics. It is only looking at the center of black holes or looking at the whole universe at the moment of the Big Bang that you need both. But so far using both leads to nonsense—that the probability of some process is not 20 percent or 90 percent, but infinite. Obviously something is very wrong.

By shining light of ever-higher frequency on electrons their position can be measured with ever-greater precision. But high-frequency protons have a lot of energy and give the electrons a sharp "kick" significantly changing their velocities. Even in the quietest region of space there is a tremendous amount of activity. And this activity gets increasingly agitated on ever-smaller distance and time scales. As we know, $E = M C^2$ so energy can be turned into matter and vice versa. If an energy fluctuation is big enough it can, for example, momentarily cause an electron and its anti-matter companion to erupt into existence, even if the region was initially empty. These particles will quickly annihilate each other, relinquishing the energy borrowed in their creation. And the same is true for all the other forms that energy and momentum can take: other particle eruptions and annihilations, wild electromagnetic-field oscillations, and weak and strong force field fluctuations. Quantum mechanical uncertainty tells us the universe is a teeming, chaotic, frenzied arena on a microscopic scale. Empty space looks calm and placid when examined with all but microscopic precision. This frenzy is *the* obstacle to merging general relativity and quantum mechanics.

Physicists working in the 1930s and 1940s found that Schrödinger's quantum wave equation was only an approximation. The central piece of physics that Schrödinger ignored in his formulation of quantum mechanics was Einstein's special relativity. Schrödinger had sought and found a mathematical framework encompassing the experimentally discovered wave-particle duality, but he did not, at that early stage of understanding, incorporate special relativity. So he ignored the malleability of matter, energy, and motion. Physicists tried to incorporate special relativity and by doing so they created quantum electrodynamics, which has come to be called relativistic quantum field theory or, simply, quantum field theory.

Toichira Kinoshita, a particle physicist from Cornell, spent 30 years using this theory to calculate certain detailed properties of electrons. His calculations yield predictions about electrons that have been verified by experiment to an accuracy of better than one part in a billion! Physicists have been able to solidify the role of photons as the "smallest bundles of light" and to reveal their interactions with electrons in a mathematically complete, predictive framework. Following this success, physicists were able to construct quantum field theories for the strong and weak forces, called quantum chromodynamics and quantum electro weak theory. At high enough energy and temperature levels, such as those existing a fraction of a second after the Big Bang, electromagnetic and weak force fields dissolve into one another and are more accurately called electro weak fields. When the temperature drops, the electromagnetic and weak forces crystallize from their common high-temperature form in a process known as symmetry breaking.

So physicists call the theory of the three non-gravitational forces and the three families of matter particles the standard theory or more often the standard model of particle physics.

The photon is the smallest constituent of an electromagnetic field. The smallest constituent of the strong force is the gluon. Those of the weak force are weak gauge bosons (or more precisely, the W and Z bosons). The standard model instructs us to think that these particles have no internal structure.

Einstein's theory implies that the absence of mass means that space is flat. When Einstein first posited the idea of curved space, the speculation was that anyone looking straight ahead for a long enough time would see the back of his head—that two parallel lines in space would eventually meet. But "flat" space does not mean two-dimensional space, but that space is curved in the vicinity of large masses, such as stars, but not in the larger sense. "Flat" in this context means that two parallel lines out into space will *not* eventually meet. Quantum theory shows that on average the space is zero, but that its actual value undulates up and down due to quantum fluctuations. The uncertainty principal also tells us that the size of the undulations gets larger as we focus on smaller regions of space. Quantum mechanics shows that nothing likes to be cornered. Narrowing the spatial focus leads to ever-larger undulations.

The smallness of the Planck's constant governs the strength of quantum effects. It also governs the intrinsic weakness of the gravitational force. These two team up to yield a result called the Planck length, which is small almost beyond imagining—a billionth of a billionth of a billionth of a billionth of a centimeter (10^{33}). As Brian Greene suggests, if we were to magnify an atom to the size of the whole universe, the Planck length would barely expand to the height of an average tree.

Chapter 5

String Theory

At the end of Chapter 3, there were two tables. One listed the three families of fundamental particles found in nature, and the other listed the four forces. The fundamental particles appear to have no further substructure, but string theory says they do. String theory says that if we could examine these particles with a precision many times our present technological capability, we would find that each is *not* a point, but instead a tiny, *one-dimensional* loop! The theory is that each particle is like an infinitely thin rubber band, a vibrating, and oscillating, dancing filament—a "string." Matter is composed of atoms. Atoms are composed of electrons and a nucleus of protons and neutrons. Protons and neutrons are composed of quarks. String theory holds that both electrons and quarks are composed of strings.

Many physicists believe that string theory may provide the final answer they have been seeking. The idea that everything at the ultra-microscopic level consists of combinations of vibrating strings provides a single explanatory framework capable of encompassing all matter and all forces. Strings are very, very small, about the size of the Planck length, so small that they appear pointlike even when examined by our most powerful equipment.

String theory proclaims that the properties summarized in the table on particles are a reflection of the various ways in which a string can vibrate.

Just as the strings of a violin or piano have resonant frequencies at which they prefer to vibrate, so do the loops of string. Some of the preferred patterns of vibration appear as particles. The mass of a particular particle is determined by the oscillatory pattern of the string. The electron is a string vibrating one way; the up-quark is a string vibrating another way, and so on.

The same idea applies to the forces of nature as well. Force patterns are also associated with particular patterns of string vibration.

The work done in the period from 1984 to 1986 is called the "first superstring revolution." This work showed that many features of the standard model emerged naturally and simply from string theory. But the arithmetic was very difficult, involving equations that are extremely hard to understand or analyze. So the scientists used approximations. Then at a conference on strings in 1995, Edward Witten announced a plan for taking the next step and ignited the "second superstring revolution."

Think about the strings on a violin. Each string on a violin can undergo a huge variety of different vibrational patterns, called resonances. Just as the different vibrational patterns of a violin string give rise to different musical notes, *the different vibrational patterns of a fundamental string give rise to different masses and force charges.*

From special relativity we know that energy and mass are two sides of the same coin, that $E = MC^2$. Greater energy means greater mass and vice versa. Thus, according to string theory, the *mass* of an elementary particle is determined by the *energy* of the vibrational pattern of its internal string. Heavier particles have internal strings that vibrate more energetically, while lighter particles have internal strings that vibrate less energetically.

There is a direct relation between the pattern of string vibration and a particle's response to the gravitational force and to the other forces. The electric charge, the weak charge, and the strong charge carried by a particular string are determined by the precise way it vibrates. Exactly the same idea holds for the messenger particles themselves. Particles like photons, weak gauge bosons, and gluons are yet other resonant patterns of string vibration. And of particular importance, one of the vibrational string patterns matches perfectly the properties of the graviton, ensuring that gravity is an integral part of string theory.

Each elementary particle is in fact a single string, and all strings are absolutely identical. Differences between particles arise because their respective strings undergo different resonant vibrational patterns. What appear to be different particles are actually different "notes" on a fundamental string. The different particles are just strings under different tension. The bottom line is that string theory offers a "Theory of Everything."

Tension

So the graviton, for example, is one particular pattern of string tension. The calculations show that the strength of the force transmitted by the proposed graviton pattern of string vibration is inversely proportional to the string's tension. Since the graviton is supposed to transmit a very feeble force, investigators found that this implies a colossal tension of a thousand billion billion billion billion (10^{39}) tons, the so-called Planck tension. Fundamental strings are therefore extremely stiff when compared with more familiar examples.

As Brian Greene points out, this has three important consequences. First, high tension causes the strings to contract to a minuscule size. Being under Planck tension causes a typical string to contract to Planck length (10^{-33}).

Second, because of the enormous tension, the typical energy in a vibrating string is extremely high. The greater the tension a string is under, the harder it is to get it to vibrate. In a similar way, it is easier to pluck a violin string than a piano string, which is under much greater tension. So, two strings that are under different tension and are vibrating in the same way will not have the same energy. The string with the higher tension will have the higher energy since more energy must be exerted to set it in motion.

Two things determine the energy of a vibrating string. More frantic patterns correspond to higher energies, and higher tension corresponds to higher energies. The minimal energies are huge multiples of the Planck energy. Translating the Planck energy into mass using $E = M C^2$, they correspond to masses ten billion billion (10^{19}) times that of a proton. This gargantuan mass (by elementary particle standards) is known as the Planck mass.

Through the weirdness of quantum mechanics, the energy associated with the quantum jitters of a string is negative. This reduces the overall energy content by an amount that is roughly equal to the Planck energy. This leaves relatively low net energy vibrations. Their corresponding mass equivalents are in the neighborhood of the matter and force particle masses shown in Brian Greene's two tables given in Chapter 3. As an important example, scientists found that for the vibrational pattern of the graviton messenger particle, the energy cancellations are *perfect*, resulting in a zero-mass gravitational force particle. *This is precisely what is expected for the graviton—the gravitational force is transmitted at light speed and only massless particles travel at this maximal velocity.*

Note that low-energy combinations are the exception. The more typical vibrating fundamental string corresponds to a particle whose mass is billions upon billions times greater than that of the proton.

Third, strings can execute an infinite number of different vibrational patterns.

Doesn't this mean that there would have to be an infinite number of elementary particles seemingly in conflict with the tables above? The answer, Greene says, is yes. But the high string tension ensures that all but a few of these will correspond to extremely heavy particles (the exceptions being the lowest-energy vibrations that have near-perfect cancellations with quantum string jitters). And heavy means many times the Planck mass. Since our most powerful accelerators can reach energies only a thousand times the proton mass, less than a millionth of a billionth of the Planck energy, we are very far from being able to search for any of these new particles predicted by string theory.

The energies in the Big Bang would have been high enough to produce these particles copiously. But such particles are highly unstable, relinquishing their enormous mass by decaying into a cascade of ever-lighter particles, ending with the familiar ones in the world around us. However, it is possible that such a super-heavy vibrational string — a relic of the Big Bang — did survive. As Brian Greene says, it would be a monumental discovery to find such a particle.

Theoretically, at ultra-microscopic levels there is violent and devastating quantum foam. But there is a limit that comes into play before you encounter such foam. Since the string is supposed to be the most elementary object in the universe and since it is too large to be affected by the violent sub-Planck-length undulations of the spatial fabric, these fluctuations cannot be measured and hence, according to string theory, do not actually exist.

The sub-Planck fluctuations are an artifact of formulating general relativity and quantum mechanics in a point-particle framework. So in a sense, the problem has been one of the scientists' own making. Through its graviton pattern of vibration, string theory is a quantum theory containing gravity.

Spin

All particles are endowed with a fixed amount of spin—always a multiple of a universal quantum that does not depend on mass, charge, or any other attribute of the particle. Wolfgang Pauli guessed that spin exists because of the way that the time dimension must be added to the other three dimensions. Spin signals the correctness of Einstein's theory of relativity.

By the end of the 1920s it was understood that there was a remarkable difference between particles whose spin is an integral number (such as photons) and those whose spin is half an integral number (such as electrons). The former are called bosons and the latter fermions. The difference is important because Pauli's exclusion principle applies only to fermions. That explains why stars, which consist primarily of neutrons (which are fermions), do not collapse.

Paul Dirac concluded not only that Pauli's spin was necessary but also that electrons must have an opposite number. Oppenheimer persuaded Dirac that these could not be protons. So Dirac predicted a particle identical to the electron but carrying a positive charge, the positron. If electrons are particles of matter, positrons are particles of anti-matter. One will annihilate the other, producing photons.

An electron orbits its nucleus. Does it also rotate, i.e. spin? Yes, every electron in the universe *spins at one fixed and never-changing rate*. It is an intrinsic property, much like its mass or electrical charge. If an electron were not spinning, it would not be an electron. All the matter particles and their anti-matter partners have spin. Physicists say that electrons all have spin—1/2 where the 1/2 is a quantum-mechanical measure of how quickly electrons rotate. Moreover, non-gravitational force carriers — photons, weak gauge bosons, and gluons — all possess an intrinsic spinning characteristic that turns out to be *twice* that of the matter particles. Gravitons have twice the spin of photons, i.e. spin-2. Strings *necessarily* have a vibrational pattern in their repertoire that is massless and has spin-2 — the hallmark features of the graviton. Where there is a graviton there is also gravity.

The idea of supersymmetry is that nature must come in pairs whose respective spins differ by half a unit. Since matter particles have spin-1/2 while some of the messenger particles have spin-1, supersymmetry appears to result in a pairing of matter and force particles. As such, it seems like a wonderful unifying concept. As Brian Greene says, the problem is in the details.

Physicists discovered that none of the known particles could be superpartners of one another. So if the universe incorporates supersymmetry, then every known particle must have an undiscovered superpartner particle whose spin is half a unit less than its known counterpart. There should be a spin-0 partner of the electron, and so on for all the other particles.

None of these particles has been discovered. But physicists are reluctant to give up. First, it is hard to believe that nature would respect some, but not all supersymmetries. Second, certain processes remain consistent only if the standard model is fine tuned to better than one part in a million billion. Supersymmetry changes this drastically because bosons whose spin is a whole number and fermions whose spin is half a whole (odd) number tend to give canceling quantum-mechanical contributions. The quantum jitters of a boson are positive and those of a fermion are negative. So cancellations are automatic and tend to calm the frenzied quantum effects. So with supersymmetry you don't need the delicate numerical adjustments of the standard model. As Brian Greene says, this makes supersymmetry very attractive.

The third piece of circumstantial evidence for supersymmetry comes from the notion of grand unification. One of the puzzling features of nature's four forces is the huge range of their intrinsic strengths. The electromagnetic force is 1 percent of the strong force. The weak force is 1,000 times feebler than that, and the gravitational force is some hundred million billion billion billion (10^{-35}) times weaker still. But it turns out that the quantum cloud of particle eruptions and annihilations amplifies the strength of the strong and weak forces. So if the haze of microscopic quantum activity is penetrated by examining the forces not on everyday scales but on distances of about a hundredth of a billionth of a billionth (10^{-39}) of a centimeter (only ten thousand times larger than the Planck length) the three non-gravitational force strengths appear to become equal.

The high energy necessary for all this occurred very early in the Big Bang. There is, however, a tiny discrepancy in their coming together. But the new super-partner particles required by supersymmetry are just right to nudge the three together.

Why haven't the scientists discovered any of these superpartner particles? The reason may be that it looks like these are very massive—one thousand times as massive as a proton. The present accelerators cannot reach such energies.

Then a new theory of string theory began to emerge, incorporating supersymmetry. The bosonic and fermionic patterns of vibration appeared to come in pairs. Supersymmetric string theory — superstring theory — had been born. It is only the supersymmetric version of string theory that has fermionic vibrational patterns that can account for the matter particles constituting the world around us. Superstring theory comes hand-in-hand with string theory's proposal for a quantum theory of gravity as well as with its grand claim of uniting all forces and all of matter. If string theory is right, Brian Greene says, physicists expect that supersymmetry is also right.

In 1919, Theodor Kaluza formulated some equations on the modest assumption that there was a fourth space dimension. He found extra equations beyond those developed by Einstein. To his amazement, the equations were the same as those that Maxwell had written down in the 1880s for describing the electromagnetic force! By adding another space dimension Kaluza had united Einstein's theory of gravity and Maxwell's theory of light!

His theory argued that both gravity and electromagnetism are associated with ripples in the fabric of space. Ripples in the familiar three space dimensions carry gravity, whereas ripples involving the new, curled up dimension, carry electromagnetism.

At first glance, Einstein liked the theory, but then changed his mind and discouraged Kaluza. Then two years later, Einstein had second thoughts and offered to present the theory to the academy. Isaac Klein augmented Kaluza's theory, but more study showed that the electron's mass and its charge were vastly different from their experimental values. Kaluza's idea was ahead of its time. At the time he was writing, everyone was interested in developing what became the "standard model." That success and the formulation of a quantum theory linking three of nature's forces emboldened physicists to try to bring the fourth, gravity, into the fold. The Kaluza-Klein theory was revived.

Since Kaluza and Klein's work, quantum theory had been developed and verified by experiment. The strong and weak forces, unknown in the 1920s, had been discovered. Some physicists felt that since Kaluza did not know of these forces, he had not been bold enough — more forces meant that more dimensions were needed! The essential requirement is that all of these dimensions have a spatial extent smaller than the smallest length that present equipment can probe; i.e., smaller than the Planck length. Although the equipment could probe a billionth of a billionth of a meter, it was not enough. It became clear that bits and pieces of a unified theory were surfacing but that a crucial element capable of tying them all together was missing. Then in 1984 the missing piece—string theory—dramatically entered the story and took center stage.

String theory solves the incompatibility between Einstein's theory of general relativity and quantum mechanics. But to accomplish these feats, string theory *requires that the universe have extra space dimensions.*

The reason is that one of the main insights of quantum mechanics is that our predictive power is limited to saying that something will happen with such and such a probability. This was repugnant to Einstein and others. But let us accept it. Now, probabilities are numbers between 0 and 1, or when expressed as percentages, between 0 and 100. The key signal that quantum mechanical theory had gone haywire was when particular calculations yielded probabilities that were *not* within this range. For example, the grinding incompatibility between general relativity and quantum mechanics *in a point particle framework* is that calculations *result in infinite probabilities.* String theory cures these infinities. But then physicists discovered that certain calculations yield *negative* results, which are also outside the acceptable range.

Finally, physicists found the cause of the unacceptable feature. If a string is forced to lie on a two-dimensional surface, the number of independent directions in which it can vibrate is reduced to two. If the string is allowed to leave the surface, it can vibrate in three dimensions. Calculations showed that if strings were allowed to vibrate in a total of *nine* directions, all the negative probabilities would cancel out. The Kaluza-Klein theory provides a loophole. Strings can vibrate in the large dimensions of our world, and they can also vibrate in tiny, curled-up dimensions. So Kaluza and Klein assumed that in addition to our three spatial dimensions, there are six curled-up spatial dimensions. Moreover, string theory *requires* them. The universe should have 9 space dimensions and 1 time dimension; i.e., 10.

But why 9 space and 1 time? Actually, the calculations that lead to this conclusion are *approximate.* One physicist calculates that there are 10 space dimensions and 1 time, for a total of 11. (Described below.)

Second, why are the three space and one time dimensions large and all the rest tiny and curled up? (Also discussed below.)

Third, if there are more than three space dimensions, why not more than one time dimension? If there are curled-up time dimensions, it might be possible to return to a prior instant in time! (This will *not* be discussed below because no one has even been able to speculate on it!).

Strings vibrate through all spatial dimensions. So the precise way that the extra dimensions are twisted up and curled back on each other influences the properties of particles that we see. This means that *extra-dimensional* geometry determines the particle masses and charges that we see in the usual three large space dimensions. *Because the patterns of string vibrations appear to us as the masses and charges of the elementary particles, we conclude that these fundamental properties of the universe are determined in large measure by the geometrical size and shape of these extra dimensions.* This, according to Brian Greene, is one of the most far-reaching insights of string theory.

The equations that emerge from the theory severely restrict the geometrical form that the extra spatial dimensions of string theory can take. In 1984, scientists showed that a particular class of six-dimensional geometric shapes could meet these conditions. Known as a Calabi-Yau space or shape from the two mathematicians who developed it while working in another field, the picture from Brian Greene's book, (page 207) gives an idea of what might look like if you could see it.

Edward Witten is fond of saying that string theory predicts gravity. Through its massless spin-2 graviton pattern of vibration, string theory has gravity thoroughly sewn into its theoretical fabric. As Brian Greene says, this *prediction* is more of a *postdiction*, since physicists had made theoretical descriptions of gravity before they knew of string theory. Most physicists would be happier if string theory made a prediction that could be verified by experiment. With a bit of luck, one central feature of string theory could be verified experimentally within the next decade. With a good deal more luck, indirect fingerprints of the theory could be confirmed at any moment.

Physicists can probe down to a billionth of a billionth of a meter with accelerators that are a few miles in size. Since the Planck length is some 17 orders of magnitude smaller than can currently be accessed, using today's technology would require an accelerator the size of the Milky Way galaxy to see individual strings. The calculations of one scientist indicate the accelerator might have to be the size of the whole universe! Although the energy required is only enough to run an air conditioner for 100 hours, the seemingly insurmountable technical problem is to focus all this energy on a single particle, i.e. on a single string. The Congress canceled the much smaller Superconducting Supercollider, which was to be only 54 miles in circumference. So testing string theory experimentally will have to be done in an indirect manner.

Recall that the elementary particles fall into three families with the particles in each family being successively massive. A typical Calabi-Yau shape contains holes analogous to the holes found in a doughnut (but these holes are multidimensional!). There is a family of lowest-energy string vibrations associated with each hole in the Calabi-Yau shape. So string theory proclaims that the family organization observed experimentally is not of random or divine origin but is a reflection of the number of holes in the geometric shape comprising the extra dimensions! Greene says that this is the kind of result that makes a physicist's heart skip a beat. The problem is that no one knows how to deduce from the equations of string theory which of the Calabi-Yau shapes constitutes the extra spatial dimensions.

If string theory is right, then some of the string vibrations will correspond to the known elementary particles. And due to supersymmetric pairing, string theory makes the *prediction* that each known particle will have a super partner. No super partners of the known elementary particles have yet been observed. This might mean that they do not exist and that string theory is wrong. But many physicists feel that it means that the super partners are very heavy and are thus beyond our current capacity to observe experimentally. A mammoth accelerator is being constructed in Geneva called the Large Hadron Collider, and when it is operational it may confirm supersymmetry. It should be ready before 2010.

A string is typically the Planck length, but strings that are more energetic can grow much larger. The energy of the Big Bang would have been high enough to produce a few strings that might have grown to astronomical scales. This kind of string left over from the Big Bang might sweep across the sky leaving an unmistakable imprint on data collected by astronomers, such as a small shift in the cosmic microwave background temperature. As Witten has said, "... nothing would settle the issue quite as dramatically as seeing a string in a telescope." Other possibilities listed by Greene on pages 224 and 225 are:

1. The standard model says neutrinos are massless. If they turn out to have some mass, which recent work indicates may well be the case, a challenge to string theory would be to explain why.

2. The standard model forbids certain processes, such as the decay of a proton and various combinations of quarks. If observed, they would offer fertile ground for string theory to explain.

3. Certain choices of the Calabi-Yau shape should produce patterns of string vibration that can contribute new, tiny, long-range force fields. If the effects of any such new forces are discovered they might reflect the new physics of string theory.

4. The puzzle about the nature of dark matter is another opportunity. String theory suggests a number of candidates.

5. String theory might settle the question of the cosmological constant.

In 1854, Georg Bernhard Riemann developed the mathematics for describing warped space. Einstein used Riemann geometry in general relativity. String theory asserts that this works only if the fabric of the universe is examined on a large enough scale. On scales as small as the Planck length a new kind of geometry is needed—quantum geometry.

The traditional notion of a point particle does not exist in string theory—an essential element in its ability to give us a quantum theory of gravity. Riemann's geometry relies fundamentally on distances between points. Physicists routinely model whole galaxies as if they were points, since their size in relation to the whole universe is tiny. So Riemann's geometry is a very accurate approximation. But in the ultramicroscopic realm, Riemann's geometry won't work. It must be replaced by the quantum geometry of string theory.

The universe has been expanding since the Big Bang. If the average matter density is greater than five hydrogen atoms for every cubic meter of the universe (the critical density), then a large enough gravitational force will be generated to reverse the process and lead eventually to a Big Crunch. If the average matter density is less, the universe will continue to expand forever. Visible matter is much less than the critical value. But, as we have seen, there is overwhelming evidence that the universe is full of dark matter that cannot be seen. Calculating the forces at work on a galaxy always adds up to considerably less than the visible light coming from that galaxy.

The Standard Model says that if the density is more than critical and there is a Big Crunch, the universe will shrink faster and faster until the whole universe becomes the size of our galaxy, the solar system, the Earth, an orange, a pea, a molecule, an atom, a point—*and finally to nothing at all*. The Standard Model says that the universe began from nothing and if the density is more than critical, it will return to nothing. But when the distances are around the Planck length, quantum mechanics invalidates the equations of general relativity. If string theory is valid, then the ultimate fate is quite different. String theory proclaims that the universe cannot be squeezed to a size smaller than the Planck length in any of its spatial dimensions.

Summary

To many scientists, superstring theory seems to offer the best hope for a "unifying theory." In this theory the basic entities are strings rather than points or particles. They are very tiny, 10^{20} times smaller than an atomic nucleus. Most superstring theories require 10 dimensions. We don't notice these many dimensions because they are "compactified"—as if a piece of two-dimensional paper is rolled up so tightly that it looks like a line.

The appeal of superstring theory is that it explains not only the basic particles but also the properties of *space*. Einstein's theory, which interprets gravity as curvature in four-dimensional space-time, is built into superstring theory. The quantum of gravity, the graviton, is the simplest vibration mode of a superstring loop.

Chapter 6

What Next?

Einstein refused to take his own theory at face value and to accept that it implies that the universe is neither eternal nor static. Alexander Friedman *did* accept Einstein's theory at face value and found what is now known as the Big Bang solution to Einstein's equations. This is that the universe emerged from a state of infinite compression and is currently in the expanding aftermath of that explosion. Einstein wrote an article claiming to have found a fatal flaw in Friedman's work. Eight months later, Friedman convinced Einstein that there was no flaw, and Einstein curtly retracted his objection. Five years later, Hubble's observations confirmed that the universe was in fact expanding.

About 15 billion years ago, to repeat, the universe erupted in an enormously energetic, apparently singular event that spewed forth all of space, matter, and energy. You don't have to look for where it occurred. It took place where you are right now and everywhere else as well. All locations in the beginning were all the same location. The temperature at a mere 10^{-43} seconds after Big Bang, the Planck time, was about 10^{32} Kelvin, some 10 trillion trillion times hotter than the deep interior of the Sun.

As time passed the universe cooled and as it did, the initial homogenous, roiling, hot, primordial, cosmic plasma began to form eddies and clumps. At about a hundred-thousandth of a second after the Big Bang, things had cooled sufficiently (to about 10 trillion Kelvin—about a million times hotter than the Sun's interior) for quarks to clump together in groups of three, forming protons and neutrons. About a hundredth of a second later, nuclei of some of the lightest elements in the periodic table started to congeal out of the cooling plasma of particles. For the next three minutes, as the simmering universe cooled to about a billion degrees, the predominant nuclei that emerged were those of hydrogen and helium, along with trace amounts of deuterium ("heavy" hydrogen) and lithium. This is known as the period of *primordial nucleosynthesis*.

Not much happened over the next few hundred thousand years, other than further expansion and cooling. But then, when the temperature had dropped to a few thousand degrees, the wildly streaming electrons slowed down to the point where the atomic nuclei of hydrogen and helium could capture them, forming the first electrically neutral atoms. This was a pivotal moment. From this point forward the universe became transparent. Prior to the era of electron capture, the universe was filled with dense plasma of electrically charged particles—some with positive charges like nuclei and some with negative charges like electrons. Photons, which interact only with electrically charged objects, were bumped and jostled incessantly by the thick bath of charged particles, traversing hardly any distance before being deflected or absorbed. The charged-particle barrier to the free motion of photons would have made the universe appear almost completely opaque, much like what you may have experienced in a dense morning fog or a blinding, gusty snowstorm. But when negatively charged electrons were brought into orbit around positively charged nuclei, yielding electrically neutral atoms, the charged obstructions disappeared and the dense fog lifted. From that time onward, photons from the Big Bang have traveled unhindered, and the full expanse of the universe gradually came into view.

About a billion years later, with the universe having substantially calmed down from its frenetic beginnings, galaxies, stars, and ultimately planets began to emerge as gravitationally bound clumps of the primordial elements.

How much faith can we have in the Big Bang theory? As already described, the most convincing proof was accidentally discovered—the Cosmic Background Radiation. The universe is filled with microwave radiation whose temperature is about 2.7 degrees above absolute zero. In every cubic meter of the universe, including the one your body occupies, there are on average 400 million photons, the echo of creation. A percentage of the "snow" you see on your TV screen when you disconnect the cable and tune to a station that has ceased broadcasting for the day is cosmic background radiation.

Physicists can make definite predictions about the lighter elements produced in the period of primordial nucleosynthesis between one-hundredth of a second and a few minutes after the Big Bang. According to theory about 23 percent of the universe should be composed of helium. By measuring the helium in stars and nebulae, astronomers have amassed impressive evidence that this prediction is right on the mark. Even more impressive is the estimate of deuterium, since there is no astrophysical process other than the Big Bang that can account for its small but definite presence in the universe. The same is true of lithium.

Prior to about 10^{-35} seconds after the Big Bang, the strong, weak, and electromagnetic forces were all one super force. But as time went by and the universe expanded and cooled, this symmetry was reduced in a series of abrupt steps. Consider a container of water. It looks the same in every direction. But as it cools and suddenly turns to ice, it is no longer symmetrical. This is a phase transition. Water goes from being a gas, with a very high symmetry; to water, with somewhat less symmetry; to ice, with still less. Physicists believe that between the Planck time and a hundredth of a second after the Big Bang the universe passed through two analogous phase transitions. At temperatures above 10^{28} Kelvin, the three non-gravitational forces appeared as one, as symmetric as they could possible be. But as the temperature dropped the universe underwent a phase transition in which the three forces crystallized out from their common union in different ways. Their relative strengths and how they act on matter began to diverge. So the symmetry evident at higher temperatures was broken as the universe cooled. But not all the high-temperature symmetry was erased—the weak and electromagnetic forces were still deeply interwoven. As the universe further expanded and cooled nothing much happened until things simmered down to 10^{15} degrees, about 100 million times the Sun's core temperature. Then the universe went through another phase transition in which the electromagnetic and weak forces crystallized out. The two-phase transitions are responsible for the three apparently distinct, though deeply related, non-gravitational forces at work.

The Horizon Problem

The cosmic background radiation is the same in every direction you look. Two regions of space can exchange energy and so come to have a common temperature only if the distance between them is less than the distance light can have traveled since the Big Bang. At a billionth of a second after the Big Bang, they were one foot apart—and there was just not enough time since the Big Bang for light to have traveled the distance between the two regions. Even at a billionth of a second after the Big Bang, the two regions still cannot influence each other, since light could not have traveled the 12 inches between them. Alan Guth in 1979 supplied the missing link—inflation. He found another solution to Einstein's equations in which the very early universe undergoes a brief period of enormously rapid expansion—it inflates in size at an unheralded exponential expansion rate.

During a tiny window of time—around 10^{-36} to 10^{-34} seconds after the Big Bang—the universe expanded by an unbelievably huge factor of at least 10^{30}. So in a brief flicker of time, about a trillionth of a trillionth of a trillionth of a second after the Big Bang, the universe increased in size by a greater percentage than it has in the 15 billion years since! Matter was closer long enough for a common temperature to come to pass. This solved the horizon problem.

What happened before the Big Bang? One answer is that it does not matter because it does not affect the state of our universe today. Dr. Andrei Linde in 1986 put forward a theory known as eternal inflation that the Big Bang was only one of many in a chain reaction of big bangs by which the universe endlessly reproduces and reinvents itself. "Any particular part of the universe may die, and probably will die," Dr. Linda said, "but the inverse as a whole is immortal."

Einstein's theory says that nothing can travel faster than the speed of light, but this does not restrict the speed at which a bubble of space-time can itself expand. This is why Guth's inflationary universe does not conflict with Einstein. So, one microsecond after the Big Bang, the observable universe would have been 300 meters in diameter, just over five times as big as the standard football field in diameter. At that stage the temperature would have fallen to 10,000 billion degrees and the density of the particles of matter would have been comparable with that in an atomic nuclei or in neutron stars. So the full rigors of the general theory of relativity would apply. Space–time would have been tightly curved.

Below is a time line provided by Brian Greene (page 356) of key moments in the history of the universe. In the standard model at time zero the universe vanishes, and the temperature and density soar to infinity. Greene argues that this is a warning that something is wrong with the theoretical model, that nature is telling us that at this point we must merge general relativity and quantum mechanics. In other words, we must make use of string theory.

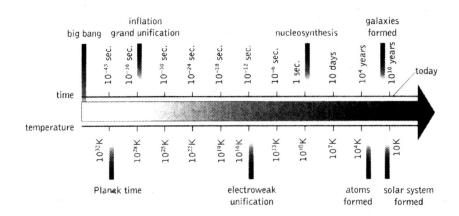

Much is still unknown, but physicists believe that string theory modifies the standard cosmological model in three ways.

First, Greene calls attention to a sliver of time between the Big Bang and the Planck time. String theory implies that the universe does not vanish before the Big Bang, but at this point is at its minimum size. As Greene says, this has profound consequences. Second, string theory has a small-radius/large-radius duality. Third, string theory has more than four space-time dimensions.

In the beginning all the spatial dimensions of string theory were tightly curled up to their smallest possible extent, which is the Planck length. The temperature and energy were high, but not infinite. All the spatial dimensions of string theory were completely symmetric—all curled up in a multi-dimensional, Planck-sized nugget. At about the Planck time, three spatial dimensions expanded and the rest retained their Planck-scale size. The three expanded to their current form.

Why three? Robert Brandenberger and Cumrun Vafa came up with a possible explanation. When a dimension is curled up like a circle, a string can wrap around it and keep it from expanding. If a wrapped string and its anti-string partner come into contact, they will annihilate each other, producing an *unwrapped string*. If these processes happen with sufficient rapidity and efficiency, enough of the rubber band-like constriction will be eliminated allowing the dimension to expand. Brandenberger and Vafa suggested that this would happen to only three of the dimensions.

In the first moment of the universe, the high temperature drove all the circular dimensions to try to expand. But wrapped strings restricted the expansion, driving the dimensions back to their original Planck-size radii. But sooner or later random thermal fluctuations will drive three dimensions to grow larger than the others, and strings, which wrap these dimensions, are highly likely to collide. About half of these collisions will involve string/anti-string pairs leading to annihilations that continually lessen the constriction, allowing these three dimensions to continue to expand. The more they expand, the less likely it is for other strings to get entangled around them, since it takes more energy for a string to wrap around a larger dimension. And so the expansion feeds on itself, becoming ever less constricted, as the dimensions get ever larger. They continue to expand to a size as large or larger than our current universe.

Cosmology and Calabi-Yau Shapes

In the tumultuous, hot moments after the Big Bang, the curled-up Calabi-Yau components of space stay small but go through a frenetic dance in which their fabric rips apart and reconnects over and over again, rapidly taking us through a long sequence of Calabi-Yau shapes. As the universe cools and three of the spatial dimensions get large, the transitions from one Calabi-Yau shape to another slow down, with the extra dimensions ultimately settling into a Calabi-Yau shape that gives rise to the physical features we observe in the world around us.

As Brian Greene says (p. 383) among the several features of string theory, the following are perhaps the most important to keep in mind:

First, gravity and quantum mechanics are part and parcel of how the universe works and any unified theory must incorporate both. String theory does this.

Second, other key ideas, many of which have been confirmed by experiment, appear central to our understanding of how the universe works. These include such concepts as spin, the family structure of the particles of matter, messenger particles, gauge symmetry, the equivalence principle, symmetry breaking, and supersymmetry. All of these emerge naturally from string theory.

Third, unlike the standard model, which has 19 free parameters that can be adjusted to ensure agreement with experiments, string theory has no adjustable parameters. Its implications should be thoroughly definitive—they should provide an unambiguous test of whether the theory is right or wrong.

Laymen stand in awe of the achievements of science, but even so they occasionally have an uneasy feeling that string theory is not the final answer. The notion of seven, curled-up dimensions is just too reminiscent of mathematical gimmicks used in the past to salvage theories that started off with an inadequate basic assumption. In particular it brings to mind the marvelous mathematical solution that Ptolemy used to reconcile the observed movements of the planets, the "wanderers," with the assumption, so deeply held that it was rarely questioned, that the Earth was the center of the universe. He was able to develop orbits for the planets with the Earth as the center, but only by making them enormously complicated, as shown in the illustration given below (from Robert Wilson, *Astronomy through the Ages, The story of the human attempt to understand the Universe*, (Princeton University Press, 1997, p. 36). Astronomers used Ptolemy's model for 1,000 years.

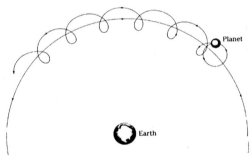

A team of astronomers led by Dr. Richard Ellis combined the natural magnifying power of a galaxy 2 billion light years away to detect the faint light from 13.4 billion light years away. By bending the distant light, the gravitational lens makes the image of a baby galaxy 30 times brighter. With this discovery we may be witnessing the birth of one of the first stars.

In 1964, Dr. Val Fitch and Dr. James Cronin discovered in an experiment for which they were awarded the Nobel Prize, the kaons or neutral k's, behaved differently. Such differences may explain why the Big Bang did not produce equal amounts of matter and anti-matter, which would then have annihilated each other and left nothing but light. New findings show with a statistical certainty of 99.997 percent, that the effect also occurs in another type of particle, the B meson. What the scientists want to find is a crack in the standard model.

String theory, to repeat, hypothesizes tiny strings vibrating in nine-dimensional space, with some strings manifesting themselves as matter-particles like protons and neutrons and others manifesting themselves as force-particles like the photon and the graviton. But these are smaller than the Planck length, and the instruments now available cannot detect them. Also as we have seen, about 90 percent of our universe is made up of so-called dark matter that neither emits nor absorbs light, but makes itself known only through gravity.

A photograph of a distant exploding star has given the first direct evidence of a mysterious "negative gravity" that swept through the universe and still pervades it. The Hubble space telescope photographed the exploding star, the most distant ever observed, in 1997. Scientists say that subsequent detective work on the relative intensity of its light confirms one of Einstein's conjectures about the universe—that all of space is bobbling with an invisible form of energy that creates a mutual repulsion among objects normally attracted to each other by gravity.

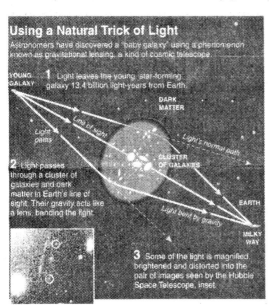

Using a Natural Trick of Light
Astronomers have discovered a "baby galaxy" using a phenomenon known as gravitational lensing, a kind of cosmic telescope.

YOUNG GALAXY 1 Light leaves the young, star-forming galaxy 13.4 billion light-years from Earth.

2 Light passes through a cluster of galaxies and dark matter in Earth's line of sight. Their gravity acts like a lens, bending the light.

3 Some of the light is magnified, brightened and distorted into the pair of images seen by the Hubble Space Telescope, inset.

In 2003 a 12.7 billion-year-old planet was discovered in the constellation Scorpius, 7,200 ligh-years from Earth. This challenged a long-held view that planets could not have originated so early because the universe had not yet generated enough heavy elements to make them. The conclusion is that planet formation is more widespread and happened earlier than was believed.

Einstein called the force the cosmological constant, but he thought it so strange he repudiated the conclusion. The idea gained support in 1998 with findings suggesting that the expansion of the universe was accelerating and that the force accelerating the expansion, negative gravity, overtook the force of gravity in the last few billion years.

The new observation is of a star that exploded about 11 billion years ago when, scientists theorized, the cosmological constant, called "dark energy," was less powerful than gravity. Until recently, scientists felt that the gravitational attraction among the galaxies would slow the expansion. If Einstein's explanation is correct, extremely distant supernovas should appear to brighten relative to some standard, rather than continue to dim. A difficult and time-consuming analysis of light from the star showed that it was twice as bright as it would have been if cosmic dust had been obscuring it. Cosmologists will have to cope with a universe that seems increasingly filled with mysterious stuff that scientists cannot see and do not fully understand.

The supernova researchers will have to go to space and employ a wide network of people and telescopes to detect these explosions, diagnose their type, and watch them fade. An orbiting telescope would perfrm all three functions, the Supernova/Acceleration Probe, or SNAP, would combine an 80-inch diameter mirror, a giant electronic camera with a billion pixels, and a special spectroscope. The device could be launched in 2008, and in three years of operation could harvest about 2,000 supernovas. To distinguish the difference in ideas about dark energy, observations would have to be refined to the level of one to two percent uncertainty.

Recently, theorists have expanded superstring theory to include vibrating membranes—called branes for short. These "surfaces" can be tiny like strings, but they can also span across light years. Dr. Lisa Randall of Princeton and Dr. Raman Sundrum of Stanford have proposed a revision of string theory in which at least one of the extra six dimensions would be large enough to be tested. Suppose that our entire universe is a 3-dimensional brane floating inside a 4-dimensional megaverse. Assume that most particles are open-ended vibrating strings and that the reason we cannot explore the surroundings is because the strings that make up our universe are stuck to the surface of the gargantuan home brane. We cannot peer into the extra dimension because photons, the carriers of light, are also anchored to our home brane. But gravitons are thought to be generated by vibrating loops with no ends to stick to the brane. So how do you get gravitons to stick to the brane? The gravity we know is weak. A magnet can pick up a paper clip even though the full force of the Earth's gravity is pulling back at it. It can be shown mathematically that if gravity were allowed to roam through all four dimensions it would be much stronger than the gravity we experience. But the theory proposed by Randall and Sundrum holds that if hyperspace is curved in just the right way, the gravitons could be kept from escaping and becoming unreasonably strong. If hyperspace were shaped like a funnel, it would encourage a kind of feedback effect. Gravitons would be channeled back to the brane, preventing them from wandering off into the extra dimension. Randall and Sundrum suggest that this might explain why gravity is so weak. It may seem weak because gravitons are concentrated on a different brane from our own. The region surrounding this other brane might be so severely warped that it would suck in most of the available gravitons. If so, only stray gravitons would appear in our brane, just enough to provide the weak gravitational force that we see.

It follows that dark matter could be just ordinary matter waving to us from another brane. The photons in the other brane can only move along the surface of the brane, but the gravitons could seep across the fourth-dimensional light.

The theory also suggests why dark matter tends to be found in halos around galaxies. Large masses on the other brane would line up with large masses on ours. So we could feel the gravity of that matter without being able to see it on our brane. Sitting behind a galaxy in our brane separated by the void of hyperspace would be a dark galaxy in the other brane. Because most of its gravity would be occluded, it would be apparent only around the edges. Conversely luminous matter on our brane would be dark to observers on the other brane. The only way we could communicate would be by signaling with gravity waves.

Since gravitons are not so tightly confined as other particles sometimes they will stray into hyperspace becoming heavier than the ordinary variety, and this may provide the basis for a test of the string theory approach. The Textron accelerator at Fermilab slams protons into antiprotons to produce energies measured in trillions of electron volts. Using this accelerator, physicists would not be able to detect heavy gravitons directly, since they would immediately fly off into a higher dimension. But their existence might be inferred. The energy going into a particle collision must equal that going out. If some were missing, it would indicate that they were being spirited away by gravitons flying off into hyperspace. In fact, if enough gravitons were packed into a tiny volume of space, they would collapse into miniature black holes. Creating black holes sounds scary, but they will pose no danger, since they would rapidly evaporate. In any case, experiments like this will be on the agenda when the Large Hadron Collider begins operation at the CERN accelerator in Geneva Switzerland.

Part Two:

The Earth

Chapter 7

The Earth, the Moon, and the Continents in Collision

The gas cloud from which the Sun formed was the remnant of an earlier supernova explosion and so contained the heavy elements necessary for the world, as we know it. The gas cloud also spawned nine planets, thousands of asteroids, and billions of comets. As the Sun's planets condensed out of the parent cloud of gas, they continued to accrete debris for several hundred million years. The surface of the rocky planets (as opposed to the gaseous ones) was made molten by the persistent high-velocity impacts of debris, and this inhibited the formation of complex molecules and so of life.

The planet Earth, unlike the others, was formed in a zone around the Sun in which the Sun's heat kept most of the water as oceans. Had the Earth been closer to the Sun, the water would have vaporized. Had the Earth been further away, it would have frozen. In either case, life as we know it could not have evolved.

Inside the chemically rich oceans a simple anaerobic bacteria emerged by a mechanism still not known. These bacteria transformed the Earth's atmosphere from one rich in carbon dioxide and deficient in oxygen into one with enough oxygen to allow aerobic organisms to develop.

The emergence of life also depended on another piece of good fortune. Ultra-violet light, which is emitted from the Sun in great quantities, is hostile to life. However, although oxygen atoms are normally found in pairs

(O_2), some exist in threes (O_3) to form ozone, and ozone serves as a shield that protects the Earth's surface from most ultra-violet light.

The Moon

Various theories were proposed about the origin of the moon. An early one was that the moon and the Earth formed together from the disk of material surrounding the newborn Sun. This is the way that most other planets spawned moons. If so, both would have had the same composition, but the moon is poor in iron. Another theory was that the moon was formed elsewhere in the solar system and was captured by the Earth. But studies of orbital dynamics have shown that this would have required the intervention of a third planetary body, which is very unlikely.

Also, the moon is too big for this explanation, since it is more than a quarter of the diameter of the Earth. Only Pluto has a satellite so large in relation to itself. The moon is also made of the wrong stuff; not green cheese but matter that is very much like the crust of the Earth. The Earth has an iron core. The moon, as already mentioned, is poor in iron. Its density is about the same as the Earth's mantle or crust. The moon has no water that we know about, although some may exist in a frozen state. But many minerals and their isotopes on both the moon and Earth are the same. Finally the moon's orbit is all wrong. Every other major satellite in the solar system orbits above its planet's equator. But the Earth's axis is tipped relative to the plane of its orbit by 27 degrees, and the moon orbits along the Earth's orbital plane, not its equator.

A recent theory, dubbed the "Big Splash," visualizes the following scenario: About 4.5 billion years ago the young Earth, still red-hot beneath its thin, new crust, had been constantly bombarded by thousands of asteroid-sized objects. It had grown in size but was still considerably smaller than what it is today. Most of its iron, still molten, had sunk to form a dense core. Suddenly a fast-moving, fully formed planet the size of Mars or perhaps larger loomed from space. Traveling at a speed of 40,000 kilometers an hour, it struck the Earth a glancing blow. Most of its material was incorporated into the liquefied Earth, adding to its mass. The intruder's iron core looped around the Earth, struck again, and this time penetrated the Earth and merged with the Earth's own iron core.

The heat generated by the impact vaporized most of the intruder's crust along with a good part of the Earth's. A great, expanding, fiery cloud of gasified rock was squirted out into space. There it finally settled into orbit at a height of about 22,500 kilometers and eventually condensed as the moon. This explains why the moon is lower in density than the Earth, and why it lacks iron, since all the material came from the crust of the intruder and the crust of the Earth itself and none from their iron cores.

After about one year, the cloud of gasified rock condensed into solid particles and formed a ring around the Earth. The particles slowly clumped together, and over a period of about 100 years, they formed a single body—the infant moon. At that point the Earth and the moon resembled a double planet. The moon circled the Earth rapidly at a small fraction of its present distance from the Earth, and the Earth spun rapidly, thanks to the glancing blow it had suffered from the impact.

The infant moon was covered by molten rock—magma. As the lunar surface hardened, meteors, asteroids, and comets peppered it. About 3.2 billion years ago, large objects ceased to hit the moon, but smaller ones continued to hit it, forming many craters. Mountains on the moon were not formed by folding, as on Earth, but by piled up debris from these impacts.

Over the following millennia, lunar tides caused the Earth's spin rate to slow to once every 24 hours, the moon to move away from the Earth to its present distance of about 385,000 kilometers, and to slow the moon's spin until today it presents only one face toward the Earth.

Continental Drift

Mountains have been a puzzle to humankind. They occur not at random, but in long, narrow belts, and on some of the highest peaks are found fossilized sea creatures.

Archbishop James Ussher, Anglican Primate of All Ireland and confidant of Charles I, enjoyed international respect in the first half of the seventeenth century. His major work was a history of the Earth and humankind. For him, as for his western contemporaries, the only reliable source for such a history was the Holy Bible. He regarded the ancient Greek, Egyptian, and Chinese accounts as unreliable compendiums of mythology and legend. Ussher recognized that in the Bible several peoples tell a story in another time and in different voices and languages, so it had inconsistencies and contradictions. He set about to sort out them all out. He concluded that heaven and Earth had been created during the night preceding Sunday, October 23, 4004 B.C. On the following Tuesday, the waters had gathered together, and dry land emerged. Humankind and other forms of life appeared on the following Friday. The Deluge followed 1,655 years later. Noah entered the Ark on Sunday, December 7, 2349, B.C., and left it on Wednesday, May 6, the following year. Ussher's work was universally acclaimed, and his chronology was often printed in the margins of new editions of the Bible.

Some doubt was expressed when travelers to China reported that recorded genealogies of ancient Chinese families went back to a time before Ussher's dates for the both the Deluge and the Creation. During the so-called Enlightenment that swept the western world during the eighteenth century, doubts increased as scientific enquiry revealed the presence of fossilized marine creatures in high mountains. After the voyages of discovery in the sixteenth century, mapmakers noticed the strange similarities in the coasts of Africa and South America, and it was suggested that the two might have once been joined. But the Ussher supporters argued that what had separated them was the Flood!

A French naturalist observed that rain, wind, and waves were wearing away the continents so rapidly that soon no land would remain unless new rock grew to take its place. The Church denounced him for heresy.

René Descartes in 1634 concluded that the creation of the Earth had been the result of natural processes. But he did not dare publish his conclusions because of what the Church had done to his friend Galileo for saying only that the Earth revolved around the Sun.

In 1911, Alfred Wegener, a lecturer in astronomy and meteorology, was browsing in the library at the University of Marburg, when he chanced on a paper theorizing that a land bridge had once existed between Brazil and Africa. He read descriptions of identical fossils of creatures that could not possibly have crossed an ocean and yet were found on opposite sides of the Atlantic. This came as a surprise, and the subject became an obsession with him. The idea that the continents could have moved such fantastic distances seemed inconceivable. But he eventually became convinced that this was the explanation. He proposed the theory in Frankfurt in 1912.

His ideas were ridiculed. He kept working on the theory and published his conclusions in 1915. But they received little attention. Three more editions followed in 1920, 1922, and 1929. Wegener identified eight geological features that matched perfectly and suggested that all the continents were once joined in one single land mass. He named it Pangaea and calculated that it existed 300 million years ago.

Wegener's theory also explained the creation of mountains, which had been particularly puzzling to scientists. When the leading edge of a drifting continent hit another continent, he speculated, the target continent crumpled and folded into great mountains. As America drifted westward, for example, with the Atlantic ocean opening up in its wake, the resistance of the cooled bedrock of the ancestral Pacific caused the folding of the Rockies and the Andes.

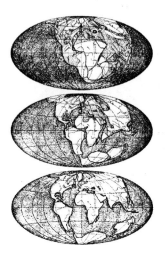

The sea floor between Europe and America is moving apart at just about the same speed that your fingernails grow! Quite fast, although not so fast as toenails! Similarly, India drifted northward after separating from Antarctica, collided with Asia, and uplifted the Himalayas.

As to what provided the enormous force that moved the continents, Wegener speculated that there were two. The first was the centrifugal force generated by the spinning of the Earth. Centrifugal force tends to move rotating objects away from the center of rotation. The second was the gravitational attraction of the Sun and the moon, which causes the ebb and flow of the tides, working in the opposite direction.

Wegener died, apparently of a heart attack, on a trip to Greenland, with his theory of continental drift still not accepted.

Maurice Ewing later developed a technique of exploding a stick of dynamite on the surface of the ocean and measuring the seismic waves reflected from the ocean bottom. He founded Columbia University's Lamont Geological Observatory and eventually discovered a deep canyon down the center of the mid-Atlantic ridge. Comprising millions of square miles of jagged peaks, jumbled cliffs and valleys, the ridge snakes in a great S bend down the center of the Atlantic, then curves east around the African continent and into the Indian Ocean, where it forks in two. One chain goes north into the Gulf of Aden; where it splits again into the Red Sea and the East African rift system. The other strikes off south of Australia and New Zealand into the Pacific where, several thousand miles from the tip of South America, the ridge curves north, eventually entering the Gulf of California and joining the San Andreas fault zone. Almost entirely hidden under the ruffled surface of the oceans, its great peaks thrust a mile or more above the rift valley floor, occasionally poking above the waves to form rocky islands like the Azores and Iceland.

Sea Mounts

During World War II, Harry H. Hess, a professor of geology, was in command of an attack transport fitted with an echo sounder that drew continuous profiles of the ocean floor to permit the troop carrier to move as close inshore as possible. Hess kept his switched on all the time, and he noticed a number of strangely shaped submarine mountains. He named them guyots after the distinguished nineteenth century Princeton geologist, Arnold Guyot. Like most old volcanic islands subjected to aeons of scouring by wind and wave, the guyots had extremely flat tops. What was puzzling was that they were all well below the surface of the ocean, beyond the reach of erosion. Also puzzling was the fact that the deeper they were, the farther they were from the mid-ocean ridge. Hess concluded that they had formed as volcanic islands along the ridge, had been truncated by erosion while on the surface, and then had somehow submerged and drifted away from the ridge.

Hess, like most of his colleagues, placed no credence in the theory of continental drift. But the suggestion that the mid-ocean ridges were part of a continuous underwater mountain chain set him to thinking. His guyots, the absence of ocean-floor rocks older than about 150 million years, the missing sediment in the rift areas, the heat flow from the rift, and the thinness of the oceanic crust—all these led him to conclude that the ocean floors were moving like conveyor belts, carrying the continents along with them. The mid-ocean ridge is a crack in the crust of the Earth through which hot material from the underlying mantle constantly wells up and spreads outward. He estimated that new crust is generated at the rate of 1/2 inch a year on each side of the ridge. At this pace all of the ocean floors in the world would have been formed during the last 200 million years —less than 5 percent of the Earth's geological history. As new crust is generated, old crust is being destroyed by subduction as it plunges into the deep trenches that lie at the edge of the continents. The continents are carried passively on the mantle and do not themselves plow through the ocean crust.

His theory was met with skepticism. But confirmation finally came from a different field. As molten lava solidifies and cools tiny crystals of magnetite within it become permanently magnetized in parallel with the Earth's magnetic field as if the rocks were recording magnetic compasses. P. M. S. Blackett invented a device that could detect extremely weak magnetic fields. He and his colleagues took samples from all over Britain, and their findings could be explained only if Britain had, starting some 200 million years earlier, rotated clockwise through 30 degrees of longitude and at the same time drifted northward from a lower latitude.

Another team of researchers doubted that the continents had moved. They believed that the Earth as a whole had shifted its position relative to the magnetic axis, causing the poles to "wander." They traced the wanderings of the north magnetic pole as indicated by the rocks in Britain and the continent along a 13,000-mile path that started in western North America about one billion years ago, curved across the northern Pacific and northern Asia, and finally reached its present position in the Arctic about 20 million years ago. They concluded this did not indicate continental drift. But they were soon to change their minds.

Another team took measurements in North America that indicated that the Pole had followed a similar course, but in a completely different location—30 degrees of longitude separated it from the path charted in Europe. They then realized that the only way to explain such a divergence was to suppose that when the North American rocks had formed, they had been 30 degrees of longitude closer to the European rocks—that there had been no Atlantic ocean, and that the two continents had been joined. When this was assumed, the two plots of the separate paths fitted almost perfectly! The poles may have wandered, but the continents had also drifted.

Plate Tectonics

The theory of plate tectonics holds that the Earth's outer shell is divided into nine large plates and a number of smaller plates. The continents ride on the plates like logs stuck in an ice floe. The ocean floors are constantly being reduced at the subduction zones and regenerated at the mid-ocean ridge. The continents are permanent features of the Earth's crust. Because they are lighter and thicker than the basalt of the ocean crust, they never sink.

About 60 miles thick, rigid, and immensely strong, the plates float on a soft, hot, semi-viscous layer of the Earth known as the asthenosphere. Beneath this lies the Earth's deep mantle. High temperatures and tremendous pressures on its top layers cause the asthenosphere to deform and even to flow plastically, thus permitting the plates to inch along. The African and Antarctic plates are almost totally surrounded by sea-floor-forming ridges, and are nowhere being destroyed.

The whole jigsaw puzzle of plates is interlinked. No one plate can move without affecting the others. The Atlantic Ocean is getting wider, but the Pacific plate is being consumed in deep oceanic trenches. The plates move an average of two inches a year—30 miles in one million years. This is very fast by geological standards. It took only 150 million years for a mere fracture in an ancient continent to turn into the Atlantic Ocean! The driving force is heat, generated deep in the Earth by radioactive decay.

The most famous fault is the San Andreas, stretching for 1,000 miles in California. The Pacific plate on the west side of the fault moves northward at the rate of two inches a year relative to the American plate on the east side. When two plates become locked, tremendous forces build up—eventually relieved by a major earthquake. At 5:12 A.M. on April 18, 1906, in less than a minute one plate lurched 20 feet northward along a 270 mile stretch of the fault, releasing energies that had been building up for over a century, and causing the San Francisco earthquake. An example of when two plates containing continents collide is the Himalayas. These are the highest mountains in the world and are still being thrust up as India, embedded in the Indo-Australian plate, continues to crunch relentlessly into Tibet on the southern edge of the Eurasian plate. The European Alps formed in a similar fashion, when some 80 million years ago the outlying fragments of the African plate collided with the Eurasian plate. The pressure continues, slowly closing the Mediterranean.

The Hawaiian Islands are another dramatic example of plate movement. Stretching to the west and north of the big island of Hawaii is a string
of smaller islands and submerged volcanoes or seamounts 3,700 miles long,
and every one seems to have formed at the spot where Hawaii now stands.
This "hot spot" causes a massive thermal plume to rise up and melt holes
through the plate like a blowtorch. This subterranean blast furnace is nearly
stationary, unaffected by mantle convection, perhaps because of its great
depth. The Pacific plate slides over the hot spot at the rate of about 5 inches
a year, and when a hole is melted through the plate a new volcanic island
appears.

Chapter 8

From the Great Dying to the Great Flood

Sixty-five million years ago, which is less than two percent of the Earth's current lifetime, over ninety percent of all species on Earth suddenly died out. Walter Alvarez, a geologist, and his father, Luis Alvarez, a Nobel Laureate physicist, proposed in their book, *T. Rex and the Crater of Doom* (Princeton University Press, 1997) that the mass extinction was caused by the impact of a meteor weighing 10 trillion tons. It hit the Earth near to what is now the Yucatan peninsula, and its debris blocked sunlight and obliterated over 90 percent of the Earth's flora and fauna. This included the dinosaurs, which had been the dominant land animals until that time.

However, the tragedy opened an opportunity for Earth's small surviving mammals to fill the vacated niches. One branch of these were primates, which produced the several species of *Homo*, then *Homo sapiens*, and eventually *Homo sapiens sapiens* who were intelligent enough and curious enough to find out how their world had come to be, and how they, themselves, had emerged.

In the early 1970s, Walter Alvarez was puzzling over a layer of rocks in Italy. Oddly, it was rich in iridium, rare on Earth, but common in comets and asteroids. After a year of pondering, Walter and Luis developed the thesis that the iridium had come from a comet or asteroid that had hit the Earth in a killer impact. The first test was to see if iridium was found in the same strata all over the Earth. It was. The same strata in Spain, Denmark, New Zealand, and on the Pacific floor north of Hawaii yielded abnormally high iridium concentrations. The same strata also contained globules of shocked quartz, grains of soot, and tiny spheres of fused silicates characteristic of an impact.

Geologists then traced the ghostly outlines of the buried Chicxulub crater in the Gulf of Mexico and the nearby peninsula. The crater is 125 miles in diameter, caused by a meteor one or two miles in diameter.

There were two riddles: First, more shocked quartz debris was found in sediment cores taken from the Pacific ocean floor west of the crater than the equivalent distance east of the crater. This was a puzzle, until someone recalled the perfectly obvious fact that unlike the moon, the Earth rotates, so the dust lofted high by the explosion fell to the west of the impact.

The second riddle stemmed from the fact that two kinds of ejecta fell in the western United States: shocked quartz and melted rock. They were not intermingled but segregated, the quartz layered just above the melted rock. This suggested twin impacts, and presented a real puzzle.

An expert on impact dynamics, Susan Kieffer, found the answer. The region of the impact is rich in limestone, which when vaporized would release an enormous cloud of carbon dioxide. So, there must have been two fireballs: First, a cloud of extremely hot vaporized rock; second a cloud of carbon dioxide vapor at a less elevated temperature, given off by the more lightly shocked limestone. So there were two fireballs, and two patterns of fallout.

Another crater, the Boltysh in the Ukraine, which is 15 miles in diameter, is 65 million years old. Another in the British North Sea close to the coast, the Silverpit crater, is also 65 million years old. It is 12 miles in diameter. These two are in addition to the Chicxulub crater. There are 170 confirmed craters on Earth, not counting the ones in the deep sea, which are unknown.

Other Mass Extinctions

In addition to the mass extinction in the Cretaceous period 65 million years ago, there were three mass extinctions in the Cambrian period (570 to 505 million years ago) that destroyed much sea life such as Trilobites and reef-building organisms. The impact rate of comets and asteroids came to an all-time low 500 million to 600 million years ago and then rose nearly fourfold over the past 400 years. A 1997 study of the craters on the far side of the moon suggested that the impact rate had doubled over the past 300 million years. Richard A. Muller of the University of California at Berkeley believes that the increased impact rate seeded the Earth with water and other compounds essential for life during the past 500 million years and could have sparked the Cambrian explosion. Muller theorizes that the Sun has a stellar companion, so far undetected, that periodically flings comets into the inner solar system.

Another mass extinction occurred in the Ordovician period (505 to 438 million years ago) that also destroyed much sea life. Another extinction occurred in the Devonian period (408 to 360 million years ago) that destroyed jawless fish, early-jawed fish, and ammonites. Still another occurred in the Permian period (255 to 245 million years ago) that destroyed as much as 90 percent of all species. Finally a mass extinction occurred in the Holocene period (11,500 years ago) that destroyed a wide variety of plant and animal species including many unknown to science.

Only one of these mass extinctions is certain to have been caused by a meteor from outer space, the one that destroyed the dinosaurs in the Cretaceous period. The extinctions in the Cambrian period may have been caused by cold, oxygen-poor water welling up from the depths as a result of tectonic activity.

In the case of the Ordovician extinction, the cause seems to have been an ice age, possibly as a result of fluctuations in the Sun's output of heat. However, a meteor may also have been the cause of the Devonian dying, after plants and animals had colonized the land. The evidence is a large amount of iridium in rocks from this period. Iridium is rare on Earth, as already mentioned, but plentiful in comets. If so, a large amount of dust would have obscured the Sun.

A contrary theory is that the Devonian dying occurred over a long period of time, suggesting another ice age, when as many as 90 percent of all forms of life became extinct. But an ice age is only one possible cause. Geologists have found many glacial deposits from this period, so another possibility is massive volcanic eruptions. Vast lava flows from this period have been found in Siberia. These eruptions would have spewed thousands of cubic kilometers of ash into the atmosphere, blocking sunlight around the world and lowering temperatures.

The most devastating of all the mass extinctions was in the Permian age. The Triassic extinction is poorly understood. The fossil record indicates that both land and sea animals were destroyed, and the land extinction occurred several million years earlier than that in the oceans. Possible explanations range from global cooling to the impact of an asteroid.

GEOLOGICAL PERIODS

Geological Eras	Geological Epochs	Glacial Periods	Years Ago
Precambrian			5 billion (?)
Paleozoic:	Cambrian		570 million
	Ordovician		500 million
	Silurian		430–440 million
	Devonian		395 million
	Carboniferous		345 million
	Permian		280 million
Mesozoic	Triassic		225 million
	Jurassic		190–195 million
Cretaceous			136 million
Cenozoic	Paleocene		65 million
	Eocene		54 million
	Oligocene		37 million
	Miocene		24 million
	Pliocene		7 million
	Pleistocene	Günz	2 million
		Mindel	
		Riis	
		Würm	
	Holocene		9–12 thousand

Many biologists believe that by destroying tropical forests and other habitats, modern humans are driving species into extinction at an accelerating rate and that if the destruction continues it will result in one of the major extinctions of history. A study by Dr. James W. Kirchner and Dr. Anne Well in the journal *Nature* in early 2000, came to the startling conclusion that it takes about 10 million years for the planet to recover from an extinction and that the same amount of time is required to recover whether the extinction is a minor one or a major one. The reason is that the loss of a species brings the loss of opportunities for other organisms as well, those that would make their living preying upon or parasitizing that organism.

The Ice Ages

The Earth was subjected to an ice age in the late pre-Cambrian period, about 700 to 800 million years ago; in the early Cambrian period, about 600 million years ago; and in the Permian period, about 230 million years ago. The Earth gradually cooled beginning with the age of the dinosaurs, 65 million years ago. During the past 3 1/2 million years a series of four great ice caps covered much of the northern hemisphere. The third interglacial period began 175,000 years ago and lasted 60,000 years. During this period Neanderthal spread throughout Europe and Western Asia. Then the fourth glacial period, the Würm, began 115,000 years ago. In North America the center was at Hudson's Bay, and ice piled up from 8,000 to 10,000 feet thick. The pressure of its weight caused the ice to flow westward and southward, covering most of North America down to what are today the valleys of the Missouri and Ohio rivers. In Europe, the Scandinavian Peninsula was the center. The ice flowed southeast almost to Moscow and covered northern England, western Denmark, and Germany. At their height, the ice sheets turned so much water to ice that the oceans dropped almost 300 feet.

As the glaciers slowly spread out, they pushed soil and loose rocks ahead of them like giant bulldozers. They left scratches (striae) on rocks over which they moved, and the soil and rocks left behind when the ice melted formed mounds of many shapes called moraines. At their farthest extent where they reached the sea, they melted, depositing the debris they had collected. This is how Long Island, Block Island, and so on were formed.

The low places scoured out by the glaciers became lakes when the glaciers retreated, such as the Great Lakes, and they gouged out U-shaped gorges in old river valleys. Yosemite is a spectacular example. Other examples that are today under water are the fjords.

The modern horse and camel first appeared in the Ice Age, originating in North America and then crossing what is now the Bering Strait to Asia. Elephants, bison, deer, and bears evolved in Europe and Asia and used the same route to North America. Horses, llamas, giant ground sloths, and armadillos migrated to South America.

A few scientists believe that it was the change in climate that caused the big Pleistocene animals to die out. But most believe that *Homo sapiens sapiens* hunted them to extinction. In Europe, mammoths, bison, and cave bears all died out not very long after humankind appeared. In North America, mammoths, ground sloths, bison, and other large mammals were living in fantastic abundance as recently as 15,000 years ago, when humankind first appeared in the region. Shortly thereafter they disappeared.

The Mediterranean

The Mediterranean became separated from the Atlantic about seven million years ago. Gradually the Mediterranean basin dried up until it became a dry, salt lakebed. Then, about five million years ago, the dam that was Gibraltar broke through, and within a hundred years the Mediterranean became a salt sea again. It went from being part of the world's oceans to a desert several thousand feet below sea level and then back to being part of the world's oceans in the space of about two million years. After the Gibraltar breakthrough the Mediterranean's transition from dry, salt lakebed to a mile-deep abyss of salt water took no more than a century.

Underneath the delta of the Nile is a vast landscape of buried river valleys—what had been a badlands. Six million years ago the ancestral Nile flowed through a canyon just as deep and impressive as the Grand Canyon of the Colorado. No wonder there is little oil or gas in the area—all the strata that might have been reservoirs or traps for hydrocarbons had been washed away. In the broiling hot eastern Mediterranean valley, elephants and hippopotami evolved into dwarf forms that could cope with the hellish conditions.

Eels in American and European rivers flowing into the Atlantic and the Baltic breed in the Sargasso Sea in mid-Atlantic, and their progeny return to their parents' homeland rivers. Eels living in European and North African rivers that flow into the Mediterranean breed in the area immediately east of Gibraltar at the foot of the long-destroyed ancient dam that prevented them from joining the other eels in the migration to the Sargasso Sea. It is awesome to think that this pattern was established seven million years ago!

The Black Sea

The Black Sea went from a salt sea not to a desert as the Mediterranean did, but to a fresh-water lake, the largest in the world. Then it went back to being a salt sea. The break-through at the Bosporus that made it into a salt sea took place 7,600 years ago, in 5600 B.C., well within the collective memory of humankind.

Pliny the Elder described the Black Sea as having swallowed up a large area of land that retreated before it. Historical records date the foundation of the earliest seaports on the Black Sea to the middle of the eighth century B.C., 2,800 years ago.

The Black Sea is a huge basin more than 6,000 feet deep. It receives more water from rain and rivers than it loses by surface evaporation. The excess flows through the Straits of the Bosporus and the Sea of Marmora to the Dardanelles and the Mediterranean. In places the velocity exceeds five knots (six miles an hour).

But at the bottom of the straits, the water flows in the opposite direction, from the Mediterranean to the Black Sea. From the time of Jason and his search for the Golden Fleece, the ancients knew that there was another current at the bottom of the straits flowing from the Mediterranean to the Black Sea. From the eighth century B.C., 2,800 years ago until the time of steam power, mariners lowered stone-laden baskets to the bottom of the straits and the bottom current from the Mediterranean to the Black Sea dragged their boats northward against the swift-flowing surface outflow. In 1680, an Italian tied white-painted corks to a lead-weighted line and watched them stream north as the weights neared the bottom. The Bosporus channel continues far out into the Black Sea.

Coral can live only in shallow water, and a study of the Barbados reefs show that when the ice caps melted the level of the ocean never rose more than six feet a *century*. The Black Sea rose about six feet or more *every week!* The pre-flood beaches of the Black Sea were 400 feet below today's sea level.

Much of the total ice cap melting had occurred in two brief and rapid spurts separated by a thousand years, during which the climate returned to ice-age conditions. The first pulses of melt water from the vast ice sheet covering the northern parts of Europe, Asia, and America began 14,500 years ago. It fed dozens of huge lakes that no longer exist. These lakes filled the sag in the Earth's crust caused by the weight of the great ice dome. They were dammed at their southern margin by the temporary bulge where the enormous weight of the ice sheets had pushed the softer Earth aside. These lakes swelled until one by one they breached the dam and spilled one lake into the other like the Great Lakes in America. The second melt water spike began 11,400 years ago. But this melt water did not reach the Black Sea. The bulge in the Earth's crust prevented it, and the water flowed away from the Black Sea westward across Poland and over Berlin to the North Sea.

The world ocean continued to rise, but the Black Sea evaporated more rapidly. By 12,000 years ago the Black Sea had dropped below the level of the external ocean. By 7,600 years ago its shoreline was 350 below the top of the Bosporus dam. It was then, when the world's oceans were 50 feet below today's level but still 300 feet higher than the Black Sea, that the trickle of salt water began to flow through the Bosporus and rapidly became a torrent.

The flow was astonishing. The speed was 50 miles an hour. The level of the Black Sea rose half a foot a day!

Part Three:

Life on Earth

Chapter 9

How Did Life Begin?

Inside the chemically rich oceans there emerged by a mechanism still not understood a simple anaerobic bacterium. This transformed the Earth's atmosphere from one rich in carbon dioxide and deficient in oxygen into one with enough oxygen to allow aerobic organisms to develop.

The emergence of life also depended on another piece of good fortune. Ultra-violet light, which is emitted from the Sun in great quantities, is hostile to life. However, although oxygen atoms are normally found in pairs (O_2), some exist in threes (O_3) to form ozone, and ozone serves as a shield that protects the Earth's surface from most ultra-violet light.

The earliest life on Earth appeared at least 3.5 billion years ago. It consisted of prokaryotes, such as bacteria. These one-celled organisms lack a nucleus, a cellular skeleton, and many other features. These missing parts evolved later in eukaryotes—the group including animals, plants, fungi, algae, and such unicellular creatures as amoebas.

The atmosphere of the young Earth was very different from what it is today. It was virtually devoid of free oxygen. Most oxygen was locked up with hydrogen as water (H_2O) and with carbon as carbon dioxide (CO_2). There would also have been some carbon monoxide (CO). Other carbon would have been present in the atmosphere as methane (CH_4). Nitrogen, which is now 90 % of the atmosphere, would have also been present in the form of ammonia (NH_3). Interestingly, these are the elements that compose the atmosphere of Jupiter today.

A. I. Oparin, a Russian scientist, guessed that simple organic compounds, the stuff of life, could be formed from these components by chemical reactions induced perhaps by ultraviolet light from the Sun. In 1956, Stanley W. Miller, a graduate student at the University of Chicago passed a high-voltage electrical discharge similar to a lightning flash through such a mixture and recovered at the bottom of the vessel several amino acids, the building blocks of proteins. However, after that discovery little progress was made. One problem was that attempts to reconstruct the original composition of the nebula of gas and dust from which the solar system was formed about 5 billion years ago suggests that ammonia would *not* have been present in the quantities necessary for this process. How could life emerge without ammonia?

In 1977, oceanographer Jack Corliss was exploring a volcanic ridge at the bottom of the Pacific Ocean in a tiny research submersible when he came across hydrothermal vents on the ocean bottom spewing out a hellish mixture of shimmering brines. What was even more amazing was that around the vent was a biological wonderland—shoe-sized clams, 6-foot tubeworms, and blizzards of strange microbes. If these creatures could subsist in a bath of searing heat and scorching chemicals from the planet's interior in which the Earth's more familiar creatures would quickly die, Corliss speculated, perhaps this was where life got its start.

Günter Wächtershäuser an organic chemist in Germany conceived of an assembly-line process at the ocean floor that transforms basic inorganic chemicals into organic chains, the building blocks of life. Following this line of enquiry, Jay A. Brandes at the Carnegie Institute in Washington confined water, powdered rock, and gases like those spewed out by a volcano in a small gold capsule and subjected the capsule to high temperatures and crushing pressures, forces like those in a seafloor geyser. Only 15 minutes at 500 degrees centigrade created ammonia—lots of it. What is more, the ammonia was stable up to 800 degrees centigrade. So all the ingredients for the creation of life existed around hydrothermal vents...

If life on Earth originated in hydrothermal vents it seems very possible that life will also be found in other parts of the solar system. Both Mars and Europa, the ice-covered moon of Jupiter, show evidence of geothermal forces. Such conditions would also be common on many of the planets of other stars.

On the other hand, the problem of the missing ammonia may be solved. Some as yet unknown process may have supplied it in the necessary quantities or life may have appeared in the oceans by some process that did not require ammonia.

While the *how* of the beginning of life on Earth is still unknown, the *when* has been pinned down. The Earth is 4.5 billion years old. Fossils are scarce, and the earliest life forms did not have the bones and skulls that help preserve fossils. But there are fossil structures with the size and shape of modern bacteria in sedimentary rocks dating from 3.8 billion years ago. A little later in the fossil record there are structures called stromatolites. These are found in Australian rocks 3.5 billion years old. They appear to be relics of accumulations of huge conglomerations of single-cell organisms, either bacteria or algae, comparable to the great bacterial "mats" found floating in modern oceans.

Some scientists, including Francis H. C. Crick, the co-originator of the structure of DNA, took the position that the chances are so small as to be negligible that the long polymer molecules that vitally sustain all living things, both protein and DNA, could have been assembled by random processes. This prompts the question whether the surface of the Earth was fertilized from interstellar space.

But this hypothesis just moves the puzzle of how life arose from Earth to some other place in the universe. Even if some form of life could migrate through the hostile environment of space, which is very doubtful, it seems more likely that life arose at different places at different times. Also, life did not originate in its present extremely complex form, but in some much, much simpler form that has evolved into the present-day version.

The starting point for life need not have been an organism in the sense that is now familiar, but simply molecules with the property of being able to catalyze their own formation from raw materials in the environment. Starch, which is branched chains of simple glucose molecules, for example, is not alive, but it does replicate itself. This is the *prebiotic* phase in the history of terrestrial life. Recently discovered in Antarctica is a meteorite that had originated in Mars containing what appears to be the fossil of some form of life. If so, the formation of organic molecules from inorganic materials is more probable than was thought.

The fact is that life is not only universal on Earth but also ubiquitous. Bacteria have been discovered in apparently inhospitable regions of Antarctica, often in pools of water appearing only in the brief Antarctic summer. In semitropical regions bacteria have been found in ponds and lakes in which the concentration of salt is so great that the more familiar bacteria could not survive. As already mentioned, bacteria and even invertebrate animals have recently been found at depths of thousands of meters on the floor of the world's oceans, including shrimp-like creatures, clams, and tube worms. Through these vents in the ocean floor, as we said, gush hot water laden with inorganic chemicals of all kinds—sulphates, nitrates, and phosphates, together with toxic materials such as hydrogen sulphide and carbon dioxide in solution as well as methane gas. There can be no true plants at these depths, because there is no sunlight.

All this suggests not only that life arose spontaneously on Earth, but also that it probably arose more than once and in slightly different ways. The most likely hypothesis, in other words, would seem to be that there is not one ultimate ancestor of all the different forms of life living on Earth today, but two or three. Some forms of life may have originated at great depths in the ocean around vents in the ocean floor. Other forms may have originated in the primordial sea, sparked perhaps by lightning, and nurtured by sunlight.

Peculiarities in Life

Squid grow big. Squid are intelligent and fast moving and very hard to capture in the deep ocean where they live. In 1954 one was washed ashore in Norway that measured 9 meters from the end of its body to the tip of its outstretched tentacles. In 1933, in New Zealand one was recorded at 21 meters. It had eyes that were 40 centimeters across. Sperm whales dive deep to hunt squid. Scars on whales that have battled squid suggest their suckers were 13 centimeters across. Squid beaks have been found in whale stomachs even bigger than the one recorded in New Zealand.

Why did the dinosaurs grow so big? Two reasons. The big ones like Brontosaurus were vegetarians, as we can see from the teeth. The plants of the time were tough and needed a great deal of digestion. The dinosaur teeth were not good for grinding like modern cows. Although there is evidence that some dinosaurs may have swallowed pebbles just as some birds today use grit in their gizzards, most dinosaurs must have relied on the biochemical and bacteriological powers of their digestive juices. So their stomachs had to be huge. A huge stomach needs a huge body to carry it. Carnivorous dinosaurs would in turn need big stature to prey on the giant vegetarians. Also the bigger the body, the longer it retains heat and the less susceptible it is to short-term temperature changes.

The debris from the meteor 65 million years ago that caused the great dying obscured the Sun, and much vegetation simply died. For dinosaurs, vegetation was the bottom of the food chain. Another result was very cold weather, which the dinosaurs were not adapted to endure. No large reptiles survived. Only a few smaller ones made it, those that could also take refuge in water, which retains heat better than air. So it is no accident that the only reptiles from the time of the dinosaurs that survive today make their homes in water or whose ancestors did—crocodiles, lizards, tortoises, and turtles.

Life Elsewhere than on Earth

As Stephen Jay Gould writes:

> [F]aced with the data we now possess—that life appears as soon as it could and remains pervasive forever after—our thoughts must move to ideas with almost predictive inevitability. Given a planet of earthly size, distance from a central star, and composition, life of simplest grade may originate with virtual certainty as a consequence of principles of organic chemistry and the physics of self-organizing systems.

By the middle of 2001, over 50 planets had been discovered orbiting stars other than the Sun. The telescopes available are not capable of seeing these planets, so their existence has been inferred by studying the wobble they cause in the stars they orbit. For this reason only planets that are rather massive compared to the Earth have so far been discovered. The one planet that has an Earth-like orbit rotates around Iota Horologii, 56 light years from Earth. Its elongated orbit takes it around its star once every 320 days. Its closest approach to its star is about the distance of Venus from the Sun, and at its farthest is about the distance of the Earth from the Sun, 93 million miles. The planet is far larger than Earth, about twice as massive as Jupiter. There may also be a second, smaller planet orbiting the same star.

Of the Sun's planets only Mars and Earth have at some time in the past met all the conditions for life, as we know it. However, Jupiter's moon Europa seems to have ample water and methane and it probably has an internal supply of heat comparable with that of Earth.

The broad stages of the evolution of life on Earth are plain. First there was a period lasting between 200 million and 500 million years—the prebiotic phase—during which molecular evolution threw up molecules capable of replication that were potentially the founders of the first truly living things. There followed a period of between 2 billion and 3 billion years during which all organisms were essentially single-celled creatures. Multicellular organisms appeared later, probably more than 1 billion years ago. And they were abundant by the Cambrian explosion of life about 550 million years ago.

The emergence of organisms consisting of specialized cells may have occurred as recently as 1 billion years ago or may go back to 2 billion years ago.

The first emergence of eukaryotic organisms, which include fungi and protists as well as multicellular organisms probably occurred about 2.5 billion years ago.

The cells of all modern organisms but bacteria convert the energy of simple chemicals into energetic chemicals by means of a specialized structure called mitochondria. In plants, cells called chloroplasts specialize in converting sunlight into energy.

Life probably began when the first molecule of RNA, DNA's elder cousin, got itself more or less accurately replicated in some natural stew of chemicals on the primitive Earth. The first living cells, the first plants and animals, emerged merely because they were better mechanisms for repeating that first ancient accident of replication. DNA has been blindly pursuing the same plan ever since.

The more complicated life forms developed in the oceans. Some migrated to the land and developed even more complicated life forms. Some, like whales, later migrated back to the oceans.

Birds

Flying creatures that were *not* the ancestors of modern birds ruled the skies about 240 million years ago—the pterosaurs. Some were as small as sparrows, but some, the pterodactyls, had a wingspread of 39 feet! Their wings were made of skin, like a bat's wing, that stretched from the side of the body and along the arm to the end of a very long fourth finger. They lived side by side with both birds and dinosaurs until 65 million years ago at the time of the great dying.

The debate about whether birds descended from dinosaurs or both birds and dinosaurs descended from some common ancestor continues hot and heavy. The fossil of a theropod dinosaur, Sinosauropteryx, with bristle like impressions that seem to be feathers or proto-feathers was discovered in China in 1996. Another candidate also discovered at the site in China is Proto-archaeopteryx robusta, a chicken-sized creature with what appeared to be feathers attached to its tail.

Two theories about the origin of birds developed, the tree-down theory and the ground-up theory. Both theories agree that dinosaurs and birds had a common ancestor, the archosaurs.

In the tree-down theory, both dinosaurs descended from archosaur and thecodonts. From dinosaurs descended theropod dinosaurs. From thecodonts descended the first birds and from them descended two other branches. One branch was flightless birds and from them descended the Caudipteryx zoui and the Proto-archaeopteryx prima—both of whom died out 65 million years ago in the great dying. The other branch was archaeopteryx, from it

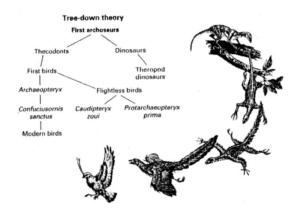

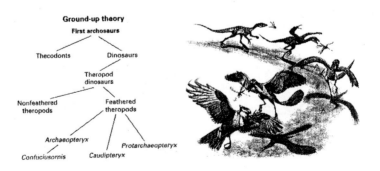

90

Confuciusornis sanctus, and from it modern birds.

In the ground-up theory, from archosaur also descended dinosaurs and thecodonts. From the dinosaurs, descended theropod dinosaurs. From the theropod dinosaurs descended non-feathered theropods and feathered theropods. From the feathered theropods descended Caudipteryx zoui and Proto-archaeopteryx that died out, as we said, 65 million years ago. From the feathered theropods also descended Archaeopteryx, from them Confuciusornis sanctus and from them modern birds. So far neither school of thought has won the victory over the other.

Recently in China six specimens of a four-winged dinosaur were discovered. The dinosaur had a body the size of a pigeon but an overall length of three feet. It was named Microrapter gui, honoring the chinese paleontologist Gu Zhiwei. It lived about 128 million years ago. This creature had two sets of feathered wings, one on its forelimbs and one on its hind legs. Both wings were used for gliding, and this supports the gliding-in-trees theory. Scientists have seen gliding dinosaurs before, but never one with feathers and never one with four wings. It developed about the same time as the first two-wing birdlike dinosaur, Archaeopteryx, which is believed to have flown by flapping its wings.

The Genome Project

By two billion years ago, DNA had become the genetic material in all but a few organisms. Viruses, such as HIV, which causes AIDS, are an exception.

Two teams, one a publicly funded consortium and the other, Celera Genomics, a privately funded organization, reported early in 2001 that there are only 30,000 human genes, only a third more than are found in the ordinary roundworm. The fruit fly, the staple of laboratory genetics has 13,601 genes. The roundworm, the staple of laboratory studies in development, has 19,098. It was thought that the human had as many as 142,634 genes. But it turns out that the human has only between 30,000 and 40,000 with the final figure lying nearer the lower number. In other words our bodies develop with only half again as many genes as the tiny roundworm. A small portion of the remaining 100,000 to 140,000 genes may play a useful role.

The consortium's report suggested that 223 of the human genome's 30,000 human genes appear to have been acquired directly from bacteria. The implication is that vertebrate and human genomes might have been shaped not by just inheritance, but by weird accidents like bacterial infection of the egg or sperm cell.

Dr. Steven L. Salzberg, a senior director of subsidiary of Celera Genomics, said the method was simply wrong. The issue has been hotly debated.

Physically the genome is miniscule. Two copies are packed into the nucleus of every ordinary human cell, each of which is about a fifth of the size of a speck of dust the eye can see. But the genome is vast in terms of the information it holds. Composed of chemical symbols designated by a four letter alphabet of A's, T's, C's, and G's, the human genome is some 3.2 billion letters long. If printed in a standard type it would cover 75,490 pages of a newspaper.

The favored explanation is that the genes of multicellular organisms are composed of coding segments. Each gene can generate non-coding regions, and if the order of splicing changes then several distinct messages can be sent by a single gene.

Mammals have been around for 200 million years. Modern, placental mammals had a common ancestor some 65 million years ago (about the time of the great dying that killed off the dinosaurs), although they were probably around for some time before that.

The DNA of *Homo sapiens sapiens* is only 20 percent different from that of a mouse. So in sequencing humans, we will be sequencing 80 percent of all placental mammals. Our closest living relative is the chimpanzee. Our DNA and theirs differ by only 1 percent. Chimps and humans diverged from a common ancestor about 5 million years ago. We differ from gorillas by about 3 percent. Two humans of the same sex differ in their DNA by only 1/10th of 1 percent. This means that Dan Quayle and Albert Einstein differed by only 1/10th of 1 percent —if you can believe it!

One chimp differs from another six times as much as one human differs from another—which means that they have been around six times as long as humans. All this and other data show that *Homo sapiens* originated about 80 to 90 thousand years ago in Africa, in what is now Ethiopia and Kenya, and *Homo sapiens sapiens* originated about 50 to 60 thousand years ago. So we are the very youngest of the mammals!

The idea that man had descended from monkeys prompted the John T. Scopes trial. What would have happened if the idea had been that man had descended from an insect?

The Icelandic DNA Project

The enormous promise of knowledge of DNA is illustrated by a recent project in Iceland, described in an article by Michael Specter, "Decoding Iceland" in *The New Yorker* (January 18, 1999. pp. 40-51), from which the following has been drawn.

A small band of Norsemen and a handful of their Irish slaves settled Iceland in the ninth and tenth centuries, and there was almost no other immigration until the Second World War. In the middle of the eighteenth century the population stood at fewer than 50,000, no more than it had been 500 years earlier. In the early fifteenth century, the black plague killed as many as 40,000 people, two-thirds of the population. In 1707, smallpox killed more than 15,000 people, one-third of the population.

These disasters also cut down on the population's genetic diversity. Then in 1783, the Lakagigar volcano erupted. The eruption itself killed only a few people, but the sulfur dioxide it released blanketed the region with a dusty poison. The resulting famine killed 25 percent of the people, and almost all the livestock.

As a consequence of the small original population, the almost negligible immigration since then, and the series of natural disasters, the people of Iceland are very closely related. Few leave and even fewer come. So Iceland is populated by what seems to be one single, rather large family. As a result Icelanders all have a family resemblance. They all look like each other. The hereditary instructions for blue eyes and blond hair have been passed undiluted through 50 generations, and their genetic makeup reflects this fact. Iceland consists of 270,000 of the most genetically similar people on Earth. The phone books are organized by first names! As a result, Iceland is the richest natural genetics laboratory on Earth.

An Icelandic cleric living in the sixteenth century named Einar was missing five units of DNA. This was not a large mistake. It is as if a stenographer mistyped one letter in a book containing all of Shakespeare's plays. Such mutations are rather common, but they are usually harmless. But in the case of Einar, the mutation he carried deleted a few of the basic units of DNA from a gene known as BRCA2 and is responsible for almost every case of hereditary breast cancer in Iceland. Such mutations lie dormant unless the remaining good copy of the gene is lost or damaged. At that point a still mysterious chain of events begins that results in cancer. Research has shown that the Icelandic population has only one BRCA2 mutation, Einar's. Knowing the root of a disease is the first step in finding a way to cure it.

Kari Stefansson, born in Iceland, is a neurologist who spent 15 years at the University of Chicago and became a tenured professor. He returned to Iceland briefly to run the Institute of Pathology, the country's most distinguished scientific research organization and then spent five years at Harvard as a professor of neurology and pathology. In the early 1990s, he realized that Iceland was an ideal place to research the origins of almost any common disease that had a genetic component. It reflects the gene pool of Northern Europe as of about 800 A.D.

Stefansson established a biotechnology firm, Decode Genetics, and developed a plan to create a gigantic electronic database containing the genetic information of the entire Icelandic population. One reason this is feasible is that Iceland has a national system of medical insurance that has kept meticulous records since 1915 and an immense and well-documented tissue bank. Another is that its people trust their doctors.

It is against the law in Iceland for anyone to change his or her last name, the patronymic, and the government exempts most genealogical data from basic privacy laws. Also, Icelanders have from the beginning been fascinated with their ancestry. Individual families have kept scrupulous records of their forebearers. As a result, Decode has already compiled a database with the family history of about 75 percent of all the 800,000 Icelanders who have ever lived. Another reason the project is feasible is that the old sagas, in which the history of Iceland is preserved, almost always begin with a long list of genealogical information. Since the Icelandic language, unlike English, Swedish, or Norwegian, has changed very little over the generations, if you can read a magazine article in Icelandic, you can read the ancient sagas.

In February, 1998, Decode signed a contract with Hoffman-La Roche, based in Switzerland, to pay Decode more than $200 million over five years if it managed to identify the genes involved in such diseases as schizophrenia, Alzheimer's, stroke, heart disease, and emphysema. Roche got the right to develop diagnostic tests and drugs based on the genes discovered. In addition to the payments to Decode, the Swiss company agreed to provide free of charge any tests and drugs developed to all Icelanders who need them.

In the past, such tests and drugs were discovered almost by chance. Researchers would identify the proteins that seemed to be associated with the disease, and would then try out thousands of animal and plant compounds in the hope of finding one that blocked the protein without doing serious damage to the rest of the body. But if they knew that a particular gene played a role in the disease, they could design drugs to repair or prevent the damage. This explains the interest of the pharmaceutical companies. Both the health and financial implications will be enormous.

Another possible benefit is on aging. Decode has established that Icelanders who live to be 90 are much more closely related than the general population. If Decode can identify the gene or set of genes that permits longevity, it might be possible to benefit everyone in the world.

The estimated cost, to be raised from private sources, is at least $150 million. In return the government of Iceland will grant the firm exclusive rights to market the results abroad for 12 years. The prime minister, the government, and a very high percentage of the Icelandic population support the project. But although the opposition is small, it is passionate. Partly this is because of Stefansson's flamboyant personality, which makes it impossible for him to suffer fools or almost any other kind of opposition gladly. Partly it is because of jealousy on the part of other Icelandic scientists. Partly it is because of fears of the invasion of privacy and the violation of medical ethics, and partly it is because of fears that other researchers will be prevented from taking advantage of this fantastic new tool. There is also a widely shared feeling that the enormous profits to be made should go to the Icelandic people, and not a private firm.

Life Elsewhere

By the spring of the year 2001, a total of 50 planets had been identified outside the solar system orbiting nearby stars. Most of these planets are probably giant balls of hydrogen and helium gas, but at least 5 of them could have water, which is a fundamental requirement for life as we know it. According to one of the scientists based in California, one of these planets has a temperature of 108 degrees Fahrenheit, "like a hot day in Sacramento."

The existence of most of these planets was inferred from very slight wobbling of the stars that are their suns caused by the gravitational pull of a large planet orbiting them. But late in 1999 telescopes recorded a distinct dimming of light as a planet crossed in front of a Sun-like star, HD 209458 in the constellation Pegasus. From the amount of dimming, astronomers calculated the size and density of the planet. It is very close to its star and consists solely of gas, probably hydrogen and helium. The exact composition will be revealed by further study.

Just after the Big Bang the universe consisted of hydrogen, helium, and a tiny amount of lithium. It took several million years for large enough stars to develop to manufacture the elements necessary for life and to explode and scatter these elements around. It took another 4.5 to 5 billion years for stars like our Sun and its planets to form and for life like ours to develop. The universe we know is about 15 billion years old. So in our own galaxy there has been time enough for several hundred million stars about the size of our Sun to be born and reach the age of the solar system. Perhaps 20 or 30 million of these stars have planets that replicate the conditions on Earth. So it is a reasonable guess that our galaxy harbors as many as several million planets with life, many with life as intelligent as ours, and quite a few with life more intelligent than ours. This is, to repeat, just in our own galaxy.

And in the universe? John Gribben has calculated in his book, *In The Beginning, After COBE and Before the Big Bang* (New York, Little Brown, 1993, p. 255) that the number of planets suitable for life-forms like ourselves in all the universes may be 10 to the 20th power—that is, a total of 100,000,000,000,000,000,000 planets suitable for life forms like ourselves.

What made humankind think that it was anything special?

Chapter 10

Homo Sapiens Sapiens—Us

Research on 57 proteins from organisms spanning all the kingdoms of creatures living today indicates that they descended
from a common ancestor who lived about 2 billion years ago.
This research assigns dates to such events as the emergence of land animals
(tetrapods) 400 million years ago, and these dates agree with those of the
fossil record. This suggestion that there may have been a single common
ancestor of all life on Earth is surprising. As described in Chapter 9, we
would expect not only that life arose spontaneously on Earth, but also that
it arose more than once and in slightly different ways.

But we are concerned with humankind and its ancestors. Fifty million
years ago there were lemurs and other prosimians (pre-monkeys) in both
Europe and North America. Around 30 million years ago more advanced
primates developed and displaced the lemurs. However, these advanced primates never reached Madagascar, which had been separated from Africa by
the Mozambique Channel, so the lemurs proliferated there and survived.
Elsewhere only a few can be found, such as the bush babies in Africa. What
enabled these few to survive is the fact that they are nocturnal. They crawl
along the branches of trees in the dark, while their competition, the monkeys, swing from branch to branch and tree to tree and so need daylight.

The earliest primates appeared 55 million years ago, apparently in Asia.
In gradual stages they migrated to Africa. In March 2000, paleontologists

announced that they had found in China the fossil bones of a tiny primate, about the size of a human thumb that was an early ancestor of monkeys. They named it Eosimias, dawn monkey.

Eosimias lived on insects and fruit 45 million years ago in a rain forest in China. Paleontologists had assumed that an animal made the transition to anthropoids larger than the prosimians. But the tiniest living primate, the one-ounce mouse lemur in Madagascar, is twice as heavy as Eosimias was.

Eosimias is not only the smallest member of the primate lineage that led to monkeys, apes, and *Homo* yet found but also the earliest. All primates, lower or higher, are distinguished from other mammals by their larger brains, grasping hands and feet, nails instead of claws, and eyes in the front of the skull.

Humans have 46 chromosomes, 23 distinct pairs. The great apes have 48 chromosomes, 24 distinct pairs. The common ancestor of both humans and apes must have had 48 chromosomes. The missing chromosome did not disappear but in humans was substantially incorporated at the end of the long arm of chromosome 2.

This translocation constitutes the most conspicuous difference between the great apes and humans. Much remains unknown about the process by which species differentiate, but at least one mechanism seems to be such chromosome translocation. This process is not always as gradual as Darwin visualized, but it does seem to bear out Stephen Jay Gould's theory of "punctuated equilibrium." This theory holds that a species regularly produces sports that simply die out until some change in the environment is fatal to the species but favorable to the sport or that permits the sport to find a mate and prosper even though the parent species survives.

Dating fossils has been a problem. The radiocarbon method works to about 40,000 years. Accelerator mass spectrometry works to about 75,000 years. The radioactive isotope of potassium, with a half-life of 1.3 billion years, works well in some cases, and so does the argon-argon method. This was used to date the famous Lucy fossil, described below, at 3.2 million years. Still other methods are used in the range of 40,000 years to 300,000 years. Hominids were relatively rare animals until the appearance of *Homo sapiens sapiens*, so the fossils of a variety of other animals found in the same strata have been very useful in dating them.

In all mammals, teeth are very revealing, and identity can often be established from a single tooth. Each of the different species of

Australopithecus, for example, can be distinguished by a unique constellation of dental traits. Sometimes the size of a canine tooth permits an investigator to determine sex. Teeth can also permit him or her to determine age. One of Lucy's wisdom teeth, for example, was just beginning to emerge and show wear. So she was fully adult when she died.

A tree climber who lived 6 to 8 million years ago was the common ancestor of humans and African apes. After the hominids split from the ape line they became bipeds. The apes developed a way of walking on their knuckles after the split with *Homo* but before they diverged into their three existing species. Knuckle walking was not a trait in the human lineage.

Humans and chimpanzees are more closely related to each other than to gorillas. Human DNA differs from that of a chimpanzee by 1.6 percent and from that of a gorilla by 2.3 percent. The split between the ancestors of chimpanzees and humans occurred between 6.3 and 7.7 million years ago while their common ancestor with gorillas lived 8 to 10 million years ago.

Another species with a possible upright stance was the *Orrorin tugenensis*, found in Kenya. It is dated at 6 million years ago.

Then came *Ardipithecus ramidus kadabba*, from 5.8 to 5.2 million years ago. The fragmentary remains of five individuals constitute the present find. They display dental features found in other hominids, but not in any other fossil or living ape. Moreover, the fossil contains a toe bone shaped like those of Lucy and her kind (Lucy's remains were found just fifty miles away). This is subtle but clear evidence that *Ardipithecus* like *Australopithecus* walked on two legs.

This raises a puzzling question. Researchers have often regarded a two-legged stride as an adaptation to trekking across hot, grassy savannas. Yet *Ardipithecus* lived in shady foorests where a hominid would have less need to stand up to dissipate heat or walk long distances.

The fossils of several individuals of *Ardipithecus ramidus*, who lived about 4.4 million years ago, were found in Ethiopia beginning in 1994. *Ardipithecus ramidus* is thought to be a direct ancestor of the *Australopithecines*. Since it appears to be much like a modern chimpanzee, the conclusion is that the great apes have not changed very much since then.

In 1994, Meave G. Leakey and Alan Walker found 21 fossils of what has been named *Australopithecus anamensis* and dated between 4.2 to 3.9 million years ago. It seems to have walked on two legs like later hominids.

Paleontologists in the past have held that walking upright on two legs was the hallmark of the *Homo* line, the ancestors of modern humankind. As already mentioned, the great apes use their knuckles to walk upright, and are better adapted for climbing trees. Fossils show that in the course of human evolution there was a threefold increase in the size of the skull and therefore of the brain. Today, understanding spoken speech, reading written words, making sense of them, and articulating a reply is taken as an even more specifically human attribute than walking upright.

During the past four million years, there were long periods when different forms of hominids were alive at the same time: *Homo erectus* and *Homo robustus* at similar locations in East Africa, for example, and *Homo sapiens sapiens* together with Neanderthal as recently as 28,000 years ago.

Richard Leakey says in his book, *The Origin of Humankind* (New York: Basic Books, 1984), that although anthropologists argue a lot, there are four stages on which they agree:

1. Seven million years ago an apelike creature evolved that was bipedal, i.e. that moved about on two legs.

2. Between seven and two million years ago bipedal apes evolved, each adapted to slightly different ecological circumstances in a process called adaptive radiation. Calculations based on adaptive radiation indicate that there might have been 16 bipedal species between their origins 7 million years ago and today.

3. Between 3 and 2 million years ago, one species developed a significantly larger brain. This is the origin of the genus *Homo*, the branch that led through *Homo erectus* and eventually to *Homo sapiens* and *Homo sapiens sapiens*.

Homo sapiens sapiens, our own species, was the fourth stage, and its members possessed language, consciousness, artistic imagination, and the ability for technological innovation.

No one knows whether language was part of the equipment of *Homo erectus*, but several lines of evidence suggest that he did have some language, perhaps two or three dozen words.

Darwin argued that bipedalism, technology, and an enlarged brain must have evolved in concert. But it turns out that in this Darwin was wrong. The earliest examples of stone tools appeared 2.5 million years ago. So almost 5 million years passed before the ancestors of humankind began to use tools. However, many anthropologists believe that the advent of technology did coincide with at least the beginnings of larger brains.

The human brain has 100 billion neurons, as many as stars in the Milky Way, and a trillion glial cells to support those neurons. It is three times larger than it would be for a non-human primate of our body size. The primitive parts of the hindbrain have not changed much as the human brain evolved during the last two million years. There was some enlargement in the mid brain, but the real difference was in the cortex, the forebrain. The primitive forebrain was mainly concerned with the sense of smell, but even though the forebrain is still connected with the olfactory lobes, these are reduced in size, and the forebrain now serves a different function. The much larger parts of the forebrain are those associated with language. The part concerned with motor skills takes up only one-third of what it does in a monkey brain, so we won't be leaping from branch to branch any time soon.

But the possibility does exist. In the spring of 2000 scientists at MIT reported that they had reconfigured the brains of ferrets to hook up the animals' eyes to the part of the brain where hearing normally develops. The surprising result was that the animals can see the world with the part of their brain that scientists thought was only for hearing. The implication is the brain regions are not set in one at birth but develop specialized functions based on the kind of information that flows into them after birth.

Between 2 million and 700,000 years ago the hominid brain size doubled from about 440 cc to more than 900 cc. Another, even bigger burst of brain size occurred around 500,000 to 100,000 years ago, the span of time from *Homo erectus* to early *Homo sapiens*. The average size of the brain of a modern human is 1350 cc. Elephant brains are four times as big, and whale brains are even bigger, corresponding to their larger body size. Neanderthal brains were also bigger than ours, about 1580 cc. But this was not because they were smarter. The reason for their bigger brains had to do with the relationship between body size and ambient temperature. Neanderthal was adapted to a cold climate and part of that adaptation was a relatively larger brain corresponding to their stout stature. Similar patterns occur in modern populations living at high latitudes, including the Lapps and the Greenland Inuit. In addition to a large brain, Neanderthals had somewhat shorter arms and legs and stouter body proportions.

A major biological transformation, as well as a major adaptive one, was bipedalism. The bipedal skeleton is very, very different from that of a tree-dweller. And being bipedal carried much evolutionary potential, since the upper limbs would one day be free to manipulate tools. This led Leakey to argue that bipedalism ought to be recognized as the beginning of *Homo*. Leakey also says that the image of *Homo* stepping out of the forest into savannah is wrong. Fifteen million years ago, there was no savannah. The

Earth's crust was tearing apart at what is now the Great Rift Valley. Here and there in Ethiopia and Kenya the land rose like blisters forming great domes 9,000 feet high, and the lands to the east were thrown into rain shadow. The continuous tree cover began to fragment into patches of forest, woodland, and shrub land. But not as yet into open grassland.

About 12 million years ago, the Rift Valley formed an east-west barrier for the common ancestor of humans and apes. All the creatures on one side of the Rift Valley had to adapt to a humid, arboreal milieu. On the other side, they had to adapt to a more open environment. It was in the more open environment that the ancestors of humankind lived.

The more open environment had dramatic highlands with cool forested plateaus and precipitous slopes that plunged 3,000 feet to hot, arid lowlands. Because such environments offer many different kinds of habitat, they are an engine of evolutionary innovation.

Sometimes the change is toward oblivion. This is what happened to the African apes. Five to ten million years ago the cooling climate brought about a diminution of the tropical forests. The fast-breeding monkeys began to adapt to the savannahs and proliferated. Apes found themselves hanging on in widely dispersed clumps of forest, and they experienced a steady decline in both their numbers and diversity. Only three species exist today: the gorilla, the common chimpanzee, and the pygmy chimpanzee. The hominids, on the other hand, were blessed with a new adaptation that allowed them to survive and prosper—bipedalism.

Attempting to answer the question of why our remote ancestors became bipedal, anthropologists at first assumed that a big brain came first. Some speculated that intelligence was necessary to make the decision to walk upright and to move out of the forests and into the grasslands. Others saw bipedalism as the first step toward freeing the forelimbs to make and use tools; bigger brains meant better tools, and better tools meant bigger brains.

But then it was discovered that bipedalism began 5 to 8 million years ago and bigger brains came only 2 million years ago. Bipedal *Australopithecines* did not make tools, and stone artifacts did not appear until 2.5 million years ago, some 1.5 million years after bipedalism. One possibility is that as the forest dwindled such food sources as fruit trees became too dispersed for efficient exploitation by tree-dwellers. Bipedalism is certainly a more efficient way to travel between dispersed sites than the knuckle walking of the great apes, but as already mentioned knuckle-walking developed much, much later than bipedalism.

In any case, bipedalism is not anywhere near as efficient as going on all fours. Any explanation of bipedalism has to consider that compared to using four legs, using only two legs is slow, clumsy, and fraught with opportunities for injury. Notions about being more efficient in picking fruit or standing up to see enemies approaching were shot down rather easily. So too was the idea that it was easier for an upright, two-legged animal to dissipate heat. The heat problem was more easily solved by spending the middle of the day in the shade of trees.

Evidence is mounting that feathers evolved before flight. In April 2001, Chinese and American paleontologists announced the discovery of a 130-million-year-old fossil in slabs of fine-grained rock. Around nearly every part of the skeleton are etched downy tufts and featherlike filaments, even some that resemble the herringbone pattern of modern bird feathers. These dinosaurs could not fly. They were more primitive than birds and the theory is that birds descended from them.

Owen Lovejoy pointed out that since bipedalism was such an inefficient mode of locomotion, it must have evolved for carrying things. How could the ability to carry things give bipedal apes a competitive advantage over other apes? He noted that three activities consume the most energy—reproduction, feeding, and safety. He argued that beyond a certain point using more energy on feeding and safety does not help a species survive, but using more energy on reproduction always does so. If a bipedal male uses his upper limbs to carry food to a female, the female can spend more time bearing and raising children. The intervals between children will be reduced, and the female will be able to care for more than one child at a time. If the male also provides better protection, admittedly a somewhat dicier proposition, the female can also spend less time worrying about safety.

So longer-term relationships between male and female and the beginnings of pair bonding had an evolutionary payoff for bipedal hominids. Pair bonding made it more likely that each generation would survive long enough to produce the next.

Presumably the females of our bipedal ancestors were like their modern sisters in that they did not exhibit the external signs of ovulation—estrus with its swelling of the genitalia along with enticing scents and dribblings. So again like their modern sisters they were presumably ready for sexual intercourse at any time of the month—except, of course, when like their modern sisters they had a headache. So the males did not have as much competition from other males as the males do in species in which there is estrus and the female exhibits obvious external signs that she is ready for intercourse. Also the males and females presumably had features, like those in modern *Homo* that served to attract the opposite sex—distinctive scalp hair, distinctive voices, and specialized scent glands in armpits and pubic regions. The male, like modern males, was twenty percent larger than the female. He had facial hair, and he also had the largest penis of all the primates. As for the female, unlike chimpanzees whose breasts are enlarged only during lactation, the *Homo* female had permanently enlarged breasts. She also had a unique distribution of body fat. And the male found both features enormously appealing.

To sum up, bipedalism permitted the male to provide a reliable source of food to the female. In return, the female provided ready sex. Both had physical features that were sexually attractive to the other. The overall result was increased survivorship for the species.

In 1924, the incomplete skull of a child was found in the Taung limestone quarry in South Africa. This was the only such fossil found at the site, for which there is an intriguing explanation. Puncture marks and depression fractures on the Taung skull are similar to those seen on animal bones found in the nests of eagles. So it is possible that the Taung child represents the leftovers of a meal by a large bird of prey. No precise dating was possible, but scientific estimates are that the child lived about 2 million years ago. It had the small brain and protruding jaw of an ape. But the jaw protruded less than it does in apes, the teeth were flatter than in an ape, and the canine teeth

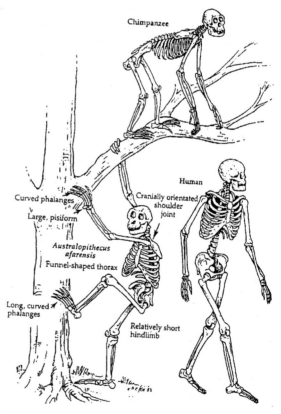

Note that the big toe is aligned with the other toes, not opposed in a grasping position, and that a pelvic basin is formed to support the viscera of an upright creature.

104

were smaller. A key piece of evidence was the position of the foramen magnum, the opening at the base of the skull through which the spinal cord passes. In apes it is far back in the base of the cranium. In humans it is more in the center, a difference that reflects the bipedal posture of humans. The Taung child's foramen magnum was in the center indicating that he was bipedal. In a bold move, Raymond Dart, professor of anatomy at the University of Witwatersrand in Johannesburg called it the "man-ape of South Africa" and named it *Australopithecus africanus*. In addition to the single individual from Taung, 120 individuals of *Australopithecus africanus* were found at Sterkfontein.

Finally, scientists agreed that there were two species—a more gracile species, *Australopithecus africanus*, who lived from 2.8 to 2.4 million years ago, and a more massive version, *Australopithecus* (later *Paranthropus*) *robustus*, who lived from 1.9 to 1 million years ago. The fossils of 200 *Australopithecus robustus* and six *Homo* were found in the cave at Swartkrans, South Africa.

Mary Leakey discovered what finally was named *Australopithecus* (later *Paranthropus*) *boisei*, on the assumption that it was an East African version of *Australopithecus* (*Paranthropus*) *robustus*. It had a massive skull and a broad, concave face like no other creature in the human line. *Australopithecus* (*Paranthropus*) *boisei* lived from 2.3 to 1.4 million years ago. Later Richard Leakey found another fossil of this same creature at Lake Turkana.

Leakey's brother, Jonathan, then found something that looked rather different. The Leakeys named it *Homo habilis*—handyman, referring to the supposition that the creature was a toolmaker.

In the mid-1970s, a rich collection of fossils between 3 and 3.9 million years old was discovered in the Hadar region of Ethiopia. The most exciting was a partial skeleton of a mature female, nicknamed Lucy, who stood barely 3 feet tall and who was very apelike in appearance, with long arms and short legs. Lucy lived about 3.2 million years ago. Other fossils found at the site were 5 feet tall. At first anthropologists thought they were two different species. But further investigation showed that Lucy and the others were the same species, examples of sexual dimorphism, i.e., the males were much bigger than the females. The females were three feet tall. The males were five feet tall and weighed twice as much. Given this difference in size, it is a fair assumption that the social organization of the *Australopithecines* was similar to that of the baboons today, with dominant males competing for access to mature females.

A study of Lucy's skeleton revealed her rib cage was conical, like an ape's, not barrel-shaped like a human's. Her shoulders, trunk, and waist also looked like those of an ape. Lucy would not have been able to lift her thorax for the kind of deep breathing that humans do when they run. Lucy's abdomen was pot-bellied with no waist, and this would have reduced the flexibility needed to run. *Homo* was a runner. Lucy was not.

The two vertical canals of the inner ear of humans are much larger than those of apes. In a bipedal animal, larger vertical canals are needed to maintain balance. In all species of *Australopithecus* the canals look like those of apes. In the genus *Homo*, the inner ear looks like those of modern humans. Although this suggests that *Australopithecus* moved on all fours as apes do, the structure of the pelvis and lower limbs speak against it. So do the fossilized footprints discovered by Mary Leakey that were made 3.75 million years ago. The footprints are the trail of a large male, a smaller female, and a still smaller child, all of the Lucy type. The footprints are very humanlike. A Lucy creature walked very much like *Homo sapiens sapiens* does. This clinched the conclusion, and Lucy and her ilk were named *Australopithecus afarensis*.

Australopithecus afarensis appeared in East Africa 3.9 million years ago and disappeared 3 million years ago. It changed very little over this rather long time span. The remains of 111 individuals were found at Hadar, Ethiopia, and 31 at Laetoli, Tanzania.

For several years it was thought that Lucy was a direct ancestor of ours and that her type lived for the longest time without another similar type living at the same time. However, in 2001 Dr. Meave Leakey, the current standard-bearer of the famous family, reported finding in Kenya a 3.5 million-year-old skull that belonged to an entirely different branch of the human family. Lucy's face resembled a chimpanzee's, and her species was assumed to be a direct human ancestor. But the flat face and small molars of the new Leakey find anticipated the human race more directly than Lucy did.

The differences were so great that Dr. Leakey decided to assign the discovery to a brand-new genus, *Kenyanthropus platyops*, the flat-faced man of Kenya. This means that the new fossil is different from any other member of the hominid family.

Scientists are not yet sure that the new find is a direct human ancestor or that a more natural one might yet turn up. However, the new find extends the pattern back to at least 3.5 million years ago.

From *Australopithecus afarensis* descended *Australopithecus africanus*, who lived 2.8 to 2.4 million years ago, and *Australopithecus* (later *Paranthropus*) *aethiopicus* (southern ape of Ethiopia), who lived from 2.7 to 1.9 million years ago. From *Australopithecus africanus* was descended, as already mentioned, *Australopithecus* (*Paranthropus*) *robustus*, who lived from 1.9 to 1 million years ago, represented by 85 individuals from Swartkrans.

Specimens belonging to only three individuals represent *Australopithecus* (*Paranthropus*) *aethiopicus*. From it descended *Australopithecus* (*Paranthropus*) *boisei*, who lived from 2.3 to 1.4 million years ago.

The pattern that emerged from these findings was that the early ancestors of humankind split into two branches between 3 and 2.5 million years ago, the *Homo* and the *Australopithecines*. The *Australopithecines* had a body built like apes. The *Homo* species had bodies that were more like those of humans, a larger brain, and smaller cheek teeth.

Homo ergaster and *Australopithecus* (*Paranthropus*) *boisei* lived at the same time in the Olduvai Gorge—*Homo ergaster* from 1.8 to 1.5 million years ago and *Australopithecus* (*Paranthropus*) *boisei* from 2.3 to 1.4 million years ago. The jaws of *ergaster* were designed for crushing and chewing. It was a wide-ranging omnivore that scavenged meat as well as gathered fruit, berries, and roots. *Australopithecus* (*Paranthropus*) *boisei* was an herbivore focusing on hard foods probably including nuts and seeds. Leakey thinks that the *Australopithecines* became extinct as a result of competition for food from the new *Homo* species and from the baboons, both of which were competing in the same new open areas.

Lewis Binford in his *Bones Ancient Men, and Modern Myth* (San Diego: Academic Press, 1981) argues that systematic hunting began with modern man only 45,000 to 35,000 years ago, when spears came into regular use. He argues that before that time rather than hunting and bringing the result to a base camp to be shared, hominids went to places like a lion kill and scavenged, mainly for marrow. At two different hominid sites dating from 1.5 million years ago, other investigators quite independently discovered marks of predator teeth on the bones found at the sites as well as the cut marks from flint tools. This strongly indicates that the carcasses were brought to the site for butchering and that the hominids were scavengers, not hunters.

The hunter-gatherers living today live in small mobile bands of about 25 people consisting of a core of adult males and females and their offspring. These bands interact with other bands forming a social and political network linked by customs and language. The network of bands is known as a dialectical tribe and totals about 500 people. They occupy temporary camps, and there is a clear division of labor—males hunt; females gather. They have a place of intense social interaction where food is shared, and when meat is available they often follow an elaborate ritual in distributing it governed by strict social rules.

To sum up, fossils of *Australopithecus afarensis*, the famous Lucy, were found in Ethiopia and dated between 3.9 to 3.0 million years ago. These and the trail of footprints left in volcanic ash demonstrated that Lucy and her relatives walked upright, unlike any of the great apes. Only one other fossil has been found of other hominids living at the same time. Lucy and her relatives lasted almost 1 million years, about 50,000 generations. In contrast, *Homo sapiens* were around for about 80 to 90,000 years, 4,000 to 4,500 generations, and *Homo sapiens sapiens* has been around for about 50 to 60,000 years or about 2,500 to 3,000 generations.

From *Australopithecus afarensis* descended *Australopithecus africanus* and *Australopithecus (Paranthropus) aethiopicus*. In 1959 Mary Leakey discovered a specimen with very robust features. She called it *Zinjanthropus*, but it is now generally recognized as a separate, extremely robust species, and called *Australopithecus (Paranthropus) boisei*. Although the exact line of descent is disputed, *Australopithecus (Paranthropus) robustus* and *Australopithecus (Paranthropus) boisei* may have descended from *Australopithecus africanus* or from *Australopithecus (Paranthropus) aethiopicus*. In any case, as already mentioned, *Australopithecus africanus* is known as the gracile and *Australopithecus (Paranthropus) robustus* as the robust form. *Ramapithecus* and *Sivapithecus*, whose remains were discovered in the Indian subcontinent, are now considered the same. It was probably the ancestor of the Orangutan.

The *Homo* line also descended from *Australopithecus afarensis*, which died out about 3 million years ago. One descendant was *Homo habilis*, "handyman," from the fact that he used tools. He lived from 1.9 to 1.6 million years ago, but had no known descendants. Recent opinion is that he was a scavenger and gatherer and not a hunter.

In 1994, an upper jaw was found at Hadar, Ethiopia, that was different from the other 324 specimens from that site. This was classified as *Australopithecus afarensis*. Its distinctive parabola-shaped dental arch immediately identified it as belonging to *Homo*. Associated with the jaw were 20 manufactured stone flakes made of basalt and chert that are very similar to the Oldowan tools. The jaw was dated very precisely at 2.3 million years old.

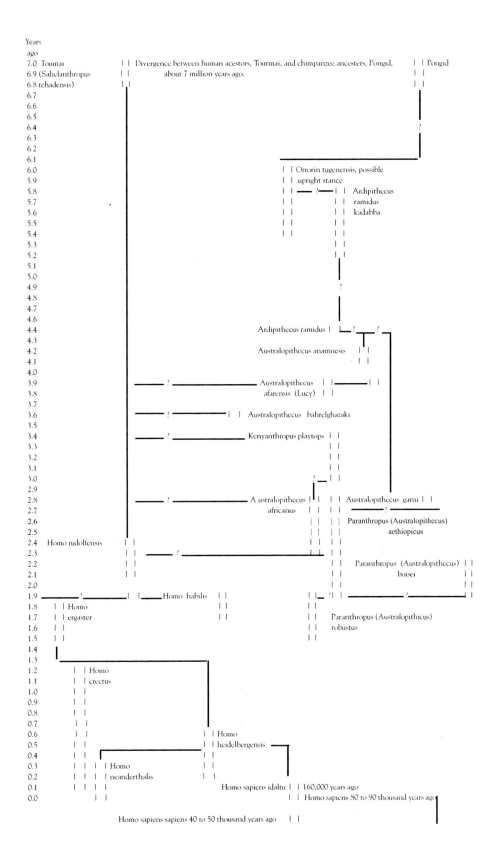

Another descendant of *Australopithecus afarensis*, was *Homo rudolfensis*, who lived from 2.4 to 1.9 million years ago. From *Homo rudolfensis* descended *Homo ergaster*, who lived from 1.8 to 1.5 million years ago. As already mentioned, fossils of *Homo ergaster* were found in the Olduvai Gorge, and it was thought that the first hominid to emigrate from Africa was its descendant, *Homo erectus*. However, in May 2000, it was announced that *Homo ergaster* fossils had been found in Georgia in the Caucasus. The tools found with the skulls were pre-Acheulean and resembled those found at Olduvai.

From *Homo ergaster*, probably before the emigration out of Africa, descended *Homo erectus*. He appeared 1.2 million years ago and lasted until 400,000 years ago, although one version may have lasted much longer as described below. But there may have been as many as six hominids intermediate between *Australopithecus afarensis* and *Homo erectus*, of whom one was *Homo habilis*, already mentioned.

All these hominids that descended from *Australopithecus afarensis* were bipedal, but apelike in appearance. They had small brains, just a little over half the size of a modern human brain. Their faces jutted forward (prognathous). The shape of their bodies was more apelike than human—a funnel shaped chest, very little neck and no waist.

Homo erectus was the first to extend its range to Asia. Its remains in China are dated at 700,000 and 800,000 years ago. Specimens from 15 individuals have been found at the Zhoukoudian site in China. Specimens from 48 individuals have been found in Java. No *Homo erectus* remains have been found in Europe.

In *Homo erectus*, brain size increased, the face was flatter, and the body more athletically built. At least one version of *Homo erectus* stood about six feet tall and was very powerfully muscled. In barehanded combat, modern man wouldn't stand a chance.

In China, *Homo erectus* may have had fire. He was the first hominid to be able to run as modern humans do, and the first to make stone tools according to some definite mental template. There is little difference between the *Homo erectus* remains found in Africa and those found in Indonesia and China, previously known as Java and Peking man. The first evidence of the use of fire outside Africa was found in a *Homo erectus* cave near Peking. However, if *Homo erectus* did use fire it was probably in the later years of its rather long existence. It has been generally assumed, to repeat, that *Homo erectus* lived from 1.2 million to 400,000 years ago and that he left Africa about 1 million years ago. But new evidence in Java, where specimens from

48 individuals have been found, suggest that he arrived there as early as 1.6 or 1.8 million years ago. The first discovery of the remains of *Homo erectus* was by Eugen Dubois in Java in the early 1890s. Later Dutch geologists discovered the remains of what they called Solo man in Java, but the consensus today is that Solo man and Dubois's *Homo erectus* is the same creature. Only recently were the Solo remains dated, and it is now thought that this version of *Homo erectus* lived between 27,000 and 53,000 years ago. If so, he coexisted with *Homo sapiens sapiens* who got to the same area about 40,000 years ago. So the evidence now is not only that *Homo sapiens sapiens* and Neanderthal coexisted for a time in Europe but that *Homo sapiens sapiens* coexisted with at least one version of *Homo erectus* for a time in Java.

From *Homo ergaster* descended *Homo erectus*, as already mentioned. Another descendant was probably *Homo heidelbergensis*, who lived from 600 thousand to 200 thousand years ago. *Homo heidelbergensis* bones from at least 30 individuals have been found at a site in Spain, from four individuals at another site in Spain, and from 20 individuals found elsewhere in Europe and Africa.

From *Homo heidelbergensis* descended *Homo neanderthalis*, who lived from 300 thousand to 27 thousand years ago. *Homo neanderthalis* branched off from *Homo heidelbergensis* 300,000 years ago and died out about 27,000 years ago. It occupied a region that included Europe, the Near East and adjoining parts of Asia. The remains of 500 individuals have been found in Europe, central Europe, and the Near East.

Also from *Homo heidelbergensis* descended *Homo sapiens*, who lived from about 80 to 90 thousand years ago to about 50 thousand years ago. Not too long thereafter modern humans appeared. The two terms, *Homo sapiens* and *Homo sapiens sapiens*, are the ones most frequently used, but some authorities prefer to use the term *Homo sapiens* for modern humans and the term *Archaic Homo sapiens* for the slightly more primitive version. Here the *term Homo sapiens* will be used for the more primitive version and *Homo sapiens sapiens* for the fully modern one.

Homo sapiens did not have modern tools, but Mousterian ones, very similar to those of Neanderthals. In other words, the culture of *Homo sapiens* was not very different from that of Neanderthals. Parts of more than 20 well preserved skeletons of *Homo sapiens* showing a number of primitive features were found in Jebel Qafzeh, a cave near Nazareth, dated from 90,000 to 100,000 years ago. Fossils of 10 more with primitive features were found at the Skhul rock shelter at Mount Carmel in Israel.

Homo sapiens include Petralona Man found in Greece; Arago Man in southwestern France; Steinheim Man in Germany; Broken Hill Man in Zambia, and Boxgrove Man in England (who had arrived before the English channel had formed). All were more advanced than *Homo heidelbergensis* and all were slightly more primitive than *Homo sapiens sapiens*.

With the appearance of *Homo sapiens*, another jump in tool making occurred. The simple hand axe of *Homo erectus* was replaced by a complex technology based on large flakes of flint. Where the Acheulean industry had about one dozen implements, the new technologies had five dozen.

A large flake of flint could cut through the toughest of hides, and this opened up a new source of food, the kills of lions and other such predators. So *Homo sapiens* was much more effective at scavenging.

A study by Nicholas Toth showed that the earliest toolmakers were predominantly right handed. Apes are both right and left handed in equal proportions. So two million years ago the brains of *Homo* were becoming more like those of humans.

Big brains require an earlier birth when the baby is still small enough to get through the female pelvis. The female pelvis of *Homo* got bigger, but reached a limit, imposed by the engineering demands of efficient bipedal locomotion. This meant a shorter gestation period and a longer infancy in which the infant is dependent on the adult. The age of weaning is later. The age of sexual maturity is also later. Individuals live longer. Apes grow at a steady pace. Humans remain children and are more easily controlled during a long learning process. They then have a spurt of growth in adolescence, during which, as any modern parent will testify, they are much more difficult to control.

Brains also require more energy. They are 2 percent of body weight but use 20 of the energy budget. Only by adding a concentrated source of protein and fat could *Homo* support a big brain. Meat was the answer. Scavenging was the principal source of meat for a rather long time, but at some stage scavenging had to be at least supplemented by hunting. Efficient hunting requires a group effort, and a group effort requires cooperation. So a better social organization is also needed.

In June 2003, the 160,000-year-old fossilized remains of two adults and a child were found in Ethiopia in an arid valley near the village of Herto 140 mils nrthwest of Addis Abba. They were named *Homo sapiens idaltu*. *Idaltu* means "elder" in the local language. They hunted and fished on the shore of a shallow freshwater lake teeming with catfish, crocodiles, and hippos. In all three the lower jaws were missing. It is speculated that the removal of the lower jaws may have been part of an ancient mortuary practice. This find is important because of the frustrating gap in fossil evidence between 100,000 and 300,000 years ago.

From *Homo sapiens* descended *Homo sapiens sapiens*, who appeared about 50 to 60 thousand years ago. Culture played a minor role until upper Paleolithic times, 40,000 years ago, and it is very clearly associated with *Homo sapiens sapiens*. Culture is taught by older individuals and learned by younger. Birds, for example, do not teach their young how to make a nest. Young birds build nests instinctively through genetic endowment. But humans do teach and learn. In passing culture from one generation of humans to another, language plays a central role. Cro Magnon was *Homo sapiens sapiens*, with modern anatomy, modern tools, and cave painting.

Neanderthal was short and stocky with a build much like today's Eskimo although taller. He had thick bones, a very heavy, beetle brow, and enormous physical strength. The first modern humans were tall, slightly built, and long-limbed. They were better suited to tropical or temperate climate. These facts support the conclusion that both *Homo sapiens* and *Homo sapiens sapiens* originated in Africa. Further support comes from the fact that fossils of *Homo sapiens* in the general neighborhood of 90,000 years old are found in both South Africa and North Africa but nowhere else.

The *Australopithecines* averaged around 4 feet 6 inches in height and weighed about 60 to 70 pounds. *Homo erectus* was generally larger. The male of Peking Man, for example, was about 5 feet 3 inches in height and the female was just over 4 feet 8 inches. Later examples of *Homo erectus* were about 6 feet, as mentioned above. For comparison, the Pygmies living today average from 4 feet 7 inches to 4 feet 9 inches, while the range of modern *Homo sapiens sapiens* runs from about 5 feet to about 6 feet, with Australians, Americans, and one African tribe, the Masai, being considerably taller. The male gorilla stands close to 6 feet tall and weighs 400 to 500 pounds.

Peking Man had considerable cranial capacity, 1,075 cc, but a low skull vault, a very thick skull wall, bony crests around the skull's horizontal circumferences, and a receding chin. All this puts Peking Man in the same league as *Homo erectus* of Java. Forty percent died before age 14; less than 3 percent reached 60. The bashed-in skulls of other members of his race are found in Peking Man's caves. But this suggests they were trophies of combat and not evidence of cannibalism, since only the skulls are found and not other parts of the body.

But the *Homo erectus* found at Peking was clearly a meat eater—70 percent of the bones were deer, and others were leopard, cave bear, saber-toothed tiger, hyena, elephant, rhinoceros, camel, water buffalo, boar, and horse. Some may have been the result of scavenging in the early years of his existence and some may have come from hunting in the later years. Charcoal remains suggest, as already mentioned, that Peking man used fire. He had many stone implements made of flakes, the raw material being vein quartz.

At one time it was suggested that *Homo sapiens sapiens* evolved from *Homo erectus* in each region where *Homo erectus* lived, the so-called multi-regional theory. But this seems highly unlikely. There is no evidence that any other form of complex creatures ever appeared simultaneously in widely separated regions. Second, the theory does not jibe with other things we know about *Homo sapiens sapiens*, as described below.

The population of *Homo sapiens sapiens* in the early years of their existence has been estimated at from 11,000 to 18,000 people. Presumably, the number grew for a while, but the data indicates that the total number suddenly declined sharply, suggesting some sort of disaster. Then the population began to expand.

Although one study puts the split between African and non-African *Homo sapiens sapiens* at 125,000 years ago, if *Homo sapiens* emerged about 100,000 years ago and *Homo sapiens sapiens* some time after that, the split must have come some time after 100,000 years ago. In any case, the genetic differences between identifiably different African populations living today are as great as the differences between Africans and the remainder of the human population. This supports the conclusion that the split occurred a long enough time ago to permit the differences to develop among the African populations and that the migration out of Africa occurred during a relatively short span of time. So it is reasonable to suppose that the crossing took place over a span of perhaps a few hundred years rather than continuing for thousands of years. Although one study estimates that the date when the ancestors of Asians, Europeans, and North and South Americans crossed from Africa to the Middle East was about 102,000 years ago, it seems more likely that the crossing was later than that, in the neighborhood of 80,000 to 60,000 years ago. In any case, it seems reasonable to suppose that different groups crossed at different times over a number of years. They undoubtedly crossed in small groups of a half dozen to perhaps as many two or three dozen people.

Recent studies suggest that both the parent population and the number of people in the crossing were remarkably small. Some estimates put the early human population of sub-Saharan Africa at the time of the crossing as 6,900 people, and the total number who left Africa as few as 500.

As already mentioned, the modern capacity for culture seems to have emerged about 50,000 years ago and with it appeared behaviorally modern humans who were capable of populating the globe. A burst of colonization occurred beginning about 50,000 years ago. The Indian subcontinent, Southeast Asia, and Australia were among the first to be settled, Asia and Europe began to be occupied about 40,000 years ago, northeast Asia about 30,000 years ago, the Americas about 15,000 years ago, and Polynesia about 3,500 years ago.

A global sample of 1,600 individuals from 42 populations concluded that the sub-Saharan population showed a large diversity, and the populations outside of Africa showed a startling uniformity. A dramatic illustration of just how recent the human settlement of the world outside Africa has been is that a person living in a remote village in the Andes and one living in a remote village in the Himalayas have been calculated to be between 1,000th and 1,500th cousins. The DNA extracted from the skeleton of a man who lived in Cheddar, England 8,980 years ago, matched that of Adrain Targett, who teaches today in a Cheddar Village school, illustrating a genetic continuity that has lasted 9 millennia. Also, the genetic sequences of two unrelated humans are 99.9 percent identical. For example, fewer than 10 genes control skin color. All humans have the capacity to have black, white, red, brown, or yellow skin. Based on the analysis of mitochondrial DNA in modern populations, Allen T. Wilson estimated that a common ancestor of all of today's humans lived 125,000 years ago. The implication is that all the people now alive are descendants of a group living in Africa 125,000 years ago who shared essentially the same mitochondrial DNA.

The number of people in this group who shared mitochondrial DNA was probably no more than a few hundred, perhaps, but certainly no more than a thousand. The group must have been so small that there were no significant variations of the marker DNA among them.

Mitochondrial DNA comes down through the mother. Only the father passes on the Y chromosome. Population geneticists believe that the breeding population of ancestral humans was only about 2,000 individuals. Because the lineages of many of this population fell extinct, a study of mitochondrial DNA goes back to a single female, nicknamed Eve. Since some men have no children or only daughters, the number of different Y-chromosomes also diminishes.

Dr. Douglas C. Wallace and his colleagues at the Emory University School of Medicine in Atlanta have studied mitochondrial DNA and Dr. Peter A. Underhill and Dr. Peter J. Oefner of Stanford University have studied the Y chromosome.

The ancestral population of 2,000 individuals mentioned above lived in Africa and started to split up at some point between 134,000 years ago and 154,000 years ago. In Africa there is a single main lineage of mitochondrial DNA that is divided into three branches.

The youngest branch, common in East Africa, is believed to be the source of both the Asian and European DNA lineages. In Asia, there is one ancestral DNA lineage, with three descendant branches.

In the Americas there are four DNA lineages. In Europe there are two main DNA lineages, one with four branches and the other with five. The data suggest that modern humans reached Europe from 39,000 years ago to 51,000 years ago. This compares favorably with the archeological data, which gives a date of about 40,000 years ago. Dr. Wallace and his colleagues identify the Vasikela! Kung of the northwestern Kalahari Desert in southern Africa and the Biaka pygmies of Central Africa as the populations that lie nearest to the root of the mitochondrial tree. Only females base all these conclusions, to repeat, on mitochondrial DNA passed on. The results of the Y chromosome study have not yet been published, but a book by one of their colleagues at Stanford, Dr. Luca Cavallis-Sforza, *Genes, People, and Languages* contains a preview of their findings. Again, the study goes back to a single individual, from whom stemmed 10 branches. Three of these, II, III, and I, are found almost exclusively in Africa. The lineage stemming from the male child labeled Son III migrated to Asia, and begat seven branches which spread to the rest of the world—Son IV to the Sea of Japan, Son V to northern India, Sons VI, VII, VIII, and IX to just south of the Caspian. Dr. Cavallis-Sforza believes that these Y chromosome lineages may be closely associated with the major language groups of the world.

To have multiplied and spread so quickly, *Homo sapiens sapiens* must have shared a powerful selective advantage. The obvious candidate is the faculty of language. Why, for example, did the Neanderthals disappear? Did *Homo sapiens sapiens* wipe them out? Or did they compete for the same kinds of food, and *Homo sapiens sapiens* was just more efficient at it? Hunting in groups would have been more efficient than by individual, and group hunting would have been more efficient if the members of the group had language.

Mitochondrial DNA recovered in 1997 from the original Neanderthal bones from the Felderhof Cave in the Neander valley dating from 30,000 years ago was quite different from that of modern humans. Russian scientists provided a sample of the bones of a Neanderthal infant, two months old, found in the Mezmaiskaya Cave in the Caucasus northeast of the Black Sea. It was carbon dated as 29,000 years old, and it, too, was quite different from that of modern humans. The DNA from the Mezmaiskaya Cave Neanderthal and the Felderhof Cave Neanderthal differed by 3.5 percent, and this suggests considerable genetic diversity. The two Neanderthals shared a common ancestor about 150,000 years ago, and the Neanderthal and modern human lineages split some 300,000 years ago. Unfortunately, no DNA has yet been recovered from very ancient *Homo sapiens sapiens* fossils, such as Cro Magnon, but the expectation is that it will be very similar to that of modern humans.

Neanderthal and *Homo sapiens sapiens* coexisted in Europe for at least 1,000 years and perhaps for 2,000. Both lived at sites in the Middle East, but it may have been at different times with no actual overlap in that area. As already mentioned, Neanderthals were adapted to a cold climate. When *Homo sapiens sapiens* came out of Africa, they were adapted to a warm, humid climate, so they turned southeast, away from the colder climate of Europe into India and Asia. They did not enter Europe until about 40,000 years ago. The speculation is that although the archeological evidence is that both Neanderthal and *Homo sapiens sapiens* lived in the Middle East at one time or another, it may have been at different times. Neanderthal may have occupied it in the cold periods and retreated north during the warm periods and *Homo sapiens sapiens* may have occupied it during the warm periods and retreated south in the cold periods. Presumably the Neanderthal did not have very much language. The position of the larynx indicates that they could not pronounce the vowels "A," "I," and "U." If Neanderthal and *Homo sapiens sapiens* coexisted for 40,000 years but were in contact for only a thousand or so, the inference must be that the Neanderthal lost the competition for resources not long after their articulate rivals entered their territory.

The important fact to remember is that it was only very recently that *Homo sapiens sapiens* learned to survive in a world that was harsh by developing specific drugs for specific diseases such as smallpox. Malaria, in which a type of mosquito must be wiped out or a drug that can be cheaply admin-istered to children every day, will continue to devastate children.

Chapter 11

Weapons, Tools, Fire, and Speech

The first animals to use weapons were undoubtedly the first who had an opposable thumb. All they had to do was a pick up a stone or a stick, and they had a weapon. Cartoons picture cave men armed with huge clubs, and there probably is some truth in the idea. Also, when *Homo sapiens sapiens* and their somewhat distant relatives, *Homo neanderthalis*, came to control fire, they hardened the point of a stick by putting it in the coals and so made a hand-held spear.

In 1999 at a 50,000-year-old Neanderthal site in Syria a sharpened, triangular, stone point was found embedded in the neck bone of a wild ass, an extinct ancestor of the donkey. Stone points ranging in size from 1 inch to several inches have turned up at many Neanderthal sites, but they appear to have been tools used mainly for scavenging carnivore leftovers. However, this two-and-a-half-inch point had been bound to a handle or a shaft. Whether it was used as a hand-held spear or as an axe, it would have been much more lethal than a wooden spear with a fire-hardened point or a hand-held piece of sharpened stone.

After the development of a spear that could be thrown, both its force and distance were greatly enhanced by the invention of the *atl atl*. This is a stick with a socket at one end in which the butt of the spear fits. The result is to lengthen the throwing arm by the length of the atl atl. The American Indians used it, and there is evidence that it was also invented and used in

Europe and elsewhere as well.

Stone of various kinds were used to make weapons. The Polynesians used jade, which is very hard and holds an edge very well indeed. But jade is scarce, and the most common stone that could hold an edge was flint. It was used to make knives, spearheads, arrowheads, scythes, and a bewildering variety of other tools.

Homo sapiens sapiens learned how to work flint into all the many shapes he needed. He also learned that some flints were better than others, and he sought out the best of them for his purposes. At Grime's Graves near Norfolk, England, 700 to 800 Neolithic flint mines pockmark 34 acres. Many were dug so close together that the chalk separating them was cut through at the base to link the two pits.

Flint occurs naturally in chalk. Nodules of flint are found at various levels, but the best, now known as floor stone, is several layers down at a depth of between 30 and 40 feet. Grime's Graves lies on the eastern boundary of a chalk zone five miles wide that runs in a north-south direction near Norfolk, England.

In a typical mine, the vertical shaft was dug down to the level of the floor stone flint, and from the base of each shaft galleries were dug radiating out to find and extract it. The galleries are up to seven feet wide and five feet high, permitting two miners to pass each other and high enough for a man with a bent back to carry a load of chalk or flint.

Archeologists estimate that the number of miners who could work in one of the diggings at the same time would be limited. Six or seven men would be the maximum number who could work effectively in the shaft. Another six or seven men would be required to take out the spoil. In the flint mine used as an example, the calculation is that it would have taken such a workforce of 12 to 14 men 30 to 32 days to dig the shaft. Digging the galleries would add another 13 to 14 days. Between 800 and 1,000 tons of chalk and sand would have to be evacuated. The yield would have been 8 tons of flint.

The skill required suggests that the miners were professional specialists and that farmers and hunters in exchange for the flint supplied their needs. Around the edge of the mining area, flint was knapped into roughed-out knife, axe, and other tool shapes. These were traded, and some ended up at rather distant points. The final recipients would apparently put on the finishing touches themselves to suit their particular needs. Neolithic farming undoubtedly followed the slash-and-burn technique, and this would have required a huge number of such tools to clear the land and till the fields. It seems likely that local specialists at the place where the tools were used did this knapping work.

Red deer antlers were used in the mines as picks. It is estimated that over 50,000 antlers were used at Grime's Graves. The great majority were cast antlers, sloughed off each year so new ones could grow, and these are the hardest and most durable kind. Anthropologists suggest that these cast antlers were most likely supplied by a service industry that grew up for the very purpose of collecting antlers.

Illumination was needed when working in a gallery radiating out from the vertical shaft, and a number of hollowed chalk "cups" have been found that were probably filled with animal fat and a wick to make a lamp. Wooden ladders were undoubtedly used to get down into the mine and leather bags and baskets used to remove the rubble and flint.

Radiocarbon dating indicates that the mines were active for about 25 to 30 generations, from about 4,330 years ago to about 3,740 years ago.

In one pit a female chalk figure, obviously pregnant, was found in a niche in one of the walls of a main shaft. A pile of offerings had been placed in front of it.

The obvious overall conclusion is that a rather complicated industry of specialists grew up around flint mining—the mining itself, gathering the cast antlers that became the miners' picks, knapping the flint into rough shapes, supplying the miners with food and necessities, distributing the product to the ultimate consumer, and knapping the rough shapes into the final tool.

Toward the end of the Neolithic age, copper metallurgy appeared in some regions. Copper was in use 10,000 years ago to make ornaments, and 6,000 years ago it began to be used to make utilitarian objects. Then came the age of bronze, an alloy of copper and tin that was much better for both weapons and tools than stone. Bronze came into use in Europe about 4,000 years ago and continued to be the most common metal for both tools and weapons until about 2,700 years ago. The Bronze Age began somewhat later in the British Isles, probably around 3,800 years ago, since radioactive dating shows that the Grime's Graves flint mines were active until 3,740 years ago.

Tools

Chimpanzees use tools—sticks to pry out termites from their hills, leaves as sponges to sop up water, stones to crack nuts. But no chimpanzee has ever been seen to *make* a stone tool. But hominids did so about 2.5 million years ago when the genus *Homo* first appeared. Leakey believes that the first tool-maker was *Homo*, not *Australopithecus*.

The tools made by the earliest hominids were simple. A jump in complexity occurred with the appearance of *Homo erectus* 1.4 million years ago, when hand axes appear. These Acheulean tools, named for the site at St. Acheul in northern France, provide evidence that the toolmakers had a mental template of what they wanted to produce, at least for hand axes.

The imposition of order is a human obsession, but without speech it would be impossible. So Glynn Isaac examined tools to try to see if the toolmakers imposed order on their implements. Oldowan tools, which date from 2.4 million years ago to 1.4 million years ago, are opportunistic. They are sharp flakes without regard for shape. Even the Acheulean tools, which followed and lasted until about 250,000 years ago, show only a minimal imposition of form. The teardrop-shaped hand axe was probably produced according to some mental template, but most of the others were like the Oldowan.

Both Neanderthals and *Homo sapiens* made tools from prepared flakes and these, including the Mousterian, comprise perhaps sixty types. But the types remain unchanged for more than 200,000 years—a technological stasis that seems to deny the workings of the fully human mind.

Fire

Burnt clay was found in a *Homo erectus* site in Kenya that is 1.42 million years old, but it is doubtful that this was anything other than an accident. In Europe at Menez-Dregan on the southern coast of Brittany there are remains of what could possibly have been a fire pit, a ring of stones enclosing charcoal and burned bones dated between 380,000 and 465,000 years ago. But both the evidence and the dating have been disputed. Two early sites in Europe, Vèrtesszöllös and Escale, also contain evidence that suggest the use of fire. There is another rather more doubtful site some 400,000 years old at Bury St. Edmund in England. The cave at Zhoukoudian in China provides some evidence that the Peking Man version of *Homo erectus* had fire. It may be doubted that early *Homo erectus* did, but the species lived over such an enormously long period of time, from about 1.2 million years ago until about 30,000 years ago, and it would be surprising if *Homo erectus* did not develop fire in the latter part of its existence. In any case, it seems reasonable to suppose that the *Homo* line had mastered fire by 100,000 years ago and used it to serve a number of specialized functions in daily life. By 40,000 years ago evidence of fires in caves is common.

The first site that shows the use of fire without any doubt is a cave at Dordogne, France. It is a Neanderthal site about 60,000 years old, and it clearly shows the remains of a fire made with lichen, which is an excellent fuel for starting and maintaining a fire, as Boy Scouts of this century will testify. It is worth noting that lichen is popular as a wick among present-day Eskimos.

Another cave with Neanderthal artifacts in Bruiquel in Southern France is so deep that torches would have been essential. It also contains burnt bones.

Warmth was undoubtedly the initial use of fire, but cooking would certainly have been quickly discovered, if only by accident. Since pottery had yet to be invented, roasting would have been the cooking method used.

Aside from using the remnants of natural fires set off by lightning, fires could have been started by striking sparks from stones or by rubbing sticks together until the heat of the friction ignited the tinder. Once a fire was kindled, tending it would have been an important function. One cannot help but wonder if the custom of preserving a sacred fire in Greek, Roman, and other temples, watched and presided over by dedicated maidens, such as the Vestal Virgins, had its origins thousands of years earlier.

Already mentioned is the fact that both Neanderthal and *Homo sapiens sapiens* had wooden spears with the points hardened by fire. Stone lamps, some with handles, have been found in a number of Neanderthal and *Homo sapiens sapiens* sites. The fuel was probably animal fat. The wicks were made of a number of substances. Lichen and moss were the easiest substances to use for wicks, but juniper, which gives off a delightful smell, was apparently a favorite.

Fire was used in the oxidation of pigments, such as ochre. Ochre provides a very dramatic red, as we see in cave art. It may also have been used for body painting. Some early peoples used fire to help flake flint in their manufacture of flint tools. A Moravian site 26,000 years old has fired fragments of clay pottery and pieces of broken clay figurines. A number of early sites have fired pieces of clay with the negative imprints of basketry and textiles.

Hominids might have carried coals from natural fires back to their caves in a skin filled with lichen or moss. Later, they obviously learned to strike flint, chert, or quartz against an iron pyrite to cast a spark on to a bed of lichen or other tinder. At some point they must have learned to rub two pieces of dry wood together to make a little pile of smoldering wood dust that could be blown to fire and then transferred to some tinder. At some stage they undoubtedly learned to do the job more efficiently with a bow drill and thong.

Speech

Only *Homo sapiens sapiens* communicates with each other by complex speech, and since the human brain is three times as large as our nearest relatives, the African great apes, the connection seems obvious. Noam Chomsky contended that speech appeared all at once. But the evidence is overwhelming that it developed gradually and in stages. At different times scientists thought that many things were unique to humans—tool making, the ability to use symbols, mirror recognition, and finally speech. Each item of uniqueness has crumbled, and recently speech has too.

The human ability to produce sounds or phonemes is only modestly better than the apes. We have 50 phonemes, apes have about a dozen. However, 50 phonemes can be used in virtually endless ways. They can be arranged and rearranged to give the average human being a vocabulary of 50,000 words and these can be combined into an infinity of sentences.

Chomsky argued that speech appeared with *Homo sapiens sapiens*, that we have no idea how physical laws apply when 10^{10} neurons are placed in an object smaller than a basketball. Steven Pinker of MIT says in his *The Language Instinct* (New York: William Morrow, 1994) that Chomsky had it backwards, that the brain is more likely to have increased in size as a result of the evolution of speech, not the other way around. He argues that "it is the precise wiring of the brain's microcircuitry that makes language happen, not gross size, shape, or neuron packing." As humankind evolved, their brain size tripled. This evolutionary transformation began with the first species of *Homo* two million years ago.

An early view was that speech grew out of the cooperation required in a hunter-gatherer culture, but hunting and gathering came much later than speech. Recent thinking is that speech might have been an extension of grooming. In any case, several people can talk together while doing other things. As a result, speech tended to integrate a larger number of people into a social group.

Richard Leakey in his book, *The Origin of Humankind* (New York: Basic Books, 1994) on which the following is based, points out that the expansion of the brain began about 2 million years ago with the origin of the genus *Homo* and continued steadily until the arrival of *Homo sapiens sapiens*. By half a million years ago, the average brain size among *Homo erectus* was 1,100 cubic centimeters, which is not too much smaller than the modern average. After the initial 50 percent jump from *Australopithecine* to *Homo*, there were no further sudden large increases. So the gradual tripling of brain size suggests a gradual development of speech. The proposition is that it was not tool use that provided the evolutionary pressure for bigger brains, but speech. As Leakey says, it does not take much brainpower to use a tool, but simple, useful speech takes a lot.

There is not just one center in the brain for speech. Speech-related areas are scattered around in the brain. Brains do not fossilize, but one part related to both speech and the use of tools, Broca's area, is visible on the surface of the brain in most people, a raised lump near the left temple. A second possible clue is the difference in size between the left and right sides of the brain. In most humans the left is larger, and this is where the speech-related machinery is packed. About 90 percent of humans are right handed, which is controlled by the left side of the brain, so right-handedness and a capacity for speech may be related. A recent study monitoring the brain activity of people answering I.Q.-type questions shows that the lateral pre-frontal cortex is the brain's center for high-level thinking.

The almost two-million-year-old fossil skull of an immature *Homo habilis* that Richard Leakey found near Lake Turkana showed not only the Broca's area but also a slight asymmetry in the left and right sides of the brain. So this *Homo habilis* probably communicated with more than the modern chimpanzee's pant, hoot, and grunt. Leakey feels that it was only with *Homo* that speech began.

Humans are able to make a wide range of sounds because the larynx is low in the throat. Humans cannot breathe and drink at the same time, while high-in-the-throat mammals can. So in animals only the oral cavity and lips make sound. Human babies are born with the larynx high in the throat, so they can breathe and drink at the same time, as they must during nursing.

After about 18 months the larynx begins to migrate down the throat reaching the adult position when the child is about 14 years old. If you could determine the position of the larynx in an ancient skull, you would know its capacity to vocalize.

Vocal chords do not fossilize. But ancient skulls do contain a vital clue. It is in the shape of the bottom of the skull, the basicranium. In the basic mammalian pattern, it is flat. In humans, it is arched. This should indicate how well the owner of the skull could articulate sounds. The basicrania of *Australopithecines* was flat. They would not have been able to produce some of the universal vowel sounds that characterize human speech. The earliest fully flexed basicranium is in *Homo sapiens*. But at least the beginning of change in the shape of the basicranium is seen in the earliest known *Homo erectus*, dating from almost 2 million years ago. This individual would have been able to produce the vowels in *boot*, *father*, and *feet*, equivalent to what is found in a modern six-year old.

So far no *Homo habilis* cranium with an intact basicranium has been found. Leakey's guess is that when found it will show the beginnings of flexion in the base indicating a rudimentary capacity for speech.

Judging by their basicrania, Neanderthals had poorer verbal skills than the early *Homo sapiens*. The basicranial flexion in Neanderthal is even less than in *Homo erectus*. As mentioned in Chapter 10, Neanderthal could not pronounce the vowels "A," "E," and "I." In adapting to colder climates, Neanderthal developed a midface that protruded to an extraordinary degree, resulting in large nasal passages in which frigid air could be warmed and moisture in exhaled breath could condense. This configuration may have affected the shape of the basicranium.

So the anatomical evidence indicates that the *Homo* line had some speech early on and that its linguistic skills improved gradually but steadily. In the Upper Paleolithic age, 35,000 years ago, innovation and arbitrary order became pervasive, and the change occurred rather rapidly, in a few millennia not hundreds of millennia. Glynn L. Isaac interpreted this pattern as implying the gradual emergence of speech in "The Food-Sharing Behavior of Protohuman Hominids." (Readings From *Scientific American*, Glynn Isaac and Richard E. F. Leakey, "Human Ancestors").

What about art? At first glance it seems to enter the archaeological record abruptly also about 35,000 years ago. The argument was that art was one of the mediums through which referential speech developed. But art had to predate speech. Various birds follow rules that govern much of human compositions. The continued analysis of whale songs shows a taste for rhyme and reliance on a statement of theme, the elaboration of a section of the theme, and then a return to a slightly modified version of the theme. Each of the music-making species makes what music it can with the tools at its disposal, and we happen to make better tools,

Leakey quotes Kathleen Gibson, one of the organizers of a conference on "Tools, Language, and Cognition in Human Evolution," as arguing that since social intelligence, tool use and speech all depended on having a bigger brain, none could have suddenly emerged full-blown. "Rather, like brain size, each of these intellectual capacities must have evolved gradually. Further, since these capacities are interdependent, none could have reached its modern level of complexity in isolation."

As Leakey says, if by some freak of nature *Homo habilis* and *Homo erectus* still existed, we would see in them gradations of referential speech. The apparent gap between us and the rest of nature would therefore be closed, and by our own ancestors.

Leakey says three revolutions mark the history of life on Earth. The first was the origin of life 3.5 billion years ago. The second was the appearance of multicellular organisms, about half a billion years ago. The third was the origin of consciousness, or self-awareness in *Homo* some time in the last 2.5 million years.

How can you tell if an animal is self-aware? The mirror test was devised to do this. First, the animal is trained to become familiar with a mirror. Then surreptitiously a red dot is put on its forehead. If the animal knows the reflection is its own, it will touch its forehead to see about the red dot. If it does not know that the reflection is its own, it will ignore the matter or touch the mirror at the red spot. When tested, chimps touched their own foreheads. So did Orangutans. But gorillas did not.

Another test would be tactical deception. For example, a chimpanzee was put in the feeding area alone. A box was opened electronically, revealing bananas. At that point a second chimpanzee was admitted to the area. The first closed the box and ambled off. He waited until the intruder departed. Then he opened the box and got the bananas. Actually, the second chimpanzee had not gone away, but had hidden himself. The would-be deceiver had been deceived. The conclusion is that chimpanzees have a significant degree of reflective consciousness.

But they seem to have no sense of the nature of death. A chimpanzee mother will sometimes carry a dead baby around for days, but no other chimpanzees show any concern or understanding. No one has seen any evidence that chimpanzees have any awareness of their own mortality, of impending death.

Among humans, ritual burial of the dead speaks clearly of an awareness of death. The first evidence of deliberate burial was by Neanderthals about 100,000 years ago. Another, more poignant example was 60,000 years ago in the Zagros Mountains of Northern Iraq. A mature male was buried at the entrance to a cave. Judging from the pollen that was found in the soil around the remains, the body had been placed on a bed of flowers of medicinal potential.

The Neanderthal also gave evidence of care giving. A partial jaw, dated between 169,000 and 191,000 years old, contains extensive bone damage and loss. This Neanderthal survived as an adult for at least six months while being virtually unable to chew food. This find pushes back by 100,000 years evidence of care giving by a *Homo* species.

Chapter 12

Language and Writing

Joseph Greenberg, who has studied and written extensively on languages, argues that most of the thousands of known languages belong to 17 language groups, listed below. Merrit Ruhlen later estimated the number of people who spoke each of these languages.

Khoisan. About 30 languages in South Africa with 120,000 speakers among the Bushmen and Hottentots.

Niger-Kordofanian. A large group of African languages with two branches. One is the Niger-Congo group including all the Bantu languages such as Zulu, Ra Wanda, and Kikuyu with 180 million speakers. The Kordofanian branch has approximately 30 languages spoken by about 30 million people in the Sudan.

Nilo-Saharan. About 140 languages with 11 million speakers in Egypt, the Sudan, Mali, and Tanzania.

Afro-Asiatic. About 240 languages with about 180 million speakers in Northern Africa and the Middle East. It includes Arabic, with 100 million speakers, Hebrew, Berber, and Hausa. Several ancient languages, including Ancient Egyptian, Akkadian, and Aramaic, are also members of this group.

Caucasian. 35 languages spoken by 5 million people in the Caucasus. The largest language group is Georgian with 3 million speakers.

Indo-European. 140 languages spoken by 2 billion people, the largest single language group, stretching from Ireland to India and including Iranian, Hindi, Slavic, Italic, Greek, Lithuanian, and Albanian.

Uralic-Yukaghir. 20 languages spoken by about 22 million people in Europe and Siberia including Hungarian (14 million), Finnish (5 million), Estonian, the Lapp language, and the Samoyedic languages of western Siberia.

Altaic. 60 languages and 250 million speakers, including Japanese, Korean, Mongolian, Turkish, the Turkic languages Uzbek and Uighur, Manchu, the Tungus languages of Siberia and China, and Ainu spoken by the Hairy Ainu of Japan.

Chukchi-Kamchatkan. 5 languages spoken by only 23,000 people in Northeast Siberia.

Eskimo-Aleut. 10 languages spoken by about 200,000 Eskimos of Siberia, Alaska, Canada, and Greenland and the Aleuts of the Aleutian Islands off Alaska.

Dravidian. 20 languages spoken by 145 million people in India and Pakistan. Tamil is spoken by the largest number of this group. Some specialists believe that Dravidian is related to Elamite, the ancient Mesopotamian language.

Sino-Tibetan. Chinese, Tibetan, Burmese, and some minor languages of Tibet and Nepal. This is the second largest language group, with one billion speakers.

Austric. A large grouping of many languages proposed by Joseph Greenberg that is controversial since many linguists regard some of them as separate. One group of 60 languages, spoken by 50 million people, is Daic or Kadai. One of these languages is Thai with 30 million speakers. Another group often considered separate is Austroasiatic with 150 languages and 56 million speakers. It includes Vietnamese and Khmer. Still another group often considered separate is Austronesian, the languages spoken by 180 million people in Malaya, Indonesia, the Philippines, Melanesia, and Polynesia.

Indo-Pacific. Also known as Papuan. Over 700 languages spoken by 3 million people in New Guinea and nearby islands.

Australian. 170 aboriginal languages with poorly understood interconnections spoken by 30,000 people.

Na-Dene. This includes, first, the Athapaskan languages of Indian tribes in Alaska and the Western subarctic of Canada. It also includes Navaho spoken in New Mexico and Arizona. And, finally it includes three languages of the Pacific Northwest coast of Canada—Haida, Tlingit, and Eyak.

Amerind. This is a category proposed by Joseph Greenberg including about 600 native Indian languages of North and South America spoken by 18 million people. Many linguists disagree. Some distinguish as many as 200 separate languages groups.

As described later in this book, the Americas seem to have been populated in four separate waves of migration. One of these were a fisher folk, who made their way along the shoreline from Siberia all the way down to Chile in South America. A second were the big game hunters who followed the game through a gap in the ice sheet to North America, and finally made their way to South America east of the Andes. A third were the Na-Dene, the ancestors of the Navajo and others whose descendants live in Canada. And a fourth were the Eskimo-Aleut. This suggests that the ancestors of the North and South American Indians other than the Navajo were two different groups rather than Greenberg's one that he called Amerind.

A study by Christy Turner concluded that American Indians, other than Eskimo-Aleut, had three distinct tooth shapes, which also tends to support the idea of three separate migrations and so three sets of languages, plus Eskimo-Aleut. Genetic studies of aboriginal Americans also indicate three separate groups.

Basque is absent from Greenberg's list, and no one has convincingly shown any connection with any other language, except one. This possible line of descent is suggested in Chapter 13 below.

Merritt Ruhlen and John D. Bengson attempted to reconstruct the primordial ancestor of all language, and to find both the meaning and the sound of words.

The word *mano*, for example, meaning man, in Ancient Egyptian is *min*, the name of a phallic god. In Somali it is *mun*. In the Nilo-Saharan Tama, it is *ma*. In Dravidian (Tamil) it is *mantar*. In Gondi it is *manja* (also person). In Austric, the Miao-Yao people call themselves, *man* or *mun*. In Amerind, among the Squamish of Canada, *man* means husband. In South America there are a number, such as *man*, *manino*, and *mino*. And, of course, the English word, *man*.

The word *kuna* meaning woman is found in Afro-Asiatic. In Altaic (i.e., in Kirghiz) it is *kunu*. In Amerind, in the Guarani language, it is *kuña*. In Kamayura it is *kunja*. The Anglo-Saxon word for the female sexual organ, *cunt*, can be added.

Writing

Writing probably began with counting. Bones and antlers with a long series of notches are often found in very early archeological sites, and they were probably preceded by notched sticks that have not survived. These were undoubtedly mnemonic devices to record things of importance, such as kills, prayers, and so on.

Language itself also had mnemonic devices. For example, as the people following reindeer herds gradually domesticated them, they had a need to count the number in the herd. Drawing on the work of the Russian prehistorian Boris A. Frolov, Richard Rugley in his book, *The Lost Civilizations of the Stone Age* (New York: The Free Press, 1999. p. 91) describes how a group of reindeer herders, the Yukaghir, counted. Since humans have 10 fingers and 10 toes, one person equals the number 20. So a herd of 94 reindeer would be expressed as "four persons (80). On top of that half a person (10) and also a forehead (1), two eyes (2), and a nose (1)." The total is 94, and the way of counting makes it is easy to remember the total number, which was probably part of the rationale in which the parts of the body were itemized.

The earliest evidence of writing is found at Uruk, the chief city of Sumeria in what is now Iraq. It dates from about 5,100 years ago. The writing precedes cuneiform (from the Latin word for wedge) and was followed by the Proto-Elamite script in what is now Iranian, and then by Egyptian hieroglyphics. Writing appeared in the Indus valley about one thousand years later.

Writing is thought to have spread from Sumeria to Iran, Egypt, and perhaps the Indus valley. Writing in both China and the Americas came somewhat later and is thought to have emerged quite independently.

In the nineteenth century it was assumed that all writing developed out of crude picture writing. But the earliest texts at Uruk were written in a script consisting of abstract characters that had little or no resemblance to picture writing. The archaeologist Denise Schmandt-Bessaret found what seems to be the answer, as she describes in her book, *Before Writing, Volume One: From Counting to Cuneiform* (Austin, TX: University of Texas Press, 1992). She was studying collections of clay objects dating from 8,000 to 10,000 years ago. Most of the items were bricks, beads, and figurines. But in the museums of Iraq, Iran, Syria, Turkey, and Israel she also found thousands of miniature cones, spheres, disks, tetrahedrons, cylinders, and other geometric shapes as well as shapes of animals, vessels, tools, and so on. She called these clay objects tokens.

The key was an article she happened to read describing a hollow, egg-shaped tablet dating 4,000 years ago in a museum in Northern Iraq. The cuneiform inscription on the tablet said:

> counters representing small cattle:
> 21 ewes that lamb
> 6 female lambs
> 8 full-grown sheep
> 4 male lambs
> 6 she-goats that kid
> 1 he-goat
> 3 female kids
> the seal of Ziqarru, the shepherd

Inside the tablet there were 49 of the tokens she had been puzzling over, specifying exactly the number of animals listed on the outside. Clearly this was some sort of accounting system.

For Schmandt-Bessaret this discovery was a revelation. She spent the next 15 years studying tokens. It seemed clear that she had come across an accounting system that had existed 10,000 years ago, beginning in the early Neolithic.

The earlier tokens, dating from 10,000 years ago to between 6,400 and 6,300 years ago, are plain, and there are only a few different kinds. More complex tokens and a wider variety have been found from the second phase, beginning around 6,400 years ago. During the sixth millennium before the present, the tokens played a significant role in the activities and administration of temples.

The conical token seems to have stood for a measure of grain, the sphere for a larger measure of grain, the ovoid for a jar of oil, the cylinder for a domestic animal, and the tetrahedron for a unit of labor. The tokens could be understood by people who spoke different languages, which would have been a great advantage in trade. In any case, they served a need for about 4,000 years.

The number of different types of tokens increased with time. Over 241 sub-types have been recovered at Uruk. The speculation is that the over-burdening of the system led to writing. At first, holes seem to have been drilled in the different tokens so they could be strung together. Putting them in a sort of clay envelope, as described above, and putting markings on the outside of what was on the inside. At some stage, the people involved must have realized that the markings on the outside made the tokens on the inside redundant. The envelopes gave way to clay tablets and the tokens to notations on the tablet.

So it seems obvious that writing was not invented overnight by some prehistoric genius, but beginning with the notches on sticks, bones, and antlers it had developed gradually over thousands of years.

By about 5,000 years ago, the practice of record keeping by using reeds to impress representational signs in wet clay evolved into a rudimentary system of writing. In the beginning the signs were pictorial, but this gradually gave way to a method by which individual syllables of speech were represented by combinations of wedge-shaped indentations in the clay—the wedge-shaped or cuneiform writing of Mesopotamia. The wedges were produced by the tip of a reed or a wood stylus modified into a sharp triangle by knife cuts.

The first writing in Mesopotamia was "logographic," that is, the signs stood for words. Using the rebus principle in which the same signs are used for things that have the same sound increased their usefulness. For example, the word BELIEF can be broken into two syllables, BEE-LEAF, and written with the image of a bee and the image of a leaf. In this way a "phonographic" dimension was introduced. The next step was to have the signs stand for syllables. For example, the word for water was the syllable "A," and the pictograph was ≈.

At an early stage, the scribes began to orient the signs vertically, ʬ. In the neo-Assyrian empire 2,900 years ago to 2,700 years ago, which is the type of cuneiform that scholars first deciphered, the sign for the sound of "A" was T╪.

The law code of Hammurabi, the sixth and most successful of the kings of Babylon who lived about 3,800 years ago, was written in cuneiform. It is worth noting parenthetically that Solon, the Athenian lawgiver lived 2,550 years ago.

Egyptian Hieroglyphics

In some cases, the system of writing evolved along with the language and if the language still lives, it is not too difficult to read inscriptions written in much earlier times. This is what happened in the case of Chinese,

Greek, and Latin. But if the inscriptions have no relationship with any existing language, they have to be deciphered as if they had been written in a secret code. Etruscan has never been deciphered. Neither has Linear A, a Minoan script found on the island of Crete. Neither has Iberian, a pre-Roman script, nor the Bronze Age script of the Indus civilization. One example of the Indus is a large wooden board with giant letters 37 cm in height. The size suggests that the ordinary people could read, and if so this could be the world's oldest billboard!

The earliest Egyptian hieroglyphics date to 5,000 years ago, and this form of writing endured for the next 3,500 years. Hieroglyphics were ideal for the elaborate inscriptions on temples—the Greek word *hieroglyphica* means "sacred carvings." But they were much too complicated for everyday affairs, so a simplified version evolved in parallel with the hieroglyphic. This was the hieratic script, in which each hieroglyphic symbol was replaced by a simplified, stylized one. Around 2,600 years ago, the hieratic was replaced by an even more simplified version called demotic, from the Greek word meaning "of the people." All three of these forms of writing are phonetic, although it took a long time before would-be translators realized this.

The Egyptians used one or the other of these forms of writing for 3,000 years. Then in the last years of the fourth century A.D. the Christian church outlawed all three in order to wipe out any link with the pagan past. The old writing was replaced with Coptic, consisting of 24 letters of the Greek alphabet plus six demotic characters for Egyptian sounds not found in Greek. The ability to read hieroglyphics, hieratic, and demotic vanished within a single generation. The ancient Egyptian language evolved into what became known as Coptic, and this was displaced by the spread of Arabic in the eleventh century A.D.

When Napoleon invaded Egypt in 1789, no one had any idea of how to read the inscriptions that blanketed the Egyptian ruins. When French troops came across the Rosetta stone, the scientists that Napoleon had brought along recognized that it might be the key to decipher the Egyptian inscriptions.

The Rosetta stone is a slab of black basalt with three inscriptions, one in hieroglyphics, one in demotic, and one in Greek. It was hoped that the stone would provide what cryptanalysts call a *crib*—a piece of plain text that can be associated with a piece of cipher text. The techniques that were used to decipher both Egyptian hieroglyphics and the Linear B writing of Crete and Mycenae were those of code breaking, and the most instructive description of how it was done appears in Simon Singh's *The Code Book, The Evolution of Secrecy from Mary Queen of Scots to Quantum Cryptography* (New York: Doubleday, 1999) from which the following account is drawn.

A translation of the Greek segment of the Rosetta stone revealed that it was a decree issued about 2,200 years ago recording the benefits that the pharaoh Ptolemy had bestowed on the people of Egypt and the honors that the priests had piled on the pharaoh in gratitude. If the other two texts conveyed the same message, it was thought that it would not be difficult to find a set of Egyptian symbols that would correspond to a set of Greek words. But the task turned out to be much more complicated than anyone realized. Also, even if the code was broken and the writing could be read, it would be no help in establishing the *sound* of the Egyptian words, which had not been spoken for eight centuries.

Since archeologists thought that the idea of phonetic spelling was too advanced for such an ancient civilization, they assumed that Egyptian hieroglyphics were picture writing. As a matter of fact, a Greek historian who visited Egypt in the first century B.C. when hieroglyphics were still a living script had also said it was picture writing. He pointed out that writing in Egyptian took the form of pictures of all kinds of living creatures, parts of the human body, and implements. He gave as an example the hawk. Since the hawk was the fastest of living creatures it was used, he said, to symbolize swiftness and all swift things.

An English prodigy, Thomas Young, became fascinated with the Rosetta stone. He focused on a set of hieroglyphs surrounded by a loop, called a cartouche. His hunch was that the cartouche meant that the particular set of hieroglyphics was of great significance, perhaps the name of a pharaoh, possibly Ptolemy since his name was mentioned six times in the Greek text. The form of Ptolemeios was used, and Young assumed that the T sound could be rendered by two different hieroglyphs. This gave him P T O L M E S. He then tackled A L, S E, T R, representing the name ALKSENTRS—Alexandros in Greek or Alexander in English. It also became apparent to Young that the scribes were not fond of using vowels and would omit them as often as possible.

But then he quit. He apparently subscribed to the scholarly consensus that the Egyptian hieroglyphics were simply picture writing. So he attributed his own phonetic discoveries to the fact that the Ptolemaic dynasty was descended from one of Alexander's Greek generals and that because their names were foreign, they were likely to be rendered phonetically and hence must be unique.

A Frenchman, Jean-François Champollion, was next to take up the task of trying to decipher Egyptian hieroglyphics, and he became obsessed with it. He learned some 12 languages to equip himself for the job and continued Young's work of translating the names of Ptolemaic pharaohs. Among them was one that turned out to be not a pharaoh but Alexander the Great. This came out as *A L K S E N T R S* and led Champollion to realize that the scribes would often omit vowels, apparently assuming that the reader would have no problem filling them in. Then he obtained reliefs from the temple of Abu Simbel, which predated the period of Graeco-Roman domination and so contained traditional Egyptian names. He discovered that they, too, were spelled out. Then he concentrated on a cartouche that contained just four hieroglyphs, ⟨☉⚶⚶⟩. The first two were puzzles, but the last two were known from the cartouche of Alexander to represent the letter S.

Although Coptic had been replaced, as we saw, by Arabic in the eleventh century A.D., it still existed in a fossilized form in the liturgy of the Christian Coptic Church. Champollion had learned Coptic as a teenager and was so fluent he used it for his journal. The ancient scribes had sometimes used pictographs as a shortcut rather than spelling the word out, and he wondered if the first sign in the cartouche, ☉ , might be a pictograph for the word *sun*. Then in a flash of genius, he wondered if the sound value might be the Coptic word for sun, *RA*. This gave him (RA SS). The name of only one pharaoh seemed to fit, Rameses—allowing for the irritating omission of vowels and assuming that the missing letter was "M." With this supposition, Champollion had solved the problem of the hieroglyphics. He had also shown that the scribes did not speak Greek, but a form of Coptic. If they had spoken Greek, the pictograph for Sun, *RA*, would have meant that the cartouche would have been pronounced HELIO-MESES rather than RA-MESES.

Linear B

The Cretan script, Linear B, is the only example of an ancient script that was solved without a crib. Heinrich Schliemann had dug at the site of Troy in Asia Minor in 1872, and between that time and 1900, archeologists uncovered further evidence that suggested a rich period of pre-Hellenic history, dating from 4,800 years ago to 3,100 years ago, and reaching its peak in its last four centuries. The civilization was centered on Mycenae on the Greek mainland. But the vast array of artifacts and treasures showed no sign of writing. Sir Arthur Evans, an eminent archaeologist living at the turn of the century, was perplexed that such a sophisticated society was completely illiterate. Antique dealers in Athens showed him some engraved stones said to have originated in Knossos on the island of Crete, the legendary capitol of King Minos. He began excavating there and uncovered the remains of a luxurious palace, riddled with intricate passageways, and adorned with frescoes of young men leaping over ferocious bulls. Evans speculated that the sport of bull jumping was linked to the legend of the Minotaur, who had fed on youths.

Evans then found a hoard of clay tablets. Apparently, the custom was to dry the tablets in the sun, rather than fire them. That way simply adding water to erase what was already on them made them reusable. Rain and moisture over the centuries would have dissolved most of the tablets, but the palace had been destroyed by fire. This had baked these particular tablets, and they were so well preserved that fingerprints could still be seen on them.

There were three sets of tablets. The first, dating from 4,000 years ago to 3,650 years ago were merely drawings, probably picture writing. The second set, dating from 3,750 to 3,450 years ago, were inscribed with characters made up of simply lines, dubbed Linear A. The third set seemed to be a refinement of Linear A and so dubbed Linear B. This third set, Linear B, contained the most recent script, and they were the most plentiful, so the focus was on Linear B.

Many of the tablets seemed to contain inventories, so it was relatively easy to work out the counting system. But the phonetic characters were puzzling. Only two useful facts could be determined. One was that the writing was from left to right, since any gap was generally on the right. The second was that there were 90 distinct characters, and this implied that the writing was almost certainly syllabic. Alphabetic scripts have between 20 to 40 characters—English has 26, Russian 36, and Arabic 28. Pictographic writing has hundreds, even thousands—Chinese, for example, has over 5,000. Syllabic scripts have between 50 and 100 characters.

The biggest problem was that no one knew what language Linear B was written in. At first, it was thought it might be Greek, but a consensus developed that it was some extinct Cretan language. Sir Arthur himself came to believe this so strongly that when a professor of archeology at Cambridge spoke in favor of the idea that Linear B was Greek, he excluded him from the excavations and forced him to retire from the British School in Athens. But forty years of effort to decipher Linear B accomplished nothing.

After Sir Arthur's death in 1941, the Linear B archives and his own notes were made available only to those who supported his theory that Linear B represented a distinct Minoan language. But somehow, a classicist at Brooklyn College, Alice Kober, got access and began a meticulous and impartial analysis of the script. She noticed that certain words seemed to have the same stem, but three different endings. She concluded that the language was inflective, meaning that the word endings changed to reflect gender, case, and tense, and she compared it to the Akkadian language of Greece, which is also inflective. Words in Akkadian often have what is called a bridging syllable. She gave as an example an Akkadian noun with the stem, SAD-. SADANU is case one. SADANI is the second case, and SADU is the third. The three words consist of a stem, SAD, and an ending, ANU in case 1, ANI in case 2, and U in case 3 with DA, DA, or DU as the bridging syllable. The consonant of the bridging syllable contributes to the stem and the vowel to the ending. At this point, in 1950 at the age of 43, just as she was about to take the crucial next step, Alice Kober died.

An English architect, Michael Ventris, took up the work where Kober had left off. Ventris had a prodigious talent for languages, he had been fascinated with Linear B since he was a child, and he had spent all of his spare time studying it. After a year of concentrating on Kober's publications, he noticed something that seemed to be an exception to the rule that all Linear B signs were syllables. It had been generally agreed that each Linear B sign represented the combination of a consonant and a vowel. Since some words do not conveniently break into consonant-vowel syllables, Ventris assumed that Minoans inserted a silent vowel on occasion. But if a word started with an "I" inserting a silent consonant before the vowel would lead to confusion. So he assumed that there must be Linear B signs that represent a single vowel. And they should be easy to spot because they would occur only at the beginning of a word.

Up to this point, Ventris had resisted the temptation to assign sound values to any of the signs. But now he decided to follow some hunches. He had noticed three words that appeared over and over again, and he guessed that they might be the names of towns in Crete. One of the words began with what he was pretty sure was a vowel, and the only town that began with a vowel was Amnisos, an important harbor town. The result was A-MI-NI-SO. The final S was missing but he decided to ignore the problem for the time being.

Using what was suggested by the first town, the second town became ?O-?O-SO. Assuming that this might be Knossos, he got KO-NO-SO. Again the final S was missing. Using what he had surmised from the first two towns, the third came out to be ??-?I-SO. The only town that seemed to fit was Tulissos. But once again the final S was missing.

When Ventris was fourteen years old he had attended a lecture by Sir Arthur Evans, who said that Linear B could not be Greek since it rarely ended in S, which was a common ending in Greek. But Ventris had now discovered that the reason Linear B rarely ended in S was because the scribes omitted it. Ventris now had a total of eight signs, and he could read two complete words, *TOSO* and *TOSA*. These were found at the bottom of inventories and were thought to mean "total." They were uncannily similar to the archaic Greek *tossos* and *tossa*, masculine and feminine nouns meaning "so much." His conclusion was that the Knossos and Pylos tablets were after all written in Greek, although a difficult and archaic Greek that was five hundred years older than the Greek of Homer.

Ventris regularly distributed his results to other Linear B researchers. Some time earlier, in "Work Note 20," he had mentioned the Greek hypothesis, but he had thought it "a frivolous digression" and labeled it as such. But now Ventris had come to believe that the language was Greek after all.

Shortly after he came to this conclusion, he was asked to appear on a BBC program to discuss the mystery of the Minoan scripts. He decided to use the opportunity to go public with his conclusion that Minoan was written in Greek, although a difficult and archaic Greek. One of the listeners was John Chadwick, who lectured on Greek at Cambridge. Chadwick had worked on Japanese ciphers at Bletchley Park, the center of the British wartime code breaking operation, and he had been interested in Linear B since the 1930s. Expecting to be peppered with questions at his next lecture, Chadwick obtained a copy of Ventris' "Work Notes," assuming that they would be full of holes. But they were not, and he was converted. So Ventris and Chadwick formed a partnership.

Since Chadwick's specialty was Greek philology, the study of the historical evolution of the Greek language, the partnership was nearly perfect.

The work accelerated each day, and soon they were writing notes to each other in Linear B.

Finally it became clear that Mycenae had been the dominant state and Minoan Crete the lesser one. But there was also evidence that until 3,450 years ago Minoa had been a truly independent state with its own language. It was around that time that Linear B replaced Linear A. So it seemed likely that the Mycenaeans conquered the Minoans, imposed their own language on them, and transformed Linear A into Linear B so that it served as a script for Greek.

Alphabet Writing

Evidence dating from about 3,600 years ago of an alphabet formed by borrowing and simplifying Egyptian hieroglyphs is found in areas where a Semitic-speaking people lived in the Sinai Peninsula and farther north in the Syria-Palestine region occupied by the ancient Canaanites. Recently, inscriptions of the same kind of alphabetic writing made 200 years earlier were discovered at a site on the ancient travel route in southern Egypt across the Nile from the royal city of Thebes. Another discovery confirms that a Semitic people were present at the site at that time. The presumption is that a Semitic people, probably serving as mercenary soldiers in Egypt or as miners and merchants, began developing an alphabet from Egyptian hieroglyphics in Egypt and an early form of this alphabet found its way to the Sinai Peninsula and the Syria-Palestine region.

Scholars working on the inscriptions say that because they are a very early form of alphabetic writing some are difficult to translate. But others look just like one would expect. The symbol for M in the inscriptions, for example, is a wavy line derived from the Egyptian hieroglyph for water (MAYM- in Canaanite and MEM in Hebrew), and it is almost identical to the symbol M in later Semitic writing.

When the alphabet first appeared, about 4,000 years ago, Mesopotamian cuneiform, Egyptian hieroglyphics, and Linear B had been in use for about a thousand years. In alphabet writing the total number of signs needed for all the sounds in most languages is fewer than 30. To become a scribe in Mesopotamia or Egypt required a lifetime of training, but most people can learn the letters of an alphabet in a few hours. By the time of the neo-Assyrian empire, 2,900 years ago to 2,700 years ago, the Aramaic alphabet was used as a medium of correspondence between different countries and with it the form of the Aramaic language modern scholars call Imperial Aramaic.

Early alphabetic writing used only consonants, and the vowel sounds were not indicated. This worked well enough for languages like Phoenician, early Hebrew, and Aramaic because in all of these languages, which belonged to the northwest Semitic group, each syllable began with a consonant sound. In Greek, however, many words and syllables begin with vowels, and it could not be effectively written without vowels. So when the Greeks borrowed the alphabet, they gave it vowels. In ancient Egypt phonetic hieroglyphs were pictorial signs that represented the initial sounds of the words for the things they depicted. For example, a sign showing the floor plan of a house was the Canaanite BAYT- . So you get B (Hebrew BET, Greek BETA). A pictorial rendering of an eye stood for the Hebrew AYIN. This was a voiced guttural sound that was not needed in Greek, so the Greeks used the simplified sign for the vowel O.

Part Four:

How Humankind Got to Where it is

Chapter 13

The Migrations of Early Man

When the small bands of *Homo sapiens* and *Homo sapiens sapiens* first came out of Africa some time between 80,000 and 50,000 years ago, some settled in the Middle East. Others turned right into Asia. The colder climate of Europe at the time must have discouraged them. Another reason may have been the presence of the Neanderthal. In any case, it was not until about 40,000 years ago that some of those who had settled in the Middle East entered Europe.

Gradually those *Homo sapiens sapiens* turned right into what is now India. The peoples who seem to have lived longest in the area are the Todas of southern India and the Veddas of Ceylon, both of whom are probably Australoid, that is they are probably the same stock as the aborigines of Australia. It seems likely that the Australoid people were among the first to pass that way. Others among the early arrivals in southern India are the short and very dark-skinned Bengali and the taller but just as dark-skinned Madrassi. In any case, it is clear from their myths, which are related to those of peoples of the Middle East, that the ancestors of the Bengali and Madrassi spent time in the Fertile Crescent and that both arrived in India very early. The Tamils are another rather early group, although they may not have started on their journey until the Black Sea flood, described in Chapter 20.

Some of the first people to come out of Africa and into India continued on to Southeast Asia. Eventually, after what were probably many generations, some of them turned south into what is now Indonesia. In due time, some of these people made their way to Australia. Those who first lived in Southeast Asia were quite different from the people living in Southeast Asia in later times.

The Australian Aborigines

The Australoid ancestors of the early inhabitants of Australia and their cousins the Melanesian people probably arrived in Southeast Asia some time before 40,000 years ago, pushed along by succeeding waves of other peoples. Eventually they made their way to Australia, probably arriving there about 30,000 years ago. Some time after the Australians and the Melanesians were pushed out of Indonesia, the seas began to rise as the ice caps melted. This created a formidable barrier to further migration to Australia and the nearby islands. Once the seas rose, there was apparently no migration of any significance until the white man came.

When the white man came to Australia in the eighteenth and nineteenth centuries, the aborigines were still hunter-gatherers. They had no agriculture and did not live in villages or even houses. Their skin is very dark brown, nearly black. But they look nothing like either Africans or Asians. Their hair, which grows abundantly, is neither lank and straight like the hair of the Bengali and Madrassi nor frizzy, like the hair of Negroids. Very young children occasionally have blond hair. All of the 300 or more aboriginal languages belong to the same linguistic family, and no connection to any other language has yet been found. The aborigines had no agriculture and no domesticated animals except the dingo, a dog they may have brought with them. They lived in camps and moved often to follow game or ripening fruit.

The Australian aborigines had no inherited or stored wealth, and this may be one of the reasons that they were the least political and least warlike people known to history. They lived in groups of fifty or so with no headman or chief. There is no evidence that they practiced or even understood warfare or the idea of one group fighting another group. However, they did have a custom in which two tribes would gather for a ritualized confrontation every one or two years. The women would hurl insults at each other, and the men would hurl spears. They were all very good at nimbly dodging the spears, but sooner later someone drew blood, and then everyone stopped to have a great dance and feast—a *corroboree*, as it was called.

However, the peaceful nature of the aborigines did nothing to protect them from the white man. There were about 300,000 aborigines when the white man arrived, and by 1900, there were only 60,000 left. As with the Indians in the Americas and the Hawaiians in the Pacific, the aborigines were devastated by the white man's diseases, such as smallpox and measles, more than his violence, although there was plenty of that.

Something similar also happened to the wildlife. The white man brought rabbits and they proliferated—like rabbits. It was not long before they threatened to overwhelm everything else.

New Guinea and Australia were connected to each other during the last ice age (the Pleistocene), but at no stage during the time of *Homo sapiens sapiens* were they connected to the mainland of Southeast Asia. During the glacial maximum, the sea distance between Southeast Asia and Australia-New Guinea was about 100 km, so a sea passage from the mainland of Southeast Asia could have been made in no more than few days, and even though it took them out of sight of land, humankind could rather easily manage such a passage. A raft-like boat that could cross 10 miles could probably cross 100. In any case, there is evidence of human occupation in New Guinea and Australia about 30,000 to 40,000 years ago. As the ice caps melted, the distance increased and a passage became very difficult, if not impossible, for primitive people.

In the interior of Tasmania there is evidence of a human presence perhaps as early as 30,000 years ago. The Tasmanians were not the same people as the Australian aborigines. Among other differences the Tasmanians had wooly hair and the Australian aborigines do not. As Sir Peter Buck says, it seems impossible either that the Tasmanians traveled through the entire continent on foot or that they made the long journey by sea. Buck concludes that they reached the Australian coast from one of the Melanesian islands by some sort of watercraft, proceeded by short coastal voyages to the Bass Strait, and then crossed over to the unoccupied island of Tasmania. In the nineteenth century, the white man arrived and brutally exterminated the Tasmanians in various ways including putting out poisoned bait.

The Bismarck Archipelago was first settled about the same time as New Guinea and Australia. The Solomon Islands in Melanesia, which were larger at that time because of the lower level of the oceans, were settled shortly afterward. Evidence in a cave in the Solomons shows that humankind was present there about 28,000 years ago.

Then for about 25,000 years, until techniques for ocean sailing were developed, there was no further settlement further east in the Pacific.

Southeast Asia

Meanwhile back in Southeast Asia, the inhabitants began to develop a primitive form of agriculture. Much, much later than the migration to Australia, about 3,300 years ago, the so-called Dong Son Bronze Age culture emerged in southern China and Vietnam and after some time spread to Indonesia. With the Dong Son culture came techniques for growing wet rice, for domesticating animals, like the water buffalo, for casting bronze, and for the so-called *ikat* weaving, still practiced in pockets in Indonesia. Also came practices such as buffalo sacrifice and erecting megalithic monuments.

The Dong Son people had some knowledge of navigation — island hopping at the least, but also some idea of keeping direction by the stars. The religion was animist — worshiping the spirits of the mountains, trees, and so on, and primitive ancestor worship. The wet rice agriculture they developed is known as *sawah* cultivation, as opposed to upland, dry rice cultivation, called *ladang* cultivation.

China, Korea, Japan, and the Americas

Some of the migrating *Homo sapiens sapiens* continued along the coast from Southeast Asia to what is now China and Korea, finally reaching the Bering Sea. At that time, all four of the main Japanese islands were connected to each other. In addition, Kyushu in the south was connected to the Korean peninsula by a land bridge, and Hokkaido in the north was connected by another land bridge to Siberia. Around 30,000 years ago, *Homo sapiens sapiens* crossed over and occupied all of the islands.

About 15,000 years ago, the descendants of those who had crossed into the Middle East from Africa so many thousands of years before finally reached the Bering Sea. It was at the end of the last ice age, and the world's oceans were low enough to create a land bridge from Siberia to Alaska. Some of the peoples who crossed made their way into the Americas. These included, as described earlier, a fisher folk who migrated down the coast and other groups who went south in stages by an inland route.

The Mongolians

After coming out of Africa into the Middle East, some peoples continued north into what is now Russia and then made their way into central Asia by a route that took them north of the Himalayas. In the last ice age a group of these, probably no more than several hundred, were trapped behind walls of ice in what is now the Gobi desert. The only ones to survive the extreme cold were those who developed stocky builds, similar to the Eskimos of today, with ample layers of fat. These included a layer that protected their eyes from freezing—the Mongolian flap, as it is called—and this survives today. As a result Westerners call Mongoloids "slant eyes," and the Chinese call Westerners "round eyes." The descendants of those who were trapped in the Gobi include the Chinese, Koreans, Japanese, Tibetans, and a number of peoples now living in Mongolia and Siberia, and the ancestors of the Finns, Hungarians, and Lapps.

The Pygmies

The pygmies seem to have a history different from all the other members of *Homo sapiens sapiens*. African pygmies are called Negrillos and Asian pygmies are called Negritos, although the two are one and the same. Some anthropologists regard them as Negroid, but others regard them as a separate race. It may not have taken too many generations living in the deep jungle to develop their pygmy form in much the same way that the pygmy elephant and rhinoceros had developed in the hot, hostile environment of the Mediterranean basin before the breakthrough of Gibraltar.

In Africa the pygmies live in the jungles of Burundi, Cameroon, Congo, Gabon, and Rwanda and number about 180,000. They are usually about 4 1/2 feet tall, with yellow-brown skin, round heads with tightly curled, reddish-brown hair. Their legs are short, and their arms are relatively long. Their abdomens swell out like those of small children. They have broad, flat noses, and prominent eyeballs. They speak the language of neighboring Negro tribes, and it is not known if they ever had a language of their own. They are hunter-gatherers. Their bows are small with limited range, and their arrows are tipped with a deadly poison.

The Asian Negritos are much the same. They live in the Andaman Islands, the central part of the Malay Peninsula and East Sumatra, the Philippine Islands, Western New Guinea, and throughout the islands of

Melanesia in the Pacific. The largest number, about 60,000, live in the Philippines. They were apparently the earliest immigrants to the Philippines, and it is believed that they arrived some time before 5000 B.C., that is, 7,000 years ago. But how much before no one knows.

Nothing is known about how or when the pygmies spread to their present locations. The guess is that they originated in Africa and that very small bands left Africa very early. If the first *Homo sapiens sapiens* came out of Africa between 80,000 and 60,000 years ago, the pygmies may have followed only a few thousand years later. But it is equally possible that their trek began only 10,000 years ago.

In any case, the pygmies made their way to Southeast Asia and the Pacific islands the same way that other humans did, but keeping rather close to the seashores along the way.

The People of the Americas

As already mentioned, three separate groups of people made their way to the Americas. The first were apparently a fisher folk who went along the coast of Asia, arriving about 15,000 years ago at a land bridge between Siberia and Alaska, called Beringia by anthropologists, which had been exposed during the last ice age. From there they continued to make their way down along the coast of North and South America. An archaeological site in Peru dates from 13,000 to 11,000 years ago, and another further south dates from 12,700 to 12,500 years ago. The Monte Verde site in Chile has a well-established date of 12,500 years ago.

Flint arrowheads, one called a Clovis point and a somewhat earlier one called a Folsom point, identified a second group people. They were big game hunters. When an ice-free passage opened between the glaciers in Western Canada, these hunters followed the big game through it into North America. Artifacts have been found at a site in Canada that is 11,200 years old.

One or more of the groups who made their way through the passage between the glaciers turned east and became the ancestors of the eastern seaboard American Indians. Others continued south, making their way eventually into South America.

Over the millennia, other small groups also probably came over these same routes to the Americas. The Navajo were apparently among the last to come and ended up with the least desirable land. Ironically, because their land was so poor, they survived the relentless advance of the white man better than those with more desirable homelands. With the coming of social security and other federal programs, they grew in numbers until today they greatly outnumber all other American Indians, although most Navajo still live in extreme poverty.

A little later the Eskimos and Aleuts made their way to Alaska, Canada, and the Aleutian islands.

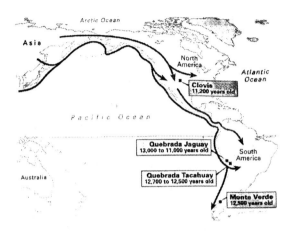

There has been speculation that an early people living in Australia might have made their way by sea to the Americas and other speculation that an equally early people living in Europe might have island-hopped to America the way the Vikings did eons later. But there is no shred of evidence for either notion.

As we saw in the preceding chapter, Joseph Greenberg lumps together the inhabitants of North and South America into three language groups, plus Eskimo-Aleut. The archeological evidence indicates that if the more recently arrived Alaskan-Aleut are included there were four groups. One was a group of fisher-folk who crossed the Bering Strait very early and came down the coast of North America, Central America, and South America and got as far south as Peru. The second group was the big game hunters who came through a gap in the ice sheet and then turned east to the plains of the Middle West and the woodlands of the east coast. The third group was the Na-Dene, including the Navajo, the Athapaskan language speakers in Alaska and the western sub-Arctic of Canada, and the speakers of Haida, Tlingit, and Eyak on the Pacific Northwest coast of Canada. And the fourth were the Alaskan-Aleut. So the archeological evidence tends to support those who argue that Greenberg goes a little too far in lumping all 600 American Indian languages into just one group. The settlement of North and South America is described in more detail in Chapters 16 and 17.

Homo Sapiens Sapiens in Europe

As already mentioned, even though Europe was closer to Africa than India and Asia, *Homo sapiens sapiens* did not get to Europe until 40,000 years ago. When they arrived, they found the Neanderthals were already there.

When a band of Neanderthal and a band of *Homo sapiens sapiens* met, they were much more likely to fight over scarce resources than fraternize. Still, it is conceivable that on occasion they might have mated. The Neanderthal had a massive, protruding brow-ridge unlike any found in modern man and looked nothing like *Homo sapiens sapiens*, but it was only recently when DNA tests were run on their remains that it was firmly established that they were not true men. Since they were not true men, if some did mate with *Homo sapiens sapiens* and if there were any progeny they would most likely have been sterile, like the mule, a cross between another set of rather distant cousins, the horse and the donkey. So it seems certain that the Neanderthal made no contribution to the gene pool of *Homo sapiens sapiens*.

In 1999, the Neanderthal bones of two adults, two teenagers, and two children found in the Moula-Guercy cave overlooking the Rhone valley in France show unmistakable signs of cannibalism. The braincases had been broken into fragments, and the limb bones shattered. The tongue of one child had been cut out. Microscopic examination of incisions on the bones indicates that the skeletons were cut apart to obtain meat. A reassembled leg bone displayed dents made by a stone hammer, fracture marks produced when the bone was smashed, and striations from a stone anvil against which it was held. Bones of red deer and other animals lying among the Neanderthal remains showed the same type of marks.

It is rare for any mammals to eat their own kind. *Homo sapiens sapiens* has often practiced cannibalism as part of religious ceremonies, as the Aztecs did on a very large scale. But the Neanderthal was not likely to have developed such a convoluted religion. Neanderthals often faced food shortages in the ice-age environments of Western Europe, and near starvation is a more likely explanation of the evidence in the Moula-Guercy cave. Shipwrecked sailors, the members of the Donner party snow-bound in High Sierras, and others in desperate circumstances have often turned to cannibalism. But there is no evidence that humankind has ever practiced cannibalism as a regular and normal source of food.

Still, there is overwhelming evidence that Neanderthal ate fresh meat during at least the later part of his existence.

The White Race

Following the mammoth and the great herds of reindeer, *Homo sapiens sapiens* made their way to the far north before the last ice age, when the climate was rather mild. Their circumstances sparked two genetic changes that persist to this day. Vitamin D is essential to life, but the only way that humankind could obtain and absorb vitamin D prior to the miracles of modern medicine was by sunlight through the skin. In the tropics there is too much sun, and a dark skin is a protection. But in the far north, days are short for several months of the year, and at some places at certain seasons, the sun barely rises above the horizon. So in the north a lighter skin is absolutely essential to ensure that enough Vitamin D can be absorbed to sustain life. Hence the white skin.

It would have taken only a very few generations to accomplish this change. Those whose skin was too dark for them to acquire the Vitamin D they required would die too young to breed or fail to breed successfully.

The second genetic change concerned the ability to digest milk. About 75 percent of adult Asians, Africans, and American Indians and about 50 percent of adult Hispanics cannot digest milk. At birth, humans and other mammals begin producing the enzyme lactase in the lining of the small intestine. This enzyme permits them to digest lactose, a large milk sugar that the body cannot use until it has been broken down. Absent lactase, when milk reaches the gut it ferments into a brew of fatty acids, hydrogen, carbon dioxide, and methane. The final result is misery—abdominal cramps, gas, and diarrhea. Most human beings begin making less and less lactase between the ages of two and seven. By the time they are teenagers they produce only about 10 percent of what they did as infants, and they stabilize lactase production at that level for the rest of their lives. They have no ill effects when they put a little milk in something like tea, but a malted milk shake is likely to put them to bed. The only exceptions are the descendants of the peoples of Northern and Central Europe—the so-called white race. The ancestors of these peoples followed the reindeer herds, killing the stragglers for meat, but also herding out lactating cows and milking them. At some stage a genetic mutation occurred that enabled about 80 percent of their descendants to produce ample supplies of lactase throughout adulthood. People with this mutation benefited from being able to digest milk in hard times, and gradually they came to be the majority of their populations. These developments, to repeat, occurred before the last ice age, probably around 30,000 years ago.

Beginning about 25,000 years ago the growing ice cap forced these white-skinned people south. Over two or three millennia some made their way into what is now Spain, Italy, and Greece. Some reached the Fertile Crescent, some the Ukraine, and some the Caucasus and the area around what is now the Black Sea.

About 20,000 years ago one tribe of these people, the Cro Magnon, made beautiful paintings in caves in France and Spain of animals that are now extinct. Later waves of *Homo sapiens sapiens* interbred with the Cro Magnon, but one group may well be their direct descendants with relatively little interbreeding. These are the Basques of the Pyrenees. They have a language, Euskera, stuffed with X's and Z's that is unrelated to any known tongue, and it is still spoken by about half of the 2.4 million Basque people. They also have an anomalously high frequency of the Rh-negative antigen, almost two times the rest of the European population. The hypothesis is, and it is also their own belief, that they are direct descendants of the ice age Cro-Magnons. In any case, they seem to have been living in the Pyrenees isolated from most of humankind for the intervening 20,000 years.

Even in very early times, one tribe of *Homo sapiens sapiens* traded with another at the boundary between their two territories. The commodities moved across tribal boundaries, but the traders themselves did not. Amber, found in Jutland, made its way south all the way to the Middle East, where amber containing a fossilized beetle, a scarab, was particularly valued. Flint to make knives and spears and arrowheads was also traded. As we have seen, flint was mined on a rather large scale in England, and there were similar flint mines scattered across Europe. Jade was mined in Burma and China. Bronze is an alloy of copper and tin and the prehistoric mines for these were in what is now Austria. Tin was also mined in what is now Cornwall in England.

Twenty thousand years ago, the ice cap extended almost to the Alps. But an ice-free corridor for both animals and man remained open between Eastern and Western Europe along the Danube valley. It was here that the famous Venus figurines of amply proportioned women were found.

In Moravia, ice age Paleolithic hunters constructed dwellings near the conjunction of two rivers in the drainage basin of the Black Sea. They chiseled out pits from the frozen peat with hand axes. The roof of each tent-like structure was arched with poles, and these were draped with animal skins stitched together with sinew. The hides were anchored to the ground by massive animal hipbones and by the skulls of reindeer, mammoths, and the occasional rhinoceros. Tusks provided the fuel for hearths. The culture produced fine, leaf-shaped blades struck from a core of flint and small bone carvings of animal heads, notably wolf and deer.

A DNA signature has been identified on the Y chromosome that goes from father to son unchanged and that is presumed to have belonged to the first of *Homo sapiens sapiens* who lived in Europe as the Neanderthals began to go extinct 27,000 years ago. Some 2 percent of the males in Turkey, 63 percent in Britain, and 78 percent in Ireland carry this DNA signature.

Dr. Daniel G. Bradley and colleagues at Trinity College, Dublin, compared the DNA in Irish men with surnames known to have originated in Ireland and found that 98 percent of those with such surnames in Connaught on the west coast had this DNA signature indicating that they descended from a population of hunter-gatherers who inhabited Ireland before the invention of agriculture.

During the last ice age, Spain was the refuge for both plants and animals that recolonized Europe as the glaciers retreated about 10,000 years ago. Dr. Bryan Sykes, a geneticists at Oxford University, traced a pattern of gene flow from Spain through Brittany, Ireland, and the west of Scotland.

Dr. Bradley estimates that the Irish versions of the DNA signature stemmed from individuals who lived 4,000 or more years ago. Ireland is believed to have been inhabited for 9,000 years, so these Irish men may well be the descendants of the original inhabitants. Outside of Ireland, the signature is most common in Basque country, where 89 percent of the men carry it.

The Ice Man of Europe

In 1991 a 5000-year-old corpse was found in a melting glacier at the border of Italy and Austria. It was given the name Ötzi from the Öztal Alps where the body was found. ("Details Emerge of Iceman Ötzi's Death," by Rossella Lorenzi, Discovery News.) A Queensland molecular biologist, Thomas Loy, did the DNA analysis, and he said it focused on four spots: one from outside Ötzi's cloak, one from a broken arrow point, one from the arrow shaft to which the point had been attached, and one from the blade of Ötzi's knife. None of these matched Ötzi's mitochondrial DNA.

One of the first people to see the frozen corpse was a mountain guide, Alois Pirpamer. He said that the man was clutching a knife in his right hand. This was dislodged when the body was removed from the glacier, but it fit the hand exactly.

Blood not from Ötzi was found on the back of his cloak, which suggested that someone was leaning on him for support. Blood from two people was found on the same arrow in his quiver, and more blood was on his knife blade.

Loy said that Ötzi shot two people with the same arrow, that he fought one person in hand-to-hand combat, and then died from a wound in the back.

The new analysis identified never-before-seen injuries on Ötzi's body—a gash on his left hand, a slash on his right forearm, and three deep bruises on the left side of his torso. These destroyed the previous theories that he had fallen asleep or was killed in a fall.

Loy speculated that Ötzi had strayed into another tribe's territory, got involved in a fight, and got shot from behind while he was struggling with at least one assailant.

The speculation is that Ötzi managed to flee up the mountain before he collapsed. Otherwise a killer would have taken the ax and other artifacts found with the body.

Questions remain: What happened to the wounded man that Ötzi was carrying on his shoulder? What about the blood of two people on the same arrow? It is possible that Ötzi killed both men and retrieved that arrow. The area may hide other mummies. Loy said that an expedition has been planned to look for more bodies.

Chapter 14

The Indians

The earliest of *Homo sapiens sapiens* to arrive in India were gatherers and scavengers, the ancestors of the Australoid people. Periodically, others followed, some of whom were hunters as well as gatherers. Eventually peoples sharing the legends and myths of the Middle East also arrived.

Scattered evidence of prehistoric agricultural settlements has been found in the northwest of the subcontinent in what is now Pakistan. In the period between 4,000 and 5,000 years ago, a great civilization arose along the rich alluvial banks of the Indus river valley. The remains of its two largest cities are found at Harappa and Mohenjo-Daro. Excavations have not found any writing or literature, but the uniformity of the architecture and artifacts suggest a centralized government similar to those in Egypt and Mesopotamia.

The city of Mohenjo-Daro was constructed of burned brick and built around a central citadel. Spacious avenues divided the city into blocks, and smaller streets divided the blocks. Some houses were two- or three-story mansions with bedrooms and bathrooms. The city's drainage system was better than anything in the ancient world until Roman times. Large templelike structures suggest a powerful priesthood, and carvings suggest worship of a mother goddess. But very little is known about the culture and what influence it had, if any, on Indian civilization.

The end of the Harappa culture may have been partly due to massive floods of the Indus River. But the deathblow came with the Aryan invasion from the northwest about four thousand years ago. The Harappa food supply depended on a complex and vulnerable system of irrigation, and their weapons were inferior. A warrior aristocracy armed with bronze weapons, on the other hand, led the invading Aryan tribes. They were mounted on four-wheeled chariots drawn by two to four horses. The chariots carried a driver and a warrior whose principal weapon was a bow and arrows.

The Aryan food supply was based on cows and other animals that moved with the tribe and on pillage from the lands they conquered. The society was rigidly patriarchal, based on clan kinship and divided into warriors, priests, artisans, and slaves.

The main source of our knowledge of this Aryan culture is the *Rig-Veda*, a collection of hymns preserved by Brahmin priests. The priestly role was to offer sacrificial prayer—the word, Brahmin, literally means prayer. As would be expected in a nomadic people, the Aryan gods described in the *Veda* were principally the elements—the sky, the Earth, rain, storm, and lightning. Indra was the storm god and Agni was the god of sacrificial fire. But a god of justice, Varuna, was also important.

The second part of the *Veda* is the *Brahmanas*, which describes the rituals required to perform sacrifices correctly. The priests had magic that could manipulate even the gods themselves!

The geographical references in the *Veda* trace a slow but certain march of the Aryan civilization down the valleys of the Indus and the Ganges. The contribution of religion to the conquest is illustrated by the greatest of all the Vedic religious rites, the Horse Sacrifice (Ashvamedha).

A king to dramatize his conquests usually celebrated the Horse Sacrifice. It took a year to perform, requiring the slaughter of hundreds of animals, and the work of a large number of priests. The king and his court toured the countryside with the sacred horse that was to be the final sacrifice, marking out the boundaries of his rule, stifling any local resistance, and instilling Aryan values. The Horse Sacrifice could not have been performed if there had not been exploitable economic resources, fixed settlements, and an established agriculture.

The Aryans created the caste system, whose importance in Indian society can hardly be exaggerated. Social distinctions based on heredity, occupation, and economic status were institutionalized in law, custom, and religion, and the result was unique in world history.

Caste was in place as early 2,600 years ago. As the Aryans gradually fought their way down from the northwest through the river valleys, they enslaved the local peoples, who were smaller and darker than they. The oldest and most archaic word for slave is *dasa,* which literally means dark. The classical word for caste is *varna,* which means color. There were four traditional castes—Brahman, Kshatriya, Vaisya, and Shudra. Brahmans were the priests. Kshatriya were the warriors. Vaisya were the merchants. Shudra were the farmers. The word *jati* indicates birth, and the specific hereditary status is commonly specified by that word and related terms that signify membership in a particular caste, clan, and family.

Historically, there have been as many as 3,000 jatis or castes. They were hedged about with taboos and barriers that prohibited all but the most limited social contacts. Only the three highest Varnas were regarded as true Aryans and admitted to the full Vedic rites and education. The Shudras were mainly excluded. But they were an integral part of the system, tied to the land or to service to one of the higher castes. Finally, there were the untouchables—outcasts who were restricted to menial and ritually unclean work.

Remarkably, the system did not impede extensive cultural and racial assimilation within at least the top three castes. Color distinctions were undercut, although they did not disappear. Intermarriage became permissible so long as the woman married up in the social scale and within Aryan society. Each village and caste had its own council of elders who enforced the laws and customs. Importantly, caste was a religious obligation and a form of religious piety. The central point was that it explained the same human enigmas that confronted Job in the Christian bible—the inequity, suffering, and misfortune in the world. For example, it is evil to kill—but not for a soldier. For a soldier to kill is a duty. These notions are spelled out in a great epic, the *Mahabharata,* and in another work, the *Bhagavad-Gita* that was composed later and inserted in the *Mahabharata.* Both are briefly described below, and both will be dealt with in detail in Chapter 26.

Beginning about 2,500 years ago, India entered an age that could be called historical. It was marked by the struggle between the leaders of Aryan society and the new religious elite imbued with the teachings of Buddha and of Mahavira, the founder of Jainism. The ferment in religious thinking is illustrated by the last section of the *Veda,* the *Upanishads,* which present a new religious theory in contrast to the older system of sacrifice and magical ritual. In the *Upanishads,* the basic human problem is one of personal salvation from bondage to the material world. The meaning of external worldly forms is questioned, and a new metaphysic is asserted. The soul of each individual person undergoes an endless cycle of rebirth, suffering, and death. The soul assumes a new physical form in each rebirth, depending upon the ethical quality, or karma, in the person's preceding life. For every thought and act there is an inevitable consequence. Overt acts of aggression that harm others are particularly destructive. The individual can ultimately obtain spiritual release from the eternal cycle—Nirvana—by practicing yoga, the autonomous, inward self-discipline of mind and body designed to eliminate the sources of human error and evil.

From the Brahminic perspective, yoga was tied to priestly hereditary rights and authority. The caste system was reinforced because obeying it was a precondition for salvation or for at least an improved position in the next incarnation.

By contrast, Buddhism and Jainism rejected the religious authority of the *Veda*. Not caste, but personal conversion was the condition for membership in monastic orders or for lay followers. The idea was that religious and social standing should be based on ability and not hereditary rights.

Buddha lived 2,600 years ago, and his original teaching was a system of ethics rather than a vision of god. Salvation entailed following a middle path between bodily self-mortification and self-indulgence. Like all religions in pre-literate societies, his teaching was reduced to numbered propositions—the "four noble truths," the "eightfold path," and so on.

The "four noble truths" are:

1. Human existence is an agonized bondage to the endless cycle of rebirths.
2. The cause of this agony is desire combined with ignorance of how illusory existence really is.
3. To break this sequence and permit salvation, desire and ignorance must be eliminated. The result is a state of bliss, Nirvana.
4. To achieve Nirvana one must follow the "Eightfold Path"—a combination of ethics and meditation.

Another prophet of the time, Mahavira, taught a yoga that placed more emphasis on physical asceticism. He also stressed the monastic ideal. However, the requirements for the laity were much less demanding. Lay ethics stressed adherence to economically efficient virtues and contractual relationships relevant to the urban commercial environment.

The new political leaders of India saw Buddhism and Jainism as valuable tools for support of the state. After provincial areas had been conquered by force, their universal ethics and pacifist teaching could help cement social solidarity. These potentialities were partially realized with the emergence of the Mauryan state, which was a centralized bureaucratic empire.

The third ruler in the Mauryan line was Asoka whose reign began around 2,270 years ago. After conquering the sub-continent, he converted to Buddhism. He tried to do away with the wasteful and expensive sacrifices and pushed for economically efficient virtues that would also contribute to political integration.

But this effort had little effect on the mass of the people. After his death, the empire split into several parts. Both the Greeks and tribal peoples invaded the northwest, and new dynasties controlled both the Ganges valley and the Deccan plateau in the south.

At this time the Brahminic core of early Indian culture came to be the dominant and finally the primary source of legitimate authority. His chief general, Pushyamitra, assassinated the last Mauryan king 2,185 years ago. Claiming to be of Brahman descent, the general founded the Shunga dynasty. The kings of this dynasty used the *Laws of Manu* as the basis for social reorganization. This contained rules governing caste and other social institutions and contained basic axioms central to Hinduism. The first axiom contained the "four goals"—religious duty (dharma), wealth, sensual satisfaction, and final salvation. The second axiom is the "four stages" that mark out the ideal development of the individual life from birth to death, centering on the need to learn and uphold the law. These stages are the student, the householder, the ascetic, and the sage.

The rapid dynastic and political shifts of this era are confusing, but the Brahman priests became more and more dominant. In the century beginning 2,100 years ago, the Shungas were overwhelmed by the Satavahana Empire. But the first Satavahana emperor celebrated his victory by the Horse Sacrifice. The Satavahana sponsored a richly diverse program in the arts and letters. So did their successors, the Pallavas. In the south, the Tamil states rose to new power in the century beginning 2,200 years ago, and produced a magnificent literature of their own.

Buddhism lost ground among the people, but many dynasties and feudal rulers still held to it. In the century following the year 100 A.D., Buddhist doctrine underwent a transformation that culminated in Mahayana (Great Vehicle) Buddhism and, later, Tantric Buddhism, both of which are described in Chapter 26. Instead of the perfect monk, the notion was introduced of the Bodhisattva, the "being of enlightenment" who sacrifices his personal salvation to help others by acts of love and compassion. The Bodhisattva concept was a source for new forms of popular religion entailing the worship of heavenly Buddhas and Bodhisattvas. At the same time, the Mahayana philosophy attracted many intellectuals to the Buddhist community.

In Hinduism the cults devoted to the lesser Vedic gods, Shiva and Vishnu became the most important and were popularized by extensive missionary activity. Many rulers converted to Shiva apparently because they thought it would strengthen their authority and stabilize the social order.

The best example of growing Brahminic control can be found in the epic literature—the *Mahabharata* and *Bhagavad-Gita*, mentioned above, and the *Ramayana*. The dramatic form was used to inculcate orthodox values. The *Mahabharata* is the story of a battle that actually took place, much as the *Iliad* is the story of the actual siege of Troy.

The *Bhagavad-Gita* was written several centuries after the *Mahabharata* and inserted in the middle of it. The *Gita* brought Hinduism into a coherent whole under the theme that everyone's supreme religious obligation was to perform the duties of his own caste.

About this time a new political power emerged, the Gupta Empire, which consolidated Brahmin orthodoxy. In 320 A.D. Chandragupta I ascended the throne and set about to conquer the whole of the sub-continent—not only to establish his dynasty but to destroy the barbarians and to bring to fruition the sacred values of Aryan culture.

The Gupta goal was to "settle the castes and orders and confine them to their duties." But the Guptas also brought the arts and sciences to new heights. The greatest of the Guptas, Samudragupta (335 A.D.–376 A.D.) was a man who could celebrate the Horse Sacrifice to dramatize his status as Supreme King of Great Kings, but also play the lute and compose poetry and surround himself with the finest artists, scholars, and scientists of his time. As the authors of the *Columbia History of the World* edited by John A. Garraty and Peter Gay (New York: Harper and Row, 1972) write (p. 106), "The drama, poetry, and musical theory of the era show a concern both for lyric beauty and for moral values.... Even Vatsyayana, the author of the *Kamasutra*, a treatise on the art of sensual love [more accurately a handbook on sex, including a catalogue of positions], insisted that his book was 'in perfect accord with the Holy Scriptures,' and that in sexual matters one must act in accordance with religious law... and not impulsively."

The Gupta era might have survived indefinitely if it had not been for a new and particularly ferocious foreign invader—the Huns. By 500 A.D. the Hun control was spreading rapidly, and by 600 A.D., the Gupta dynasty had been destroyed.

The Huns were not a united conqueror but more a collection of tribes, and in the period that followed, India was divided into a host of small states. According to Hsüan Tsang, the Chinese pilgrim who visited India in the middle of the seventh century A.D., the sub-continent was divided into 70 kingdoms.

While still based on the Vedic scripture, Hinduism, as mentioned above, was divided mainly into two great sects, the worship of Vishnu and the worship of Shiva. Buddhism and Jainism declined.

Caste was accepted everywhere. The Brahmin had the highest status, but this was in terms of ritual purity and did not necessarily result in superior economic or political position. In modern times, for example, the cook in prosperous Hindu homes is often a Brahmin because he is ritually clean. In the earlier days, however, Brahmins filled most positions of trust and responsibility in the various kingdoms.

The population in India from the first century A.D. until the nineteenth century was about 100 million. Most of the people were agrarian, but many cities were of great antiquity and fame. Many of these, such as Benares, Ujjain, and Kanchipuram, were centers of religious pilgrimage. Others grew up around great forts—Ajmer in the north and Devagiri in the south—or around a ruler's court, as in Delhi.

Staple crops were wheat, rice, and in less fertile regions millet. Cotton textiles and spices remained the main exports, as they had been for centuries. Horses from western and central Asia were perhaps the most sought after import. Much of the sea trade between India and other countries passed into the hands of Arabs.

It is against this background of a mature civilization that the political fragmentation of India must be seen. In South India, two important dynasties emerged at the end of the sixth century A.D: the Pandyas and the Pallavas.

The Pandyas with their capital at Madurai and the Pallavas with their capital at Kanchipuram controlled the rich coastal areas south of Madras. Both remained important until the beginning of the tenth century. The Cheras ruled what is now Kerala, but their history is obscure.

In the Pandya and Pallava kingdoms in the seventh century, Buddhism and Jainism were weakened by the resurgence of Hinduism, and within two centuries they had virtually disappeared. The Hindu resurgence found architectural expression at Mamallapuram and Kanchipuram in rock carvings and temples that are among the glories of Indian art.

The successors to the Pallavas and the Pandyas were the Cholas of Tanjore (846 A.D–1279 A.D.) Under Rajaraja and Rajendra I, Chola armies raided as far north as the Ganges delta. Numerous temples were erected; the largest and most splendid being at Tanjore built about 1000 A.D. When India passed under Muslim rule in the thirteenth century, it was the Cholas who preserved Sanskrit culture.

The Deccan plateau was controlled by Chalukya dynasty, which was in turn overthrown by the Rashtrakutas. It was the Rashtrakutas who built the great temple at Ellora, which was carved out of the solid rock of a cliff.

The Rashtrakutas were replaced at the end of the tenth century by a tributary chieftain who claimed descent from the Chalukyas.

Following the breakdown of the Gupta Empire in the sixth century the invading Huns established short-lived kingdoms. Early in the seventh century, Harsha (606 A.D.–646 A.D.) created an empire that included most of the Ganges plain. Harsha is famous, but mainly because his court chronicler was a writer of genius and because the Chinese pilgrim, Hsüan Tsang, mentioned above, left a memorable record of his visit to Harsha's court.

Toward the end of the eighth century two new dynasties began a struggle for control of northern India, the Palas of Bengal and the Pratiharas of Rajasthan. In time, the Pratiharas overcame Pala influence.

The Chandella kings built a great temple complex at Khajuraho that has survived almost intact. It contains several temples that are unique survivals. They are described in Chapter 26. Another great temple complex that survived is at Bhuvaneshwar in Orissa, also described in Chapter 26. Both of these are of the Tantric cults, with sculptures of erotic pleasures.

Rajput hegemony in northern India came to an end with the invasion of the Turks led by Muhammad Ghuri. For the next five centuries the focus of political history shifted from the Rajputs and their Hindu predecessors to the Muslim peoples who gained control of India. But it should be kept in mind that Hindu civilization remained dominant in most of India. Even at the height of Muslim power, probably no more than a fifth of the population embraced Islam.

The Turks' advantage lay in military organization, tactics, and equipment. They depended mainly on horsemen armed with light bows, a force far swifter and more mobile than the cumbersome Indian armies with their elephants and vast numbers of infantrymen.

The Muslim conquerors came to realize that they could not force the Hindus to accept Islam. In fact, the majority of their Hindu converts were from the lowest castes and the untouchables, for whom the appeal of escaping the caste system was very great. This is not to say that the Muslims did not try, even destroying many Hindu temples and on occasion using force in mass conversions. But in the end Hindus continued to control local government, paying the Muslims tribute.

The Islamic overlords of India never solved the problem of succession, and a factional struggle always followed the death of a ruler. After many ups and downs, including the sacking of Delhi by Timur (Timurlane) in 1398 A.D., the decline continued until the establishment of Mughal power in the sixteenth century.

A realignment of political power that began in the middle of the fourteenth century resulted in the establishment of regional political units. Several Muslim kingdoms emerged at this time. The Bahmani Sultanate controlled the Deccan plateau for 150 years. It was succeeded by five sultanates. Bengal became an independent Muslim kingdom in 1338 A.D. Following Timur's invasion, Muslim successor states were formed in the territories that had been directly under Delhi's control. In all these states, the majority of the population was Hindu, but the courts were centers of Islamic learning and culture.

Hindu power revived in Rajasthan, including modern Jodhpur. In South India a Hindu kingdom was founded about 1336 A.D., taking its name from the capital, Vijayanagar. European travelers reported that the city was larger than Rome and that its temples were splendid. It flourished for 200 years and was then defeated by the Sultanates to the north. But the small kingdoms that followed continued the religious and cultural traditions of the Hindu civilization.

The most significant result of the Islamic invasion was a permanent Muslim minority. What was visible in the continent of India in 1500 A.D. is still visible: two cultures and two religions.

In 1526 A.D., a new group of Turks under Babur began the modern era in India. Babur, the founder of the empire, was a Turkish chieftain who had been driven out of Central Asia by other Turkish tribes and established a small kingdom at Kabul. After his conquests his empire stretched from Kabul through the Punjab and down the plain of the Ganges to Bengal. His son lost the empire, but his grandson, Akbar, regained it.

Akbar expanded the territory of the empire and centralized it politically. Agra was the capital. Previous Muslim rulers had drawn their main support from their Turkish military commanders, who were not interested in strengthening the Sultan's power. Akbar's technique was to make allies of the Rajput rulers, who were Hindus, as a counterweight to the Turkish military commanders. He deposed the previous Muslim rulers, but he allowed the Rajput rulers who submitted to him to retain their lands. And he married princesses of the leading Rajput families. As a result of all this, for the next 150 years, the groups who had been most resistant to Muslim rule were its best supporters.

Whereas his Muslim predecessors had merely tolerated Hinduism, Akbar gave the Hindus what amounted to religious equality. He also abolished the special tax on non-Muslims and granted the Hindus permission to build temples.

He also changed the tax system. Previous rulers had paid officials in land, which had deprived the central treasury of income. Akbar paid in cash. He did not succeed in regaining all the land or in paying all salaries in cash. But he moved the empire in the direction of centralization and away from the old political pluralism.

Under Akbar's successors, Jahangir (1605 A.D.–1627 A.D.) and Shah Jahan (1628 A.D.–1658 A.D.) both territorial expansion and centralization continued.

The graceful elegance in both art and architecture reached a high point in the reign of Shah Jahan, when Indian and Persian artistic forms were combined in a creative synthesis. The miniature paintings of that time are admired today, and so is the Red Fort at Delhi. And the whole world stands in awe at the Taj Mahal in Agra.

Aurangzeb (1658 A.D.–1707 A.D.) came closer to uniting all of the subcontinent under his rule than any other ruler. The Mughal Empire stretched from Assam in the east, to Bombay on the Indus in the west and from Kabul in what are now Afghanistan in the north to Madras and its hinterland in the south. Only the Marathas, living east of Bombay; the independent chiefdoms in what is now Kerala; and the tiny Portuguese colony of Goa remained outside its boundaries.

But Aurangzeb had achieved this empire at great cost. He had come to the throne after a fierce struggle with his three brothers and his father, whom he imprisoned in Agra within sight of the Taj Mahal, the tomb he had built for his adored wife. Personal religious conviction and the political situation had led him to emphasize the Islamic nature of the empire. He appointed

Muslim military commanders to the higher positions and replaced Hindu officials with Muslims. There was no widespread persecution, but Hindu temples at such places of peculiar sanctity as Benares, the city of the burning ghats, and Mathura were destroyed.

He attempted to annex the territory of the Rajputs of Marwar, one of the largest of the Rajput states, and they rebelled. In the Punjab, the Sikhs' militant desire for political independence led to a violent, but unsuccessful uprising. It was only late in the eighteenthcentury that they achieved independence.

But the chief cause of the decline was the social and economic cost of expansion. War had been carried on in the Deccan for 20 years. Also for 20 years, the Marathas had carried on guerrilla warfare against Aurangzeb from their fortresses in the hill country south of Bombay.

Early in the eighteenth century, the Marathas expanded rapidly, bringing most of central India and large parts of the Deccan under their control and at one point captured Delhi.

The Marathas reached the height of their power in 1761 A.D., but they were defeated at the battle of Panipat, the historic battlefield north of Delhi. The individual Maratha chieftains remained formidable powers, and it was they, not the Mughals who challenged the British in the late eighteenth century. In the Deccan, the local governor established his independence in the 1720s as the Nizam of Hyderabad. The governors of Oudh, the province north of the Ganges, became independent a little later and vied with the rulers of Hyderabad for control of the imperial court.

Bengal was the third of the great provinces to become independent. By the middle of the eighteenth century, the French and the English were engaged in a bitter struggle to dominate the commerce with Bengal. The French were dependent upon the financial and political support of Paris, while the English were able to use the profits of the Bengal trade to maintain a high degree of autonomy from London.

Once the French were defeated, conflict arose with the Nawab of Bengal, who had finally come to understand the threat of foreign powers. He captured Calcutta in 1756 and jammed his English captives in a cellar room with little air, the "Black Hole," where many died. The English, headed by Robert Clive and backed by Hindu merchants, supported a rival claimant to the throne and overthrew the Nawab at the Battle of Plassey in 1757. The quarrels continued with the new Nawab and in 1765, the Company forced the Mughal emperor to recognize its right to collect the revenue of

Bengal. Within 20 years, the East India Company was the actual ruler of Bengal. Thus the establishment of English power in India was not the result of military invasion but in traditional Indian fashion by taking part in a dynastic struggle.

The expansion of British territorial control beyond Bengal in the next 50 years conformed to a recognizable Indian pattern—using the resources of the Ganges heartland to take over the rest of India. The development of the railroad and the telegraph combined with the nineteenth century understanding of the role of the nation-state permitted a degree of political control that was unique in Indian history. The impact of the new inventions for manufacturing textiles was felt in India within a decade. An experimental telegraph line was constructed in 1839.

In 1923, Indians petitioned for freedom of the press, arguing that they had the same civil and religious rights as every British subject had in England. Later the writings of Giuseppe Mazzini on nationalism were translated into Bengali, and the nationalists movements in Europe and particularly the unification of Italy and Germany provided examples for Indians that gave them much fuel for thought.

In the nineteenth century, the East India Company and the English parliament both opposed the wars that added to the Company's territory. They felt that the only possibility of maintaining British power in India as well as the moral course of action was to maintain with a minimum of interference the existing laws and customs of India. But the governor-generals thought that if Britain did not control India then France or Russia would.

Some territories were annexed outright, becoming part of British India. Others were brought under control by a system, which left local rulers with much internal control of their territories at the price of abandoning all claims to carry on relations with other Indian states.

In the period 1815 to 1825 the Marathas were finally defeated and Burma was annexed. Then after a pause, a new forward movement began. The British suffered a disastrous defeat in a war against Afghanistan in 1839. But the lower valley of the Indus, the Sind, was annexed in 1843. The British commander, Sir Charles Napier, cabled news of his victory with a single word, a pun in Latin that British schoolboys have treasured ever since, "Peccavi"— "I have sinned."

In England leaders of the Evangelical and Utilitarian movements challenged the policy of not interfering with Indian law and customs, arguing that Christians should introduce light and learning into the darkness and ignorance of Hinduism through legal reform, jurisprudence, and administration. A small but very influential group of Indians in Bengal responded with enthusiasm. One of their leaders was Ram Mohan Roy who pleaded eloquently for the introduction of Western science and technology and for ending what he regarded as social evils born of superstition, such as caste, child marriage, and suttee, the practice of widows immolating themselves on the funeral pyres of their husbands.

Such pressures resulted in 30 years of effort, from 1825 to 1855, in the political unification of India and the creation of a modern state. In 1829 a law was passed forbidding suttee. The frequency of the practice has been exaggerated, but it had great significance because it represented a clear invasion by the government of an area guarded by religious sanction. Sir Charles Napier, the sharp-tongued conqueror of Sind, responded to the Brahmans who complained that suttee was a national custom, "My nation also has a custom. When men burn women alive, we hang them. Let us all act according to national customs."

Action was also taken to suppress female infanticide, slavery, and human sacrifice, which was common among the more primitive people of Orissa. Also of great importance in India, where so many mutually unintelligible languages are still spoken, was the decision in 1835 that the language of instruction in institutions of higher learning would be English. Even today, the common language of the Indian parliament and government is English.

In 1855, twenty-five hundred miles of telegraph lines were completed, the Grand Trunk Road linking Calcutta with northern India and Delhi was built, and a countrywide rail network was begun. Calcutta, Bombay, and Madras became nineteenth century cities linked to their hinterlands and to each other by banking, insurance, and government. At the same time, as part of the free trade economy of Great Britain, India had no tariffs to protect new industries, and this combined with the lack of internal markets was a major barrier to industrial growth.

The population increased rapidly throughout the nineteenth century. Partly this was a result of the fact that the British used Jenner's method of smallpox vaccination widely in India in the first years of the nineteenth century. And partly it was the fact that tea became the national drink, which greatly reduced dysentery and other water-borne diseases. The lack of industry meant that the increasing population pressed more and more heavily on the land rather than finding work in urban centers.

The East India Company administered India until 1858 but long before that date, its power had passed to the English parliament, which ruled through a governor-general. In theory he was a despot, but in fact his power was circumscribed by parliament, the system of laws under which he operated, and above all by the Indian Civil Service. This consisted of about 1,000 British officials appointed from England at first through patronage but after 1854 through competitive examination. The first Indian member was not appointed until 1869. Below the top level, Indians held almost all the thousands of posts. Entrance into the civil service became the symbol of Indian aspirations. India was divided into districts of about 1 million people each, and the district officer, who was almost always a civil servant, had a large degree of autonomy. Even a very energetic governor-general could not make much headway with measures that were not popular with the district officers, who prided themselves on knowing India better than a governor-general who rarely remained in office for more than five or six years.

The Army was never more than 200,000 men, two-thirds Indian and one-third British with all officers being British. Its mystique glorified the courage and loyalty of the Indian soldiers, the sepoys.

Faith in the loyalty of the sepoys was shaken but not destroyed by the Sepoy Rebellion of 1857. The sepoys of the time had a number of grievances and worries. At one end was a new requirement that they swear on enlistment that they would cross the sea if ordered, which would be polluting to the orthodox Hindu. At the other end, was the annexation of Oudh, the chief recruiting ground of the Army. If one of a sepoy's relatives quarreled with a neighbor, the sepoy would tell his tale to the Resident. The Resident without bothering to hear the person on the other side, who was a subject of the King of Oudh, would go to the king or his representative and demand justice. But now the Resident would have to hear both sides before acting.

Then the greased cartridge story began to spread. The paper containing the powder on the cartridges for the new Enfield rifle had to be heavily greased, and the paper had to be bitten to open the end and release the powder. The Company's Army was now to be equipped with these rifles. The grease was half tallow, which came from animals of all kinds including, no doubt, pigs and cows. On the lips of a Hindu, cow's fat would be an abomination. It was not merely disgusting. It would damn him forever. It would be almost as bad as actually killing a cow or a Brahman. To a Muslim pig's fat was just as horrible.

The cartridges were not actually distributed to the sepoys. But it was too late. In May 1857, eighty-five men at Meerut refused cartridges, which were not in fact the offending variety. They were sentenced to long terms in prison. A punishment parade was held under the guns of British troops while the sepoys were stripped of their uniforms and smiths fastened irons on them. This took several hours, and then the sepoys were put in the guardhouse, which in utter folly was left in charge of its usual guard. Three regiments broke open the jail, released the prisoners, murdered as many as they could find of their English officers and the officers' wives and children and marched on Delhi. In Delhi, there were no British troops, and the Indian troops stationed there also rose and massacred their English officers and their families. The Mutiny had begun.

The British lost control of large areas of the plain of the Ganges, including the key cities of Delhi, Lucknow, and Cawnpore. Members of the dispossessed ruling classes making a desperate last bid to regain power frequently led the uprisings among the civilian population. They argued that the changes being wrought by the British Raj were intended to destroy the old religious traditions and to force the people to become Christian. Since the rebellions were centered in areas only recently taken over by the British, the argument had considerable effect on people who did not fully understand the changes.

But many areas of India were not affected by the rebellion, and the British put it down by 1858. The British authorities concluded that social change had been too rapid and that henceforth the aim would be to provide stable government with a minimum of interference in social matters. So paradoxically the British turned increasingly for support to the most conservative elements of Indian society and looked with suspicion upon the English-educated groups in the great port cities that had most enthusiastically supported the government during the Mutiny.

An attempt was made in the 1880s to remove the restrictions on the trial of Europeans by Indian judges, but died in a storm of opposition by British officials and the British business community. This led educated Indians to form protest organizations, and the leaders of a number of these combined in 1885 to form the Indian National Congress.

The Congress wanted to participate in the structure that the British had created, not to destroy it. The people who founded it had made their careers through social structures that had been created under the British. In 1947, when the Indians did achieve victory and the British withdrew from India, it was described as a "transfer of power" not a revolution, and this was correct in every sense. Those Indians who opposed these moderates wanted an Indian nationalism that had a Hindu vocabulary and Hindu symbols. They proudly accepted the title "extremists" that the moderates called them.

Another tension was the hostility between Muslims and Hindus. The Muslims felt that the democratic, representative institutions sought by the Congress would make Muslims a permanent minority. In Bengal, Aurobindo Ghose passionately preached that the sacrifice demanded from India was a blood offering made to the goddess Kali, Shiva's consort who is always pictured with blood dripping from her mouth (see Chapter 26.)

In 1906 the Muslim League was formed. The British created a special constituency for Muslims, which the Indian National Congress denounced.

India supported Great Britain in the First World War. The British reduced their troops in India to 15,000 and raised a voluntary Indian army of 1.3 million men, and many fought in the war. Wartime shortages gave Indian manufacturers the opportunity to compete with foreign goods for the first time. Indian Muslims had been inclined to regard British rule as a necessary countervailing force to Hinduism but the war against Muslim Turkey raised doubts. Some Muslims, notably M. A. Jinnah, who became the founder of Pakistan, advocated greater Muslim participation in the Indian National Congress as a way of safeguarding Muslim interests.

The promulgation of a new constitution with a provision for political parties to form provincial ministries caused much debate. In the middle of this debate in April 1919, a British Army officer in Amritsar in the Punjab ordered his troops to open fire on unarmed political demonstrators, killing at least 400 and wounding more than 1,000. This was the incident that set the stage for Mohandas K. Gandhi.

Gandhi was a lawyer who was highly respected by both the British and the Indians for his work in South Africa on behalf of Indian immigrants in their struggle against discriminatory laws. The failure of the British to punish the people responsible for the massacre combined with his assessment of the weakness of the Indian National Congress convinced Gandhi that a radical departure was needed. His answer was non-violent resistance. In 1920, he persuaded the Congress to adopt a resolution urging non-cooperation with the government, a boycott on foreign goods, the renunciation of all British titles, refusal to attend British schools, and, ultimately, a refusal to pay taxes. Gandhi's goal was the withdrawal of the British on India's terms, rather than on British terms; and the fostering of a spirit of nationhood inspired by a spirit of nationhood defined by self-respect.

Gandhi probably neither hastened nor delayed Indian independence. But he did help maintain unity between the moderates and the revolutionaries and help make the Indian National Congress identify itself with the concerns of the masses. By using symbols such as the spinning wheel to make homespun cloth that could substitute for manufactured cloth identified with the British, Gandhi dramatized his cause with success that is probably unmatched in history.

Until the summer of 1947, the leaders of both the Indian National Congress and the Muslim League, including Jinnah, probably did not really believe that partition would be the outcome. But that was what happened. The central portion of the sub-continent became India. Pakistan was created in two parts, separated by the entire continent. One part was the valley of the Indus, and the other was the east bank and delta of the Ganges. Not long afterward, with assistance from India, East Pakistan broke off to become Bangladesh. And the suspicion and mistrust between Pakistan and India continues to this day.

Chapter 15

The Chinese

As we have seen, *Homo sapiens* and *Homo sapiens sapiens* crossed over from Africa to the Middle East between 80,000 and 60,000 years ago. Some turned right and gradually made their way along the coast of India to Southeast Asia. Of these some turned south into Indonesia and then Australia and others continued along the coast into what is now China and Japan, which was still connected to the mainland. Still others spent some time in the Middle East and then repeated the process of making their way to India, Southeast Asia, Indonesia, China, and Japan. Still others followed an interior route from the Middle East that passed north of the Himalayas. About 25,000 years ago at the beginning of the last ice age, some of these were trapped for several thousand years behind walls of ice in what is now the Gobi desert. Those who survived developed a short, squat body like modern Eskimos and a layer of fat over the eyes to protect them from freezing. This is the so-called Mongolian flap, which their descendants retained after the ice age even though they developed leaner bodies in response to a warmer climate. Following the ice age what is now the Gobi desert developed a temperate climate and became a place of lush forests, streams, and rainfall. But a thousand years before the present era it began to dry out, and the people migrated mainly south and east, with a few going west. Their descendants in Asia speak the related modern languages of Mongolia, China, Korea, and Japan. The descendants of those who went west settled in Finland and Hungary, where the related modern languages of Finnish, Lapp, and Magyar are spoken. The peoples who went south into China displaced and intermarried with the peoples who were already there, and those who went east displaced and intermarried with the peoples who were already in Korea and Japan.

Of those who went south, some settled in the big knee of the Yellow River, and archeologists have excavated one of their villages, Yang-shao in western Honan. The settlers moved from relying solely on hunting and gathering to an early form of agriculture. They lived in small villages, which were moved often in response to the demands of slash-and-burn agriculture. Their crops were millet and wheat, and their domesticated animals were dogs, pigs, sheep and perhaps goats and cattle. They had pottery, which they painted in red and black. They learned how to make silk. Gradually the Yang-shao culture evolved into the Lung-shan culture—named for an archeological site in Shantung. Rice was added to the staple crops and chickens and horses may have been added at this time to their domesticated animals. Hunting, however, continued to play a big role. The villagers learned to dig wells and to build walls around their villages. Pottery was gray and black and included double boilers and tripods with hollow legs to put among the coals.

The Shang dynasty marks the beginning of the Bronze Age in China, which began before the Lung-shan stone age ended. Orthodox Chinese chronology dates the Shang dynasty as from 1766 B.C. to 1122 B.C. The so-called *Bamboo Annals*, which were discovered in a grave in 281 A.D. and took their name from the slips of bamboo on which they were written, put it at 1523 B.C. to 1122 B.C. The orthodox and the bamboo chronologies differ before 841 B.C., but coincide after that.

Divination was important in the Shang period. Heating the shoulder blades of pigs, sheep, or cattle in the early days and tortoise shells later provided divination. The heat produced cracks and from these cracks predictions were deduced. The question and sometimes the answer were incised on the bone or tortoise shell, and occasionally what actually happened was also related. For example: "The diviner Ku asked: 'Should we hunt in Kuei?' That day we caught 1 tiger, 40 deer, 164 wolves, 159 fawns, and some foxes which were rather small."

Crops were wheat, millet, sorghum, and barley. Rice was known but perhaps was not cultivated in the central region of the Shang state. Water buffalo had been tamed.

Human sacrifices were common at both burials and the consecration of buildings and could involve more than 100 victims. Male and female shamans officiated but were sometimes themselves sacrificed if they failed—if they were trying to produce rain, for example, and no rain came.

Spears were used and composite bows of wood and horn. War chariots had two wheels and were drawn by two horses. The stirrup, which made it possible to swing a sword from the back of a horse without falling off, was invented in India and did not make its way to China until later. So horses were not ridden, at least in war. As shown by the oracle bones, writing was rather well advanced, using more than 2,000 different characters.

Chinese writing went through four stages. Neither an alphabet nor syllabic scripts were developed but each word came to be noted by a different character. The earliest characters were pictographs for concrete words. A drawing of a woman, meant a woman. A drawing of a broom, a broom.

In the second stage characters were combined to form ideographs. A woman and a broom became a wife. Some of the inventors of ideographs must have had a sense of humor: Three women together meant *treachery* or *villainy*!

In the third stage some words were phonetic. Characters were borrowed for other words with the same pronunciation.

In the fourth stage the so-called radicals, intended to determine the meaning, were added to the phonetic loans to avoid confusion. Nine-tenths of present-day Chinese characters have been constructed by the phonetic method. Unfortunately, the pronunciation was not always identical. Also, pronunciation changed. So today characters may have utterly different pronunciation even though they share the same phonetic. Although many Chinese dialects are mutually unintelligible, Chinese are still able to read each other's writing even if they cannot understand each other's speech. Neighbors to the west, the Chou, who lived in the central Wei river valley, overthrew the Shang dynasty. The orthodox chronology gives the date as 1122 B.C., while the *Bamboo Annals* place it in 1027 B.C.

The chronology of events in early Chinese history is as follows:

- 3523 to 1027 B.C. was the Shang dynasty according to the bamboo annals.
- 1027 to 771 B.C. was the Western Chou dynasty.
- 770 to 256 B.C. was the Eastern Chou dynasty.
- 551 to 479 B.C. are the traditional dates for Confucius.
- c. 500 B.C. was the beginning of the Iron Age in China.

- 403 to 221 B.C. was the age of the Warring States.
- 223 B.C. the Ch'in annihilated Ch'u.
- 221 B.C. was the unification of China.
- 221 to 207 B.C. was the Ch'in dynasty.

The authority of the kings was gradually eroded, and 771 B.C. a noble killed the last king of Western Chou. A year later a son of the dead king was proclaimed his successor. The last period of the Chou dynasties was known as the Period of the Warring States, from 403 to 221 B.C.

By the end of the Warring States period, China was unified culturally. The political unification was a political follow-up to the cultural unification already in force toward the end of the Eastern Chou. The Chou dynasty ceased to exist in 256 B.C. The Ch'in dynasty annexed the weaker states and routed its main competitor, the Ch'u in 223 B.C. It then unified China in 221 B.C.

Confucius lived from 551 to 470 B.C. He was born in the lower nobility in Lu, a small but renowned state at the foot of the sacred Mount T'ai. He studied history, ritual, and music and after a brief employment in his own state, he became a teacher and spent his life as such.

Confucius was basically concerned with the relation of man to man, and he declined to engage in metaphysical speculation. He thought men had lived in harmony under the sage rulers of the golden age, and he believed that at that time they had been truthful, wise, good, righteous, and had fulfilled their ceremonial obligations meticulously and with understanding of the moral content. Since then man had degenerated, Confucius believed, but man is fundamentally good and can be salvaged through education.

Confucius's successor was Mencius. He argued that if a dynasty did not perform well it was because it lacked moral dedication to the welfare of the people. If so, heaven would withdraw its mandate. When the people rejected their ruler, it was proof that heaven had withdrawn its mandate. This theory had an enormous influence on Chinese historiography, which generally assumed that if a dynasty fell, it was because it had lost the mandate of heaven.

A late development in Chou times was the so-called Naturalists. They explained the universe in terms of Yin and Yang, which do not oppose but complement each other. Yin is female, dark, and passive. Yang is male, light, active. They should be in balance.

177

The Confucians, the Naturalists, and the others were concerned with man as a social and political animal. Taoism, founded by Lao-tzu a little later than Confucius's time, was different. Taoists believed that everything was relative. There was no death without life, no goodness without evil. Behind all this is Tao, which cannot be understood but is a mystical state reached by meditation.

The best-known work of literature in ancient China was the *Book of Changes*. It is fundamentally an early oracle handbook, whose interpretations are brief and obscure. As one authority has said, many Chinese and not a few Westerners have read a cosmological depth into this text, which it does not possess.

The newly unified China was defended in the north by the Great Wall, which was based on earlier fortifications. Korea was not part of the unified China. In the south, Hunan and parts of Kwangtung and Kwangsi and perhaps the Red River delta were incorporated into the state. Kiangsi and Fukien in the south and Kweichou and Yunnan in the southwest were not yet Chinese. The king of Ch'in became the Son of Heaven, but since the title king had lost much of its prestige, he adopted the title Huang-ti. It means August Lord, but it is usually translated as Emperor.

Carrying standardization to an extreme it was decreed in 213 B.C. that all books not sponsored by the government should be burned, although the imperial library was to remain intact. The policy was intended to wipe out the intellectual opposition to the centralized state.

Unfortunately, the library was destroyed in 206 B.C. during the civil war. But when the book-burning edict was rescinded in 191 B.C. in the Han dynasty, it was possible to reconstruct the texts from memory, since the teachings of the school were usually memorized.

The first emperor died on an inspection tour 210 B.C. A civil war followed. The victor was a commoner who became the Emperor Kao 202 B.C. He retained Han as the name of the dynasty. His descendants occupied the throne for 211 years, until 9 A.D. The Han dynasty was then restored in 25 A.D. so it is customary to speak of the Former and Later Han dynasties.

Feudal lords came to be replaced by a bureaucracy. The upper levels of the bureaucracy had the right to appoint their own subordinates. High officials could recommend sons or nephews who were first given duties in the palace and then absorbed into the bureaucracy. The emperor at times could directly summon people, but they did not have to accept. Studying at the Imperial Academy could also lead to official appointment.

But the most important and remarkable way to enter the bureaucracy was the examination system. Its primitive beginnings were in the Han dynasty, beginning in 196 B.C. Eventually only the emperor and the bureaucracy shared power. At one extreme, the emperor could content himself with a passive role. At the other he could attempt personal rule by manipulating advice and intimidating officials.

Another device for concentrating power in the emperor was the so-called Inner Court. It consisted of secretaries and eunuchs of the imperial harems who had easy access to the emperor and could be dominated by him. Once the flow of documents to and from the throne had been channeled through the Inner Court, the influence of the high career officials and the Outer Court were automatically reduced. As a consequence, many interest groups struggled for influence. But even the most successful never achieved unlimited power. Traditional China was not despotism in any true sense of the word.

If a new emperor had not reached adulthood, the empress dowager was entitled to rule in his place. Normally, empresses appointed one of their male relatives as regent. The first regent was appointed in 87 B.C., and at first the system worked well. But the situation changed in the reign of Emperor Ch'eng who reigned from 32 B.C. to 7 B.C. He took no interest in government and was willing to delegate authority to his mother's relatives, who were members of the great Wang clan and one after the other he appointed five relatives as regents. The last was Wang Mang, who outmaneuvered everyone, and in 9 A.D. he declared the Han dynasty finished and assume the throne himself.

Wang Mang is one of the most thoroughly discussed of Chinese rulers. He followed Confucian principles and among other reforms tried to redistribute land. But the Yellow river changed its course drastically twice in his time causing great floods and famine, and these in turn triggered large-scale migrations and a peasant rebellion. Supporters of the deposed Han dynasty made the most of the opportunity, and in 23 A.D. Wang Mang was killed. Peace was not restored until 36 A.D.

The new dynasty is called the Later Han. The regency was reintroduced in 89 A.D., and the struggle between cliques became even more violent than before. At times even the emperor and the regent were pitted against each other. The eunuchs sided with the emperor, which increased their power in the Inner Court. The civil servants opposed the eunuchs— and continued to do so throughout Chinese history. In a great confrontation in 169 A.D., the eunuchs triumphed, only to be themselves annihilated in 189 A.D.

As the central government grew weaker, rebellions broke out in the provinces. Decades of fighting followed. The last emperor of the Later Han was forced to abdicate in 220 A.D., but the dynasty had really ceased to exist decades earlier.

The Han Chinese were dimly aware of the Indian and Roman world. They talked as if all other peoples were subject to them. But what they thought of as tribute from the other peoples was really a disguised form of trade, since the rich presents those peoples brought were more than matched by the Chinese gifts. Many missions to China came only because of the opportunity for profit.

It was even harder to ignore the fact that the nomads to the north, especially the Hsiung-nu, could not be permanently curbed by either benevolence or force. They raided China at will, and China bought peace by sending annual gifts and an occasional princess to be a wife. The Great Wall was begun at an earlier period, but became the important bulwark of the unified China against the barbarians.

With the collapse of the Han, China fell apart into three territories: Wei in the north, Wu in the southeast, and Shu in the southwest. A bewildering number of dynasties in the different regions followed. The period is called the era of the Three Kingdoms.

Owing to more changes in the course of the Yellow River and the pressure from the Hsiung-nu and the Tibetans in the northwest, a major migration took place in later Han times that led to the first great colonization of South China. The population of Hunan, Kiangsi, and Kwantung quadrupled. The Chinese settled on the alluvial soil of the great river valleys, engulfing, absorbing, or forcing the withdrawal of the local aborigines. In the northwest Hsiung-nu, Tibetans, and other tribesmen lived side by side with the Chinese and gradually proved stronger. In the south, the Chinese step by step displaced the aborigines. Solely Chinese inhabited the Great Plains.

Buddhism in the Mahayana form came to China 500 years after Buddha lived. The first reliable reference to it dates from 65 A.D. A monk, Kuanzang (in Pin-yin or Hsuan-tsang in Wade-Giles), traveled to India via the Silk Road to find and bring back to China the sacred texts of Buddhism. During the journey, from 629 to 645 A.D., he traveled 10,000 miles.

By 577 A.D., the long period of political disunity in China came to an end. The country was divided between two major dynasties, Chinese in the south and barbarian in the north. But the most influential statesman in the north was Chinese, Yang Chien. In 581 he dismissed the last boy emperor and ascended the throne himself, and founded the Sui dynasty. His posthumous name is Emperor Wen. He defeated the south in 589 A.D., and reunited China.

Emperor Wen died in 604 A.D. and was succeeded by his son, Emperor Yang, who was possibly his murderer. The dynasty had only the two rulers, but it was one of great activity. A centralized bureaucracy was restored. The Yangtze delta was emerging as the key economic region, and the first Grand Canal was built connecting the present Hang-chou with the Yellow river, a distance of more than 500 miles. The Great Wall was reconstructed as a barrier at the northern border.

However, the Ordos region had been lost as well as the present-day Manchuria and Korea. The Tarim basin was no longer under Chinese control. However, Fukien became an integral part of China, having been assimilated by a gradual, peaceful immigration of Chinese. The Chinese also regained possession of the Red River delta in what was later Indochina.

Emperor Yang made the mistake of trying to re-establish Chinese control over Korea. He invaded, but the campaign failed. The Chinese then came under pressure from the Turks, who had been the dominant tribe in Central Asia since the middle of the sixth century and brought vast territories under their rule. In 582 A.D., the Turks split into eastern and western regimes. A great raid in 615 A.D. caught the Emperor Yang by surprise, and he was almost captured. After he escaped, he withdrew to the lower Yangtze, and his empire swiftly crumbled. In 618 A.D. the Emperor was murdered.

The victors in the civil war that followed were the Li, a noble Chinese family from the northwest, who had formed a temporary alliance with the Eastern Turks. In 618 A.D., Li Yüan was enthroned as the first emperor of the T'ang dynasty with Ch'ang-an as his capital. He defeated his rivals in several campaigns lasting until 623 A.D. But the alliance with the Turks broke up, and the Turks invaded China in 622 A.D. and 624 A.D.

The first emperor of the T'ang named the eldest of his three sons heir apparent. This provoked the middle son, Li Shih-min to ambush and kill his brothers. He then forced his father to abdicate and took the throne himself as Emperor T'ai-tsung. He posed a problem for Chinese historiography. Although not the first of the T'ang he is depicted as the actual founder of the dynasty, the man who received the mandate. The historians distorted history and portrayed him as the only talented member of the family, a superior military genius and a leader of men. Actually, he was not a bad ruler. He was forceful and intelligent and assembled able assistants. He adopted a policy of religious tolerance. When T'ai-tsung died in 649 A.D., he left a stable empire to his son.

The danger came from a woman, Wu. She became a concubine of the new emperor in 650 A.D. and managed to have herself made empress five years later. By intrigue, strength of will, and murder, she became the dominating influence in the court. When Kao-tsung died at the end of 683 A.D., she arranged for a grown son of hers to succeed to the throne. But he showed signs of independence, and within two months she replaced him with her youngest son. This son did not interfere in affairs of state, and in 690 A.D. officially abdicated in favor of his mother. She ascended the throne and proclaimed the Chou dynasty. Since the dynastic historians were biased against her, it is difficult to get a balanced view. But although she was vindictive, cruel, and power-hungry, she was also a great monarch. In 705 A.D., when she was eighty years old and feeble, she was overthrown, and her eldest son was reinstated. She died before the end of that year. Her grandson, Hsüan-tsung reigned from 713 A.D. to 755 A.D. The T'ang dynasty under him reached its cultural zenith, but also began its steep political decline.

In Central Asia after a raid by the Eastern Turks, the Chinese took the offensive and made a vassal of their territory, the present Inner and Outer Mongolia. After a series of wars, China lost its position in West Turkestan forever.

It is interesting that among the Chinese prisoners taken by the Turks were men who knew how to make paper—an art that had been discovered by China 650 years earlier. Paper manufacture spread to Samarkand and Baghdad and from there to Damascus, Cairo, and Morocco, entering Europe through Italy and Spain.

Tibet was unified in the seventh century, and its king sent an embassy to China in 641 A.D. to ask for a Chinese princess in marriage. Chinese tradition is that she did much to civilize the Tibetans, but it was actually due more to the diffusion of Indian and Chinese culture. Tibet was converted to Buddhism about this time, but the Tibetans continued to be warlike. From 670 A.D. to 821 A.D. they fought the Chinese repeatedly. But over time, Tibet became a theocracy and lost its belligerency.

T'ang improved the Chinese examination system that had been introduced in Sui times. A candidate for office studied with a tutor in the public school of his local district or at the Imperial Academy in the capital. He then enrolled for examination in his chosen field, such as literature, law, or mathematics. If he was successful, he received a title corresponding to the type of examination. The highest was Presented Scholar, and as implied by the wording such scholars were introduced to the emperor. It was a literary degree, since knowledge of the Confucius classics were valued more highly than specialization in practical subjects. The candidate had to pass a further exam before being appointed to an official post and still more exams and merit ratings for promotion.

The government tried to monopolize the production and sale of important commodities, such as salt, iron, liquor, and tea. Tea became a truly national drink only in T'ang times.

The population remained at about 50 million during both the Han and T'ang dynasties, probably because sons were preferred and newborn baby girls were often abandoned to die. In the period following the T'ang dynasty, the custom of drinking tea enormously reduced the death rate from dysentery and other water-borne diseases, and the population increased dramatically.

Professional troops had gradually replaced the militia of earlier times, and in 755 A.D. one of their commanders, An Lu-shan, rebelled. He conquered Lo-yang and Ch'ang-an and proclaimed himself emperor. The displaced emperor, Hsüan-tsung, fled and abdicated in favor of his son. The rebellion was not suppressed until 763 A.D., and then only with the help of the Uighurs, whose reward included a daughter of the emperor.

When the empire of China's powerful allies, the Uighurs, collapsed in 807 A.D., there were important religious repercussions. The T'ang dynasty had been tolerant of foreign religions. Buddhism had flourished. Zoroastrian had made converts and so had Nestorian Christianity and Manicheism. The Uighurs had converted to Manicheism, but when their empire collapsed, so did religious tolerance. Manicheism immediately came under attack, and religious persecution was heavy from 841 A.D. to 845 A.D. Manicheism, Nestorianism, and Zoroastrianism were wiped out. Buddhism did survive, but suffered enormous economic losses. The great wealth of the monasteries was confiscated, and Buddhism never fully recovered. Islam had few followers in China at the time and was apparently not affected.

There followed half a century of turmoil, the period known as Five Dynasties. Interestingly, it was during this period that block printing was invented. The Buddhists had the oldest printed texts, but at this time the Confucian texts were printed for the first time. Movable type was invented soon after this, but block printing was cheaper and continued to be the common method.

Summation

By the end of later Han times, the main characteristics of traditional China had taken form. The territory was what modern China is today. It had a highly centralized government under an emperor who ruled according to his preference. An efficient bureaucracy ran things, based on the principle of checks and balances. The examination system was in place. Social mobility was common. There were strong divisive forces under the surface, but the rebels were rarely revolutionaries. They wanted power within the system. The writing and the literature were strong unifying forces. The bureaucracy attracted the ambitious. Confucianism offered a satisfactory explanation of man's role in society. Neo-Taoism and Buddhism appealed to those who sought greater spiritual depth. The achievements of the Chinese civilization and its geographic isolation combined to give the Chinese a sense of superiority and a claim to moral and political supremacy.

The Han period was a formative one not only for Chinese history, but also for Chinese historiography. The work which created an entirely new genre and set a trend for two thousand years is the *Historical Records*, compiled privately by Ssu-ma T'an and his son Ssu-ma Ch'ien who rank with the great historians of all times and all countries. They conceived and carried out the idea of writing a complete history of China from the legendary kings to Emperor Wu.

At great personal sacrifice Ssu-ma Ch'ien completed the work in the year 99 B.C. Thank God the treatment of scholars has changed since his time. Today scholars are unfairly criticized by political figures that do not like the way they have been treated in historical works, as I well know from personal experience. But when the Emperor Wu decided that he had been slighted in Ssu-ma Ch'ien's work, he had him castrated.

Chapter 16

The North American Indians

B y the end of the Pleistocene, the glaciers had locked up an enormous amount of water. Sea levels were so low that vast areas of the continental shelf were exposed. Along the Pacific Coast of North America the shelf was covered with vegetation and teemed with game animals. What is now the Bering Straits was a high, dry isthmus 1,000 kilometers wide. The area was free of ice down to central Alaska even at the height of the ice age. As Dean R. Snow says, Alaska to ice age hunters was simply a part of the rich hunting grounds of northeastern Asia ("The First Americans and the Differentiation of Hunter-Gatherer Cultures," *The Cambridge History of the Native Peoples of the Americas*, edited by Bruce G. Trigger and Wilcomb E. Washburn, Cambridge University Press, 1996, on which much of the following is drawn).

No remains of *Homo erectus*, Neanderthal, or any of the other relatives of *Homo sapiens sapiens* have been found in the two American continents. The only remains are *Homo sapiens sapiens*. The earliest artifacts are of the Upper Paleolithic era—stone blades, tailored clothing, spear throwers (atl atl), and the evidence of fire. Sites in the Kamchatka Peninsula in Siberia show double-walled, wigwam-shaped houses. The projectile points found at these sites are bi-facial and leaf-shaped, very similar to a North American Indian point dating to around 13,000 years ago. Radio-carbon dating puts the points from Siberia at 14,300 to 13,600 years ago, although the Russian archeologist Nikolai Dikov argues that the sites themselves are really 2,000 years older, dating from 16,300 to 15,600 years ago. Similar points dated at no more than 15,000 years ago have been found at the Dyuktai sites of the Lena River Valley in Siberia. Everything found so far suggests that no humans in significant numbers entered the high, dry area of what are now the Bering Straits and the adjoining areas of Siberia and central Alaska until some time after about 18,000 years ago. Then, about 15,000 years ago, a fisher folk began to move slowly south along the shoreline of North and eventually South America.

Until about 14,000 years ago a great sheet of ice covered the land to the south and east of Alaska, but then the warming climate and retreating glaciers opened a pathway down to what is now the United States between the glaciers along the coastal range and those in central Canada. The big game worked their way south through this pathway and the people who hunted them followed.

Then, about 12,000 years ago, rising sea levels began to flood what is now the Bering Straits. For some time the Straits were narrow and probably shallow and could not have been much of a barrier. During this period the Na-Dene peoples entered North America, from about 12,000 years ago to 8,500 years ago. In time the Straits did become a barrier, but it is difficult to say just how formidable it was. The Eskimos began to enter North America around 8,500 years ago, and even today they don't have too much difficulty crossing the Straits in their kayaks.

Christy Turner examined over 200,000 human teeth from America dating from before European contact and found variations in cusps and roots and in the ridges on incisors known as shoveling (Christy Turner and Stephen Zegura, "The Settlement of the Americas: A Comparison of the Linguistic, Dental, and Genetic Evidence," *Current Anthropology* 27, 1986). She concluded that the American Indians resembled northeast Asians and that the known rates of change indicate that they split from their Asian relatives not much before 15,000 years ago. The Eskimo-Aleut and Na-Dene populations are slightly different from other American Indians and from each other, differences that are consistent with what it known about their origins from linguistic studies. Also, the Eskimo-Aleut have the B variant of the ABO blood system, while the great bulk of the other American Indians, including the Na-Dene, do not. There is no evidence of a genetic mixture with Europeans or anyone else before 1492 A.D.

After coming through the pathway between the glaciers, one group of hunters followed the big game south. At Clovis, New Mexico, they occupied a site 11,200 years ago, where their arrowheads, the Clovis points, were first found. Clovis points have since been found in Alaska and Canada. The descendants of these people made their way into Central America and on into South America east of the Andes. The big game led other people coming through the ice gap to turn east into what is now the American and Canadian middle west and on into the woodlands of the eastern seaboard.

A third group of people, as we saw, were the Na-Dene, including the Navajo, the speakers of the Athapaskan language in Alaska and the western sub-Arctic of Canada, and the speakers of Haida, Tlingit, and Eyak on the Pacific coast of Canada.

The Eskimo-Aleut peoples were the fourth group. They came somewhat later than the Na-Dene, although apparently not very much later.

Clovis points have long, thin, flake scars called flutes and are found at many sites dating from 12,000 to 11,000 years ago in North America south of the glaciation. Fluted points were skillfully made and seem to have been items of trade, since they are often found far away from the quarry source.

The Folsom point is a later derivative of the fluted-point, and it is limited to the Great Plains. Unfluted, leaf-shaped points are found in the Rocky Mountain region and along the spine of the Americas all the way to Argentina.

In 1996 the remains of a human male estimated to be 9,300 years old were found on the banks of the Columbia River in Washington State near the town of Kennewick. The man was robust, about 5 feet 9 inches tall, and about 45 to 50 years old. He had a three-inch spear point embedded deep in his pelvis, but scientists say that he had probably lived with it in place for a long time, and that it never caused a serious infection. Analysis of the skull indicates that he did not resemble either modern Indians or Europeans. Since his dates are more recent than the peoples described above, he may turn out to have been a member of a group migrating later from Siberia or perhaps even one of the Jomon from Japan. A more precise answer will have to wait for a DNA analysis.

Mathematical modeling suggests that the number of people necessary for the long-term survival of a society is about 500, which is just about the number of face-to-face interactions that most of us are able to maintain. Comparison with living hunter-gatherers suggests that the density of the early Indians was less than 1 per 100 square kilometers. Since the habitable portion of North America at that time was about 10 million square kilometers, this suggests a population of about 100,000. For 1,000 years the early Indians hunted both the game found today in the Americas and several species that became extinct at the end of the Pleistocene, such as horses, mammoths, mastodons, camels, and a species of bison different from the buffalo. The musk ox is still found in regions that were not habitable for early Indians or for the later Eskimos, and the buffalo survives only in special, protected situations.

In the northeast, the first inhabitants were nomadic, following the mammoth, musk ox, giant beaver, and other large animals. Gradually, the big animals died out or moved north with the rising temperatures. The retreating glaciers gave way first to treeless tundra then to spruce and birch forests and finally to the present mixture of deciduous and coniferous woodland. The Indians responded by hunting smaller species and gradually diversifying into fishing and gathering.

Whether or not the early Indians caused the extinction of the big game animals is still debated. On the one hand, it is difficult to believe that 100,000 people armed with spears and spear throwers exterminated whole species of megafauna. A number of very small animals, such as songbirds, that would not have been targets of the early Indians also went extinct, and this suggests that the causes of the extinctions were rapid and broad changes in the environment. In this view, the early Indians were part of the ecological equation, but not the prime movers.

But there is also an argument that the Indians *were* the prime reason the big game animals went extinct. In the nineteenth century the European Americans drove the passenger pigeon into extinction by cutting nesting trees and by harvesting flightless squabs. If the early Indians selectively hunted the young of the big game animals, their effect could have been equally dramatic. The animals had no experience with humans and may well have been fearless at their approach. In Africa, if the large herbivores had not acquired defense mechanisms through long association with humans, they, too, would probably have gone extinct.

The argument that small birds also became extinct through environmental change has also been attacked. In Africa when large herd animals have recently become extinct, the vegetation cover changed dramatically, extinguishing many of the old niches for smaller creatures, as well as creating some new ones.

So the role of humans in the extinction of the large animals in America is still under debate.

Beginning about 4,500 years ago, the Great Plains took on their modern character. For two or three millennia various ungulates thrived. A cold snap lasting several centuries and ending in 1850 was wonderful for the grasses of the prairies and the buffalo proliferated. Vast herds of buffalo roamed the grasslands, but without horses the Indians were not very successful in hunting them. Although teams of Indians did succeed driving buffalo over cliffs—the so-called buffalo jumps—the occasions were few and far between. Killing an individual animal was also difficult. The buffalo traveled in huge herds, and even when a hunter isolated a lone straggler, it would have been a formidable opponent for a man on foot armed with a spear. Sneaking up on a herd of buffalo to kill a calf was another method that was undoubtedly used, but the herd was very easily spooked into a stampede. Even after the invention of the bow and arrow, which appeared in eastern America about 400 A.D. and in the Great Basin of the Rockies about 500 A.D., really successful buffalo hunting had to wait until the Spanish reintroduced the horse to the New World.

Agriculture

A limited form of agriculture appeared about 3,500 years ago among the mound builders of the southeast and in the middle west.

In the southwest, agriculture also had its beginnings about 3,500 years ago with tropical cultigens introduced from Mesoamerica such as maize and beans.

189

In the eastern woodlands, at least four indigenous plants were domesticated 4000 to 3500 years ago—lamb's quarter, marsh elder, squash, and sunflower. Maize was introduced around 200 A.D., but it played a minor role until the period from 800 A.D. to 1100 A.D., when it gained center stage.

In time, the Indians in the northern areas developed a strain of maize that did well in their shorter growing season. In any case, by 1500 A.D., maize was well established from Ontario to Florida. Along the Mississippi and its tributaries, the river-valley maize farmers were particularly successful, not only with maize but also in exploiting the abundant supplies of fish, waterfowl, deer, raccoon, turkey; nuts, berries, and fruits.

Around 2,100 years ago, eastern woodland agriculturists pressed into the plains along the river valleys, encountering very little resistance from the resident hunter-gatherers. A second wave of eastern farmers came to the plains in 900 A.D. Living in scattered communities, they had to retreat when occasional droughts caused their farming efforts to fail.

In the southwest, where the Mexican influence was strong, people used gold, silver, and copper for decoration. Only a tiny minority had metal tools or weapons, mainly copper. Stone, bone, wood, and obsidian were worked into spear points, arrowheads, knives, and scrapers. Further north, the Indians used fire to clear forest, drive prey toward kill sites, and in some areas to create large, park-like spaces to attract deer and other game that the early European observers found particularly impressive.

The lack of any large domestic animals ruled out the intensive plowing and manuring practiced in Europe, so the Indians used a variation of the slash-and-burn technique, cultivating an area for a few years and then moving on to a new area to let the soil recover. As a result most Indians viewed land as a common resource rather than a commodity that could be *owned*. Families and tribes had rights to hunt and fish in a particular area, but the concept of a fenced-off parcel of land being the exclusive property of an individual or family would have been utterly alien to most native Americans.

Trade

In the period just before 1492, major trade centers had developed in the southwest, centered around the pueblos of the Zuni and the Pecos. Their trade networks connected to the plains, the Great Basin of the Rockies, California, and northern Mexico.

In California, major trade centers did not develop, apparently because ample resources were equally distributed along the coast and because of the abundant game and acorn supplies in the immediate interior. In the northwest, a trade center grew up in the Dalles on the Columbia River that was probably the largest in North America. Each summer thousands of Indians came from the surrounding areas to harvest and process millions of salmon that they traded for goods from the plains, the plateau, the northwest coast, and California.

In the east, the Hurons traded surplus corn with the Algonquin peoples for pelts and dried fish. But most of their trade was in luxury items, including marine shells, copper, and fancy furs.

Exotic cherts, impure, flintlike rocks, were passed from one Indian band to another. Copper from around Lake Superior was traded east to the St. Lawrence and south into what is now the United States. Marine shells from the Gulf of Mexico, the Chesapeake, and Long Island sound were traded north and west. Pipestone (catlinite), mica, lead, flint, and buffalo hide from the plains were traded east. However, there seems to have been little trade between the Indians of the Caribbean and those of Florida.

Population

Not much is known for sure about how big the population of the Americas was before the white man arrived. California had abundant resources, as mentioned above, enough to support one person to one square kilometer, for a total of 350,000 people. But the rest of the country was not so well endowed, and the numbers are subject to grand speculation. Woodrow Borah and Sherburne Cook estimated that the population of North and South America at the beginning of the sixteenth century totaled 100 million, while Europe less Russia at that time was 70 million. Henry Dobyns thought that the population of the two Americas was somewhere between 90 and 200 million and that the population of North America and the Caribbean was 10 to 18 million. But most scholars felt that these estimates were too high.

James Mooney estimated the population north of the Rio Grande at 1,152,950—and it is something of a mystery how he got such precise numbers when the others were giving only a very wide range. Alfred Kroeber rounded Mooney's number down to 900,000, while Douglas Ubelaker doubled it and also gave a very precise range, between 1,894,350 and

2,171,125 excluding the Caribbean. Scholars now believe that these estimates are much too low.

Russell Thornton estimated the population of North America, excluding Mexico, in 1500 A.D. as about 7 million, and this is now the most widely accepted figure. In Mexico, Central, and South America the agricultural civilizations supported a much larger number, from 68 to 93 million. Thus the total Indian population for North and South America is estimated at 75 to 100 million.

The white man's superior weapons and particularly his diseases took a heavy toll. Thornton estimated that 5 million of the 7 million Indians in North America lived in what is now the United States and that the number was down to 600,000 by 1800 A.D. By the end of the nineteenth century it was down to 250,000.

Beginning in the 15th century, the kings of Portugal and Spain encouraged voyages in search of gold, silk, spices, slaves, and for sea routes to the riches of the Orient. After people realized that it was not the Orient that Columbus had reached in 1492, John Cabot and others joined the search. Balboa crossed the Isthmus of Panama in 1513 and discovered the Pacific Ocean. Between 1524 and 1527, French, Spanish, and English expeditions tried and failed to find a route to the Pacific. By 1535, hope of finding a northern passage was dead. But for the rest of the sixteenth century the search continued for rivers flowing into the Atlantic that had their headwaters near the Pacific and so might serve as a trade route to the Orient.

Contact between the Europeans and the Indians occurred near the Spanish settlements in the southeast of what is now the United States and near the summer fishing grounds at the Grand Banks and along the northeast coast. The earliest record of a cargo of cod from Newfoundland was one that arrived in England in 1502, although the English did not return to the fisheries until 1522. French fishermen from Normandy were active by 1504, Portuguese by 1505, and Bretons by 1511. Basques were active after 1512, and a whole fleet of French ships left Bordeaux in 1517. For the first few years, the cod were eviscerated, washed, lightly salted, and dried on racks built on the shore. These activities inevitably involved contact with the Indians. Later in the century, some ships did not come to shore but eviscerated and heavily salted the cod and stored it in the hold without drying.

Around 1540, French and Spanish Basques came to control the Straits of Belle Isle between the mainland of Canada and Newfoundland. Using this base they hunted whales along the coast of Labrador for forty years, until the disaster of the Spanish Armada limited the number of both ships and sailors.

By 1580, fishing and whaling were bringing as many as 20 thousand Europeans to the northeastern shores of North America each summer. To some extent, the Indians must have resented the Europeans' poaching fish and cutting timber for drying racks, and the Europeans were clearly annoyed at the Indians for their pilfering and for burning the installations during the winter to extract iron nails. But relations were often friendly. The Indians were given presents and occasionally some of them worked in the fish processing.

But the main link was a growing trade in furs and animal skins. Beaver and marten were especially valued. In addition to those engaged in fishing and whaling in the north, European ships occasionally put ashore at various places along the entire Atlantic coast of North America to trade, to avoid storms, or to take on water and provisions. Trading in furs and skins was apparently much more extensive than shown in the records, since the sailors were anxious to avoid the taxes on them.

Then there were the exploratory expeditions—the Narváez expedition of 1528-33; the de Sota expedition of 1539-43 into Mississippi and Texas; the Coronado expedition of 1540-42 into the southwest; and the Luna expedition of 1559-61 to the southeast.

It was a common practice to abduct Indians as trophies of a voyage. In 1502, Sebastian Cabot captured three Indians and presented them dressed in native costume to the court of Henry VII. Many of the captives were exhibited as curiosities, the men giving public displays of their skills as canoeists or archers and the women showing how they made clothes.

Others, mainly young men, were carried off in the hope that they would learn the Europeans' language and be able to serve future expeditions as informants and interpreters. In 1536, Cartier entrapped and carried off a St. Lawrence chief of the Iroquois, Donnacona, his two sons, and several others so they could tell the French king and other officials tales of a land rich in precious metals that lay to the west. Before an expedition could be launched all but one of the Indians were dead. As late as 1605, George Weymouth seized five Indians from New England as potential informants and interpreters. Although these kidnappings were fairly few, news of them must have spread widely along the eastern seaboard.

Disease

Among the diseases of the Indians were bacillary and amoebic dysentery; viral influenza and pneumonia, arthritis, rickettsial fevers, viral fevers, round worms, tuberculosis, and syphilis. Although North America had fewer native diseases than Europe or Asia, life expectancy does not seem to have been any greater than in Europe. In both Europe and America the childhood the death rate was very high. For those Indians who survived childhood the average life span was between 25 and 30 years, about the same as in Europe.

The Europeans had some immunities to most of the diseases common in America except syphilis. Sailors brought it to Europe as early as 1493, and within two decades it had spread into every corner of Europe and on into Africa and Asia. The diseases that the Europeans brought to the Americas were smallpox, measles, influenza, bubonic plague, diphtheria, typhus, cholera, scarlet fever, trachoma, whooping cough, chicken pox, and tropical malaria. And for these diseases the Indians apparently had no immunities whatsoever.

The white man's diseases leaped ahead of the white man himself. Sometimes as many as 90 percent of the inhabitants of a village died of the white man's diseases before they had ever heard of him. What happened was a biological holocaust.

Española suffered the first outbreak of smallpox in 1518, killing about half of the Arawak Indians. It spread rapidly through the Greater Antilles, and then accompanied Spaniards to the mainland. In the summer of 1520, the epidemic hit the Aztec capital, killing a very large number and so weakening the others that they were unable to resist the conquerors. From 1520 into the 1530s, Indian, African, and European carriers incubated the disease while traveling and infected populations along the traditional trade routes and during the European expeditions of reconnaissance, enslavement, and colonization. To the south, the disease went as far as Rio de la Plata. To the north, documentary evidence describes major outbreaks in Texas and the southeast. Although the evidence is only inferential, the disease may have gone as far as California, the southwest, the northern Plains, and the northeast.

The de Sota and other expeditions into what is now South Carolina found large, uninhabited towns choked with vegetation, and the Indians confirmed that there had been a plague and that the few survivors had moved to other towns. The pattern was repeated everywhere. In Texas some native groups described by Cabeza de Vaca had vanished completely when the sites were revisited in the seventeenth century. The pueblo Indians suffered a cataclysmic decline beginning around 1520.

In New England, the first major epidemic was in 1616 to 1618. It leveled some of the New England Indian populations but inexplicably missed some others entirely. Authorities believe the epidemic began in the sixteenth century in Atlantic Canada contracted from the European fishermen and whalers.

Between 1520 and 1600 the New World experienced at least 17 major epidemics. Some of the native remedies for smallpox, such as sweat baths and plunges into cold water, increased the chances of dying. In the initial outbreaks the casualties were often as high as 75 percent. Recurrence of the disease or the appearance of other diseases, especially measles and influenza, could in three generations wipe out an entire tribe.

Although disease first hit most Indian tribes before they had ever met a white man, there is at least one confirmed instance of the white man using disease as germ warfare. After France had been expelled from Canada as a consequence of the Seven Years' War, the Ohio and Great Lakes Indians launched what was called Pontiac's Rebellion, a series of attacks on British forts. Most of the attacks were successful but the Indians failed to take Detroit, Niagara, and Fort Pitt. When a delegation of Delaware Indians met under a flag of truce to urge the surrender of Fort Pitt, the British presented them with a gift of blankets that had been used by smallpox victims. An epidemic was started that spread among the upper Ohio Indians during the ensuing year.

Alcohol was new to the Indians, they took to it enthusiastically, and it contributed to the high death rate. Another factor was that the Indians feared and hated their old Indian rivals more than the white man and often joined the white man in wars against their old enemies. An example was when the Mohicans joined the colonists in the Pequot War of 1637. In 1636, Massachusetts's settlers accused a Pequot of murdering a colonist and in retaliation, they burned a Pequot village on Block Island. The principal Pequot chief, Sassacus, gathered his warriors, and the colonists feared retaliation. The Mohicans, who were ancient enemies and rivals of the Pequots, joined the colonists in a sunrise attack on a Pequot village on June 5, 1637. They burned between 600 and 700 of the Pequots alive in their village. Later that same month they captured Sassacus and his warriors. The colonists sold him, his warriors, and most of the other Pequots into slavery in Bermuda.

However, as Shephard Krech III in his *The Ecological Indian: Myth and History* (NY: Norton, 1999); Nicholas Lemann, in his "Buffaloed, Was the Native American always nature's friend." (*The New Yorker,* Sept 13, 1999); and James Wilson, *The Earth Shall Weep, A History of Native America* (New York: Atlantic Monthly Press, 1999) all point out, some of the Indians' troubles had nothing to do with the white man. One was the high value that some of the Indian tribes put on being a warrior, the large role that warfare played among some tribes, and such customs as taking "coup"—capturing horses, taking scalps, and so on. These attitudes and customs were entirely indigenous, although some modern writers have wrongly assumed the Indians learned scalping from whites. Female infanticide was widely practiced among the Indians. They regularly set fire to forests to clear the land and provide grazing grounds to attract game, as already mentioned, and sometimes the fires raged out of control. Indian agriculture was slash-and-burn and rather than nurturing the soil when it was depleted, they simply moved on to another site. The Hohokam of central Arizona built an extensive and sophisticated irrigation system, but in the fifteenth century they suddenly abandoned everything and disappeared. They had depleted local wood supplies by extravagant use, and even worse, they had irrigated with water from the aptly named Salt River and their fields became too salty for crops to grow.

The Buffalo

As already mentioned, a cold snap lasting several centuries was wonderful for the grasses of the prairies and the buffalo proliferated. When the Spanish brought horses to America after 1500, some escaped, and by 1850 some 2 million were wild on the prairies, competing with the buffalo for pasture. But the competition from horses was minor. By 1800 there were between 40 and 60 million buffalo on the prairies, more than there had ever been. It was not the Indian but the white man who was mainly responsible for the slaughter of the buffalo—reduced to fewer than 1,000 by 1895. "Buffalo Bill" Cody, who was hired to kill buffalo to feed the people building the railroad, and other white hunters killed an enormous number.

But the Indians also contributed. After they had acquired both horses and firearms they ate buffalo in unbelievable quantities—more than five pounds a day. The early Indians drove buffalo off cliffs, as already mentioned, and most of the carcasses simply rotted in a heap at the foot of the cliff. But it was much worse after the Indians acquired horses and firearms. Then they hunted buffalo for delicacies and totems—tongues, fetuses, or heads—leaving the rest of the carcass to rot.

In the south, the Indians also came close to wiping out the deer, not for food, but for their skins, which they traded to the white man for guns and clothing. In the north, the Indians killed millions of beavers to supply Europeans with hats. When the Indians finally began to apply the basic principles of resource management, it was at the urging of the Hudson Bay Company, the middleman in the fur trade.

But Krech in his book also argues a larger point. The Indian belief system was not an earlier version of environmentalism, as some modern apologists would have it, but the product of an animist religion. There were taboos against letting any animals escape from the hunt because of a belief that doing so would jinx the next hunt. And many Indians believed in reanimation or reincarnation. The idea that killing animals in large numbers would lead to their extinction made no sense to them. Many of the plains Indians believed that the Great Spirit would reward them for killing lots of animals by creating even more of them. They believed that any depletion of animal stocks was caused not by over-hunting but as punishment for failing to obey the Great Spirit's wishes.

Krech argues that the notion that America was a wilderness existing in a state of ecological balance is nonsense. For centuries upon centuries, Indians had intervened drastically and unwisely by pursuing a combination of self-interest and religious belief.

Customs and Religion

Many Indian tribes recognized a Great Spirit, but it was usually vaguely defined. The elements, such as storm and wind, were often thought of as gods. The Sun, the moon, and the stars, and sometimes a particular constellation were also regarded as gods. And sometimes there were animal gods, such as the bear.

Many Indian tribes had tales about a trickster, often a coyote but sometimes a rabbit, giving a picture of the world poised endlessly on the brink of miracle and disaster. Like the clown in other cultures, the trickster is often lazy, lecherous, cowardly, and deceitful, making people laugh by flouting authority and breaking taboos. Often he was too clever by half, and ended up being outwitted himself.

The Inuit, as already mentioned, were the last to cross over from Siberia to Alaska, and they continued to inhabit the arctic region from Alaska to Greenland. The word, Inuit, is their own, and means simply "humankind." The word, Eskimo, was apparently an Algonquin term meaning "eater of raw meat," which the Inuit regard as pejorative. They had no formalized system of beliefs about the gods, except their folk tales. A season of successful hunting would end in feasting and drinking, but this was also the time to bury food to be dug up in the spring when it was needed to tide them over until regular hunting could begin.

The Inuit got most of their food from the sea—fish and seals—and it was the home of the Old Woman of the Sea. The name of the Old Woman varied, but in the central area it was Sedna, the mother of all the creatures of the sea. The Inuit also had myths about the Sun, the moon, and various constellations of stars. Some tribes also had beliefs about ancestral spirits.

Contact with any of the spirits was through the shaman. Usually a candidate for shaman at puberty wandered in a deserted area, fasting, until he had a vision, a visit from one of the spirits. Following this, he would become an apprentice to an older shaman to learn the skills of curing illness, controlling the weather, divining the movements of fish, seal, and other game, and foretelling the future. The only kind of religious gathering among the Inuit was impromptu attendance at a shaman's display of shouting and drum beating until he fell into trance, during which he would make his prophesies.

Further south, across what are now Canada and the northern United States was a vast coniferous forest, too cold to support maize. In these forests nomadic peoples like the Cree, the Innu, and the Dene hunted caribou, moose, elk, deer, and beaver. In the snow-bound winter, they fished through holes in the ice, scouted for hibernating bears, and dug out beaver from their lodges. In the autumn they made pemmican by pounding meat with caribou fat and berries and preserved it in birch-bark containers. They traveled the lakes and streams in birch-bark canoes. Their clothing of skins protected them from the cold in the winter and from the hordes of mosquitoes in the summer.

The Indians of the northern forests believed in an Earth spirit who was the mother of the animals and also in a supernatural being of the sky. But their religion mostly concerned a close relationship with their ancestors who were always nearby watching over them. The Great Spirit was a vague generality that did not have contact directly with the shaman. After agriculture developed, myths of the stars and the seasons appeared. For example, among the Algonquin, who had a rudimentary agriculture but still relied mainly on hunting, there was a cycle of stories emphasizing the rhythm of the seasons. Henry Wadsworth Longfellow's "Song of Hiawatha" was based on these legends, although the historical Hiawatha was actually an Iroquois chief who was one of the founders of the Five Nations, as described below.

There were usually two village sites; one for winter and one for summer. The move from one to the other was a time of festival when stories were told and myths enacted, including myths of how the world was created. The trickster appears in many of these myths, as he does in those of many Indian tribes.

In the northern part of the far west, from southern Alaska through British Columbia and south to Northern California, lived such tribes as the Kwakiutl, whose life revolved around fishing and hunting. With stone axes and adzes they felled giant trees and made them into dugout canoes forty to fifty feet long that were able to hold crews of 30 to 40 men. On the sea, they not only fished but hunted whales as well. On land, they hunted deer, caribou, bear, and a variety of small animals. In spring, their life centered on harvesting the enormous numbers of salmon that swarmed up the Columbia river in spring to spawn.

Food was so abundant these people never developed agriculture. They lived in permanent villages and developed a complex, hierarchical society with a rich ceremonial life. Houses differed from tribe to tribe, but all were square or rectangular made of heavy wooden posts and beams with cedar planking for walls and roofs. Although there was little knowledge of metal, they beat out nodules of natural copper into ceremonial, shield-shaped plates that were of great value as a symbol of wealth. Later, copper for the ceremonial plates was taken from the bottoms of wrecks of the white man's ships.

Fishing expeditions, hunting, and war required larger groups and better organization than that found in the northern forests. Northwestern society was organized into totemic groups similar in some ways to clans of the highland Scots. The clans were named for animals that played a role in tribal myths—the Bear People, Beaver People, Salmon People, Killer Whale People, and so on. They carved totem poles that were something like a family crest. Wars against neighboring groups were frequent to take vengeance and to capture slaves.

The potlatch festival was the main ceremonial event. Its purpose was not trade, but to display wealth by giving it away or destroying it. Valuable goods were often thrown on a fire, and no matter how hot the fire became, moving away from the heat would bring shame. Mainly, however, the goods were gifts to those invited, although those who received gifts were bound in honor to hold a potlatch of their own on some later occasion and give back more goods than they had received. The mythology of the Indians of the northwest was based on the world of nature. Spirit powers could act as humans but change into animal form at will. They also had a myth of the Old Woman of the Sea and vague references to the Chief of the Sky People. Shamans saw the spirit powers in visions, but they were not formally worshiped.

When creatures of the natural world were deliberately and needlessly injured, the spirits took vengeance. For example, the reason the salmon existed was to be food for humankind. But if some people caught more than they needed and then threw the fish away or tortured the salmon, the spirits would take retribution—often in the form of the explosion of a volcano!

Still further south, in the prairies of southern Canada and in a great wedge through the middle of what is now the United States, was a huge area of windswept plains and grassland with tremendous herds of buffalo. The climate was dry and the winters extremely cold. When the white man came, the plains Indians practiced agriculture as much as hunting. They cultivated maize, several varieties of beans and squash, and like the Iroquois they had fruit plantations. They hunted both buffalo and deer. Lacking horses, they would drive the buffalo over cliffs whenever they could or trap stragglers in pitfalls. Sometimes they built stockaded corrals into which they would try to drive stragglers at the rear of the herd.

In the summer, they followed the migration of the animals and lived in tipis, tents made of animal skins. They had domesticated dogs that were harnessed to a travois of trailing wooden poles on which were loaded the tents and supplies. In the winter they returned to large, earth houses near rivers and their garden plantations. The earth houses were made of tree trunks erected as pillars to support a frame with a smoke vent. In a circle around the pillars a low palisade of stakes to form the walls of a sunken room, and poles were arranged to slope up to the central frame and covered with hides. Clothing consisted of leggings and skirt for the men and a loose shift or skirt for the women—all made of animal skins. During the eighteenth century after the Spanish had re-introduced horses to America, some tribes like the Dakota gave up agriculture and depended entirely on the buffalo, following them in their seasonal migrations north and south. Some like the Cheyenne and Crow moved westward and abandoned farming. Some, like the Mandan and Pawnee, left their villages to pursue the buffalo for only part of the year.

There were great tribal gatherings in the spring and fall festivals, and offerings were made to the spirits of the Earth and the sky and to the tribal ancestors. Various games were played—one similar to field hockey and another with a hoop and pole. Most of the young men belonged to ritual societies, such as the "Dogs," the "Bulls," and the "Stone Hammers" that had public duties to perform such as maintaining order in the camp, organizing war parties, or hunts. At the spring and fall festivals, they performed sacred rituals.

The religious beliefs centered on an ill-defined supernatural power that manifested itself in the Sun, the moon, stars, in animals and birds, and in natural forces such as the wind, thunder, and rain. The spirit world communicated with people through dreams and visions, and young men (and sometimes women) would go alone to some desolate place to fast and pray to induce such visions. The Sun Dance was also an occasion for seeking visions. The men taking part ran skewers through their chest muscles and ran a line from the skewers to a large pole. Then in the ceremony they leaned back so that nearly all their weight was hanging from the skewers and line, and then they slowly circled the pole. A warrior who succeeded in staying on his feet until Sunset won good fortune for his tribe.

The medicine bundle was also central to the religion of the Indians of the Great Plains. It contained relics of ancestors and other articles of religious significance. It could change hands, usually only within the family, and then only at a high price.

The bodies of the dead were painted, dressed in their best robes, and a buffalo skin was wrapped tightly around the body and then other robes were soaked in water and bandaged tightly to exclude any air. The body was then placed on a scaffold raised by tree trunks ten to fifteen feet above the ground and supplied with arms and provisions. Later, when the flesh had dried away, the remains were buried in rock crevices.

In the southwest, in what is now Arizona and New Mexico lived the Navajo, as we saw, a relatively recent arrival. The speculation is that because of being the latest arrival, they ended up with the harshest, least desirable land. They lived by gathering edible roots, seeds, and berries and hunting small game. They learned some agricultural techniques from the Pueblo Indians, earlier settlers. When Spanish introduced domestic livestock, they became sheepherders. They then spent summers living in temporary brush-wood shelters, and moved back to earth-covered timber huts called hogans. Their gods were the spirits of maize, the rainbow, the Sun, thunder, and the powers of nature. A powerful shaman advised on future events, and guided people in the proper rituals for curing illnesses and ensuring good crops. A boy of eleven or twelve would go out into the wild alone without seeking food, and praying to the spirits for help and protection. After he had a vision, he would return to his village and recount it to his relatives. If they found it propitious, he would join the appropriate religious society where he would learn the chants and rituals. The shaman performed rituals accompanied by a chant and by a sand painting depicting the spirits in different colored sand, charcoal, corn meal, and pollen.

The Eastern Woodlands

The Indians of the eastern woodlands, as we saw, were the first in North America to come into contact with the white man. Before the contact, the rivers and lakes provided the Indians with good fishing, and those who lived along the shore harvested a bounty of shellfish. They hunted deer and moose, and the fur-bearing beaver, marten, squirrel, and fox. And by the time the white man came, maize was playing an important role in their diet. The salmon and shad were so plentiful during the spring run that the Indians buried a fish to serve as fertilizer beside each grain of corn they planted. Their fields were carefully tended and after a few years, they would move on to a new location to let the fields lie fallow for ten to fifteen years.

Their villages were made up of two or three long houses set among the fields protected by a stockade. The long house was constructed of a framework of bent saplings in the form of arches fifteen to twenty feet high and twenty feet wide as the base. It was 100 feet long, and covered with strips of birch and elm bark to make a waterproof covering. Screens divided the long house into family compartments, each with its own ring of stones for a fire and a smoke hole in the roof.

People traveled on foot or by birch bark canoe. Canoes were light enough so that a single person could carry one on a portage from one stream or lake to another, and a larger one by two people.

The men wore leggings, a breechclout, and a cape for warmth. Women wore a knee-length skirt and a large skin cloak in bad weather.

A wampum belt was made of a large numbers of cylindrical beads of white and purple shell. It served as an article of exchange, and a string of wampum the length of a man's arm was a unit of value over the whole of the northeast. Wampum belts also served as mnemonic devices, recording tribal history. Keepers of the wampum were important tribal dignitaries. At the great annual tribal gatherings, the belts of wampum were brought out and the stories associated with them recited to the people so that everyone would be reminded of the history of the tribe.

The Iroquois formed a federation of five separate "nations" who spoke the same language—the Seneca, Cayuga, Onondaga, Oneida, and Mohawk. The Five Nations was formed in the sixteenth century as a response to the depredations of the Algonquins through the leadership of a chief of the Mohawk tribe, Haio hwa tha—pronounced Hiawatha by white men – and already mentioned. Apparently Hiawatha's vision was to unite all the Indians of North America, but as it turned out the Five Nations became involved in the wars between the French and the English, and their tribal organization was undermined. They were able to bring peace in their own territories, but they ended up organizing wars against other tribes. On one occasion they even raided the Black Hills, over 1,000 miles away, and brought back captives to be tortured to death at one of the great festivals by the ceremony of fire. The captives shared with most Indians the idea that they show no fear of pain and that they should continue singing the death song until they finally lost consciousness.

The Indians of the eastern woodlands are reported to have worshiped a Great Spirit much like Odin or Zeus, although it is suspected that this particular concept derived from their very early contact with the white man. Day to day life seems to have been governed by spirits of the river, rain clouds, the Sun, the moon, and the stars, particularly the Morning Star. They also believed that somewhere there was a land of the dead.

The Southeastern Woodlands

The most highly developed of the Indians north of Mexico were the mound builders of the southern part of what is now the United States from the Atlantic to the Mississippi. They built wooden chief's houses and ceremonial centers on top of earthen mounds, some in the form of sacred animals. A particularly spectacular one is the Great Serpent mound in Adams County, Ohio.

In the early 1600s a crew of English sailors on a raid against the Spanish in Mexico were captured and taken to Mexico City. Most died of torture or were executed, but five escaped and made it on foot all the way to the New England coast, where an English ship picked them up. It is a measure of the times that in questioning them for military information about the Spanish, the English authorities stretched the English sailors on the rack. They told a satisfying story of Natchez, Creek, and Choctaw country describing fine palaces built on Earth mounds and decorated with pearls and diamonds, fine clothes, jewelry, and plates made of gold.

The culture of the mound builders declined long before the coming of the white man, although it is likely that the Natchez, at least, were their direct descendants. However, it is known that the Creeks and others also had myths about a Trickster, who in this case took the form of a rabbit. The stories of black slaves took up some of the Indian myths, and the Trickster has survived as Br'er Rabbit.

The Southwest Mesa Dwellers

The most highly organized Indian communities were the pueblo dwellers of the Southwest. In pre-Columbian times, their villages were scattered from the plains of Texas to Nevada and to northern Mexico in the south. Today they are found in Arizona and New Mexico. In the eleventh and twelfth centuries their extraordinarily fertile lands were devastated by drought. Raids from the nomadic tribes to the north forced them to find defensible sites from which they could cultivate their remaining fields. For a time, they became cliff dwellers, and the remains of their remarkable villages can still be seen. Later they moved to the flat-topped mesas to build their towns. These were large complexes of multi-storied houses arranged around one or more courtyards, so the single-room dwellings were a little like the cells in a beehive. Access was by wooden ladders, which could be drawn up in time of danger. Underneath the courtyards were underground chambers called *kivas*, the meeting rooms of the various religious societies. Supernatural beings, such as animal spirits, tribal ancestors, and natural forces such as rain, wind, cloud, and thunder were called *Kachinas*. Religious ceremonies were held in the kivas, and members of the religious societies also conducted parades in which they dressed in costumes to represent the Kachinas.

Weaving for both clothing and rugs was highly developed, using a type of native cotton until the Spanish introduced sheep and then it was done in wool.

Another highly developed craft was pottery. Pots were made by pinching coils of clay together, smoothing out the surface, firing, and then decorating with various designs. Sometimes their fields were several miles away, and in troubled times, the warriors went to protect the women who worked the fields. The Spanish explorers gave them the name, *pueblo*, Spanish for village.

Among the Pueblo Indians there were four distinct languages. Some had been settled cultivators in pre-drought times; others were migrants from the west.

Along the eastern seaboard some Indians had begun to cultivate maize and other crops, but continued to rely heavily on fishing and hunting. Along the valleys of the Mississippi and its tributaries lived maize farmers, gatherers, and hunters who ventured into the plains for only part of the year.

In California and Oregon, the more temperate climate supported a denser population who lived on the shore primarily by fishing and inland by gathering acorns and a profusion of wild plants.

On the other side of the continent on the east coast from the Gulf of Mexico up to New England, was a humid region of mountains, valleys, and coastal plains densely covered in deciduous and coniferous woodland. In some areas, several tribes formed confederations, such as the Six Nations. In the southern part of the region the people were predominantly farmers, although hunting and, especially along the Gulf, fishing, remained important. They lived in permanent villages, tended gardens of maize, beans, squash, and other crops, and practiced ceremonies and rituals such as the Green Corn Dance.

Finally, in the hot, dry hills and lowlands of Arizona and New Mexico, several different cultures co-existed—semi-nomadic peoples such as the Navajo and Apaches, desert farmers and food-gatherers like the Tohono and O'odham, and Pima, Tewa, Zuni, and others who built compact well-protected pueblos of adobe and lived by an ingenious form of agriculture which allowed them to develop the highest population density north of Mexico.

United States Indian Policy

From the earliest times, the English government and its colonial representatives conducted business with the Indians through a diplomatic process of negotiating treaties as if the Indians were sovereign nations. The colonists were greatly outnumbered and the treaty system, accompanied by gifts and trade, was cheaper in terms of both blood and treasure. Treaties were so embedded in the pattern of relations between the colonists and the Indians that Congress and the states automatically continued the practice.

During the American Revolution, the Cherokees sided with the English and attacked back settlements during the summer of 1776. Colonial militia from Virginia and the Carolinas retaliated, burning fifty Indian towns and their fields of growing crops, destroyed tens of thousands of bushels of corn, and killed or confiscated livestock. Many thousands of Cherokees were driven into the forest to eke out an existence on nuts, berries, and game. The treaties the Cherokees were forced to sign in 1777 cost them all their lands east of the Blue Ridge.

In the north, Iroquois warriors joined the British and Loyalist militias to ravage the countryside of New York and Pennsylvania. But the tide turned and by the end of the war only two of the thirty Iroquois towns remained intact and most of the Iroquois had become displaced persons.

The Peace of Paris gave the United States the territory bounded by the Great Lakes on the north, the Mississippi on the west, and on the south, the thirty-first parallel where Spanish Florida began. The United States acquired England's territorial rights in America by the right of conquest.

South of the Ohio, where it had no land claims, Congress hoped only for peace. But the states had expansionist policies as ambitious as those of Congress. Georgia dictated a peace to some Creek headman that took three million acres. Other Creek leaders made a secret agreement with the Spanish in Florida to expel the Georgians. Under the Articles of Confederation, Georgia stood alone. But when the Constitution was adopted, Georgia could at least in theory expect the support of the armies of a central government.

The northern Indian tribes united to reject the right of conquest treaties, and they launched military attacks to preserve the Ohio River boundary. In the face of all this, Congress reversed its policy, and in the Northwest Ordinance of 1787, it repudiated the right of conquest policy.

In 1789, George Washington invited a delegation of Creeks to New York to discuss relations between them and the United States. The resulting Treaty of New York declared the rights of conquest treaties invalid. Even so, the Creeks ceded a large part of the territory already occupied by Georgians to the United States, since ousting the settlers would be impossible. The United States agreed to guarantee the boundaries of the Creek Nation, and forbade any treaties between the Indians and the states. It was a victory for the Creek Indians, but it enabled the United States government to take control of Indian affairs in the south, and it freed the government to deal with the resistance of the Indians north of the Ohio.

Following the ratification of the Constitution in 1789, Washington took office. His commander of artillery during the Revolution, Henry Knox, had been Secretary of War under the Articles of Confederation, and Washington kept him in the post. Knox believed that most of the trouble stemmed from the aggressive expansion by the states into Indian lands and concluded that they must find a way to control the states and their citizens. Knox was determined both to achieve peace and to base dealings with the Indians on honor and justice. The United States, he said, could gain nothing by war. Knox blamed Georgia for the bloodshed and believed the only way to ensure peace was to restrain the states by denying them a role in Indian affairs. The Constitution addressed this issue when it gave Congress the sole right to regulate commerce with the Indians, but Knox wanted further authority. He found it in Article I, Section 10, of the Constitution, which said, "No State shall enter into any Treaty..." So if Knox could confirm the treaty process as the proper vehicle for conducting relations with the Indians, he could deny the states any legitimate right to interfere. Washington agreed and recommended to the Senate that the proper procedure for dealing with the Indians was through the negotiation of treaties, which would then be submitted to the Senate for its advice and consent. In 1790, the Senate agreed.

Washington and Knox had agreed to the Treaty of New York partly because they believed that Georgia was the aggressor and partly because they didn't want to be saddled with two wars at once. They preferred to settle the matter of the Ohio settlements peacefully, but the refusal of the Indians' western alliance to give up its commitment to the Ohio River meant that war was inevitable and that it was also just. The goal of their policy was expansion of the United States into the lands of the Indians, but they were absolutely serious in their insistence that their Indian policy should be rooted in honor and justice. Their problem was how to accomplish "expansion with honor." Their solution was to purchase the Indian property and then open the lands for settlement.

They believed that if they could enforce the treaty and prevent American settlers from encroaching on Indian lands, peace could be maintained. But as settlement proceeded, the game would flee and the Indians would either follow the game or settle down and become farmers like the Americans. It would be an orderly and peaceful advance, although slower than their people wanted.

Neither Washington nor Knox believed there was any alternative to expansion. They believed the Indians should and would exchange their wild way of life for a civilized one. They believed that the Indians were equal in mental and other abilities to the white man, so by changing their way of life they could become exactly like other Americans. Civilized Indians would see that it was to their advantage to sell their surplus land and invest in their farms. To implement these ideas Congress passed the Trade and Intercourse acts beginning in 1790 and elaborated them until 1802 when the policy was firmly established. This law served as the basis for the United States Indian policy until a sharply divergent policy was adopted in 1834.

So the Indians were sovereign nations not the subjects of any particular state. Until 1871, relations with the Indians were by the treaty system and during that period the Senate ratified some 400 treaties.

Washington and Knox wanted to encourage trade with the Indians that was fair and honest and they wanted to hold down prices. The idea was to keep peace but also to build a loyalty to the United States that would break the economic ties that bound the Indians to the British and the Spanish. In 1796, Congress passed legislation setting up a system of trading posts called the "factory system," and it worked well until 1822, when the political power of private trading companies finally succeeded in destroying it.

When Jefferson became president, he was in full agreement with these policies. He was enthusiastic about the idea of civilizing the native peoples and deeply committed to expansion of United States westwards. The Americans never understood the division of labor among Indians, that the women were the cultivators and the men the hunters. The policy that Washington and Knox devised and that Jefferson embraced actually meant a reversal of the Indians gender roles. Jefferson was also deeply convinced of the need to acquire more land to accommodate the growing American population.

When France acquired Louisiana from Britain, Jefferson was horrified at the prospect of Napoleon becoming a neighbor. This led him to the Louisiana Purchase, first to safeguard the Mississippi River as a commercial artery. The fear that French agents would stir up the Indians led him to acquire the Indian title to as much of the land that fronted on the Mississippi as possible and as quickly as possible. Between 1803 and 1809, the United States negotiated 15 treaties of cession with the Indian owners of the land in the Indiana Territory. It was in a sense a reversal of the civilizing notion—buying the hunting lands from the uncivilized Indians would force them to become civilized or starve.

In the south settlers continued to cross the boundary and squat on Indian land, Georgia and North Carolina continued to pursue aggressive policies of land acquisition. Then the squatters would demand protection.

For an Indian male to become a farmer, defied the spirits, but males could become stock raisers and horse traders. In the south, the destruction of the deer for their hides undercut the southern Indian economy. In the north, luxury fur and beaver pelts were still going strong and they had not yet been decimated. During and after the Revolution large numbers of blacks found their way into Creek and Cherokee territory as captives, escapees, or the property of Loyalist refugees. Cherokee and Creek men discovered that they could escape the collapsing hunting economy by becoming slaveholders and a highly visible few did.

In the north, there was a rise of prophets espousing militant pan-Indianism, of whom Tecumseh was one. Finally at the Battle of Horseshoe Bend in March 1814, Andrew Jackson crushed the nativist opposition. The prophets and their followers were dead, in hiding, or in exile, and the military power of the Creeks was shattered.

The bloody warfare in the west that coincided with the War of 1812 revealed that expansion with honor had failed. The Treaty of Ghent ending the war of 1812 was a watershed, confirming the independence of the United States. William Henry Harrison destroyed the village of Tippecanoe and was later elected president with the slogan, "Tippecanoe and Tyler, too."

The war with Mexico and the annexation of the southwest and California completed the conquest of what is now the United States.

Chapter 17

The South America Indians

I n South and Central America three groups of Indians developed distinct civilizations and cultures—the Aztecs, the Maya, and the Inca.

The Aztecs

The Aztecs controlled the Valley of Mexico from 1200 A.D. until the Spanish under Hernando Cortes conquered them in 1521. Their religion emphasized human sacrifice, and many of their wars were fought simply to obtain captives for the sacrifices demanded by the gods.

The people lived in adobe huts with thatched roofs. The main staple was corn prepared as tortillas. They also grew beans, squash, avocados, tobacco, and hemp. Chili was the main spice. Turkeys and dogs were the only domesticated animals. Chocolate made from the cacao bean was the favorite drink. As noted earlier, people whose main drink was something like tea or chocolate that required boiling water had a much lower death rate than people whose main drink was water alone. Clothing was cotton or a cloth made from the century plant. The cloth was sewn into a breechcloth, a cape for warmth and protection from the elements, and sandals. Women wore short skirts and sleeveless blouses.

The capital city was built on the shallow waters of Lake Texcoco. There were both streets and canals. Earth causeways and movable bridges connected the city to the mainland. Aqueducts carried fresh water from springs in a nearby hill. The population was about 100,000.

The center of the city was a ceremonial plaza surrounded by a wall. Inside were large, flat-topped pyramids crowned with temples. A huge rack containing thousands of human skulls of sacrificed victims also stood in the area.

The usual sacrifice involved tearing out the beating heart of a living victim with a knife made of obsidian. One of the gods was Quetzalcoatl, the plumed serpent. Legend was that this god had sailed across the sea but would return.

Mexico city was larger than any city in Europe when the white man arrived, a vast expanse of canals, plazas, markets, temples and brightly painted houses, shops, and schools. An army of a thousand men kept the streets clean. Waste was removed by barge to be processed as fertilizer. The elite bathed every day. When meeting Spaniards, they often held flowers to their noses to disguise the stench. Mexican religion with its human sacrifice was appalling to the Spanish.

The Aztecs had no alphabet, but they developed a rebus writing using pictures and symbolic characters. A few of their books survive. Aztec soldiers fought with bows and arrows. They also had swords made of a hard wood set with obsidian like the teeth of a saw.

Aztec history records kings from 1375 A.D. to Montezuma II who was king when Cortes entered the capital in 1519 A.D. At first Montezuma welcomed the Spaniards, apparently believing that they were actually the god Quetzalcoatl and his followers returning as the legend had foretold. Later Montezuma plotted against the Spaniards, and Cortes took him prisoner. Still later the Aztecs launched an armed rebellion. Cortes had 1,000 Spaniards and several thousand Indians from tribes that had been subjugated by the Aztecs. He also had guns, horses, and iron weapons. When Cortes landed in Mexico, the population was about 25 million. In 1600 it was about one million. The cause was partly the Spanish slaughter, but mainly it was smallpox and the other white man's diseases that the Spaniards had brought with them and for which the Mexican population had no immunities.

The Maya

The Mayan civilization developed in Central America, in present-day

Guatemala, British Honduras, El Salvador, Honduras, and part of Mexico including the Yucatan. Its height was in the years from 300 A.D. to the 800s, and the population was about 2 million. Much of their homeland was covered by dense tropical forest from 200 to 600 feet above sea level.

The Maya were the only inhabitants of the Americas to develop an advanced form of writing. They were also successful in astronomy and mathematics, and their architecture and art is admired all over the world. They were short and stocky, with dark skins, black hair, and remarkably round heads. They admired sloping foreheads and flattened the heads of their babies with boards. Mothers also dangled beads in front of babies so they would develop a squint, perhaps to honor the Sun God, who was pictured as cross-eyed.

Maya cities were centers for religious festivals, markets, and courts of justice, but they had no permanent inhabitants. Priests lived in the cities for short periods for religious festivals. The people lived in huts scattered around the countryside.

Their food was corn, beans, and squash, all of which were spiced with chili peppers. They also ate a corn cake similar to today's tortillas. They rarely ate meat, since their only domesticated animals were turkeys and dogs.

They liked to dance, and did so on every possible occasion. But only men were allowed to participate. Almost every city had at least one ball court for a game similar to basketball in which two teams tried to hit a rubber ball through a high vertical stone ring using their knees and hips.

They worshiped a number of gods. Beginning in the 900s their chief god was Kukulcan, a feathered serpent god who was the Mexican Quetzalcoatl under another name. The Maya practiced human sacrifice, but not on the large scale of the Aztec.

Their numbering system was on the base twenty, and numbers were written with dots and dashes.

Mayan architecture featured high stone pyramids with temples on top. The priests climbed to the temple top, and the people assembled in a court below. The Maya never learned the principle of the arch. They used corbelled vaulting, building two walls without windows closer and closer together until they could be roofed with a row of flat stones.

Their agriculture was slash-and-burn, and they used digging sticks to plant seeds. Like the mountain peoples of Southeast Asia today, they let the forest take over after a few years, and cleared another field.

They did not have wheeled vehicles. Their chiefs were carried on litters. Wherever possible trade was done by canoe. People in the lowlands traded jaguar pelts, feathers, copal incense, lime, flint knives, and edible hearts of palm to people in the highlands for the highly prized quetzal feathers, jade, and the volcanic glass obsidian, which was used for knives.

The classic period began about 350 A.D. and reached a peak in the 700s. During the 800s the great cities were abandoned. No one knows why but it may have been a peasant revolt that drove out the priests who ruled.

In the 900s, the Maya of Yucatán and the Guatemalan highlands developed a culture with Mexican influence. Warriors called the Itzás enlarged Chichén Itzá, established a new capital, and ruled a large area until 1450, when dissatisfied city-states rebelled. Yucatán then split into several groups and Mayan art and learning declined.

The Spanish came in the early 1500s, and subdued most of the people with little difficulty. Bishop Diego de Landa ordered that as many as possible of the Mayan bark-cloth books be burned because they contained "nothing but superstitions and falsehoods of the devil." Only three of the books, called codex, survived.

Again the white man's diseases decimated the Maya population as much as his cruelty. About a million and a half of the Maya still live in the area. They speak the Mayan language and follow some of the old religious practices, but they know little about the achievements of their ancestors.

The Inca

The Inca civilization developed in the Andes of present day Peru and at its peak, 1450 to 1532 A.D., included Peru, Chile, Ecuador, and part of Bolivia and Argentina. The population numbered between 3.5 million and 7 million. Each tribe conquered by the Inca had to learn their language, Quechuan. The Spanish conquered the Inca after years of fighting, and then only because the Spanish had firearms, horses, and steel armor.

The Inca capital was at Cuzco at an altitude of 11,000 feet. Here stood the Temple of the Sun, which gleamed with gold and precious stones. At one stage the Inca built a magnificent fortress, Machu Picchu, on top of a high mountain. It was "rediscovered" by Hiram Bingham when he was a professor at Yale.

There were four classes: the ruling class, the nobility, the common people, and slaves. Potatoes were a staple. So was the grain, quinoa. They also ate corn, beans, squash, and tomatoes. Meat consisted of llama and guinea pig. They made a beer from corn, potatoes, or grain.

Religion involved rituals and ceremonies and was concerned mainly with guaranteeing a good food supply, curing illness, and foretelling future events. Ceremonies included dancing, heavy drinking, and animal but not human sacrifice.

Priests used magic to diagnose and treat illness. They practiced trephining, cutting out a portion of the skull. The purpose was probably to let out evil spirits. It is doubtful that it was to relieve pressure on a crushed portion of the skull since some skeletons show as many as three or four such operations.

Buildings were made of stone, some weighing many tons, that thousands of laborers brought from quarries by using rollers, wedges, inclined planes, and ropes. Walls were made without mortar, but the stones were often fitted so tightly that a knife cannot be inserted between them.

The Inca never developed true writing, but they did work out a system of knotted strings to record numbers. These strings were also used as memory aids in reciting Inca history.

They built a superb system of roads with rest houses along the route. A mail system like the American pony express was established using runners stationed every few miles. Messages often traveled 150 miles in a day.

The Spaniards led by Francisco Pizarro with 177 men invaded in 1532. They arranged a meeting with the Inca leader to negotiate a treaty, but ambushed and captured him instead. The Incas gave the Spaniards a ransom of enough gold and silver to fill a room to the height of a man. The Spaniards took the ransom, but rather than releasing the Inca leader, they tried him for crimes under Spanish law and executed him.

The Spaniards imposed heavy taxes on the Incas, and made near slaves of them. The population dropped to less than 2 million, although most of the deaths were probably due to diseases that the Spaniards brought with them, and to which the Latin Americans were not immune.

The Portuguese and the Spaniard

The Portuguese took over eastern Brazil and the Spanish took over most of the rest.

And so it continued until a revolt broke out in Haiti in 1791, which won independence in 1804. This was followed by Simon Bolivar, (1783–1830) who liberated Bolivia, Columbia, Ecuador, Peru, and Venezuela from

Spain. He won a victory over the Spanish at Ayacucho in 1824, which ended the Spanish power in Latin America. Bolivar hoped to form a union of the new South American nations and to form an alliance with the United States but one by one the states withdrew from the union. In 1828 he ruled only Columbia, and he resigned from that in 1830.

The other was Jose de San Martin (1778–1850) an Argentine general who led an army from Argentina that helped win independence for Chile.

Chapter 18

The Polynesians

Several thousand years after the early peoples had passed through and made their way to Australia, Southeast Asia was inhabited by a people who had probably evolved from interbreeding among the first group who had settled there and later Neolithic peoples who arrived from time to time. The results were the ancestors of the Malays, Indonesians, Filipinos, and Polynesians. In their migration south from Southeast Asia, the Polynesians and some of the mountain people of the Philippines were the advance guard, the Indonesians, Malays, and Filipinos were the main body, and the rear guard were the Khmer (Cambodians) and the Cham, remnants of whom now live in the mountains of Vietnam.

Some time after the last ice age these Neolithic, proto-Indonesian people began to move south because of pressure from the other peoples coming east from India and perhaps from the first of the Mongoloids coming down from the north.

As for Micronesia, most are low islands, that is, atolls. It should be noted, first, that atolls with a lagoon but no central island are a very difficult habitat, and, second, that in spite of this people have lived on them for 2,000 years or more. The oceans reached their modern level about 6,000 years ago following the last ice age, and this flooded a great many of the atolls. Coral grows only in relatively shallow water, and it was some time before the coral could catch up and still longer for a central island to build up behind the coral ring. A study of one of the atolls in the Tokelau group showed that it did not become habitable until some time between 2,300 years ago and 1,600 years ago. Except for the very few volcanic high islands the same can be said of most of the other islands in Micronesia.

In the area between island Southeast Asia, coastal New Guinea, and the Bismarck Archipelago, there is a continuous corridor of islands visible from each other. In these islands lived a people anthropologists call the Lapita. What the Lapita people shared was pottery and other similarities resulting from trade rather than culture or race. In any case, the area became a voyaging nursery, like the fjords of Scandinavia.

Parenthetically, clay is not found on atolls, and good quality clay is not found in the high basaltic islands on the eastern side of the Andesite line either. When the Polynesians got to New Zealand, which does have good clay, they had forgotten how to use it.

The Lapita appeared in the Bismarck Archipelago about 3,500 years ago. Within a few centuries different peoples first settled Western Micronesia, on the one hand, and eastern Melanesia and Fiji, on the other. One of these probably came from the mainland of Southeast Asia and the other, the Lapita, hopped from island to island.

DNA data suggest that these pre-Polynesian peoples were derived from a Southeast Asia population who were different from the early settlers of Pleistocene Australia and New Guinea. It shows that the Polynesians are homogenous and the Micronesians are a mix between Polynesians and Melanesians.

Beginning 3,500 years ago, the Lapita culture spread through the islands of what is now Melanesia to Fiji and West Polynesia. The Marianas were settled about 3,000 years ago. Belau and Yap, 2,000 years ago; and the Marquesas also about 2,000 years ago. Hawaii was settled from 1,500 to 1,600 years ago. New Zealand was settled about 800 years ago.

The regions with which we are concerned in this chapter include 1) mainland and island Southeast Asia; 2) Melanesia, to include New Guinea, the Solomons, and Fiji; 3) Micronesia, to include the Carolines and the Marshals; and 4) Polynesia to include Tuvalu, Samoa, the Cooks, Tonga, New Zealand, Hawaii, and Easter Island.

Exploration was toward the prevailing wind. The reason was that this was the only direction that one could be sure of a safe return. A voyage as long as three weeks out would take only one week to return. It was not the fastest rate of advance, but it was the surest way to survive and return.

Fiji must have been reached between 3,500 and 3,000 years ago. The Marquesas were settled about 1,700 years ago and became a dispersal point for people going to the Society Islands. The Society Islands in turn became a dispersal point for voyages to Hawaii, Easter Island, and New Zealand. Hawaii was reached 1,600 years ago. Easter Island was reached at about the same time. New Zealand was settled about 800 years ago; and Chatham, south of New Zealand, was settled about 500 years ago. Voyaging was a tradition that lasted 3,000 years!

The climate from 1,250 years ago to 750 years ago was the so-called Little Climactic Optimum, and it was very favorable for voyaging. The Little Ice Age was from 600 years ago to 150 years ago, and it was not at all favorable.

Race

Australian aborigines derive from a common ancestor of the Dravidian stock, and their closest living relatives are the Veddas of Ceylon and the Todas of southern India. Scientific study of their blood grouping proves that they are *not* Negroid. Australia-New Guinea was an island continent before any of the higher mammals such as deer, rabbits, monkeys, members of the cat family and humans arrived. The Australian aborigines and their dogs must have reached Australia when the last ice age had lowered the sea levels and shortened the distance to make the trip feasible by rafts or crude boats.

Next came the so-called Oceanic Blacks. They occupied New Guinea, driving any remaining Australian aborigines out to join their fellows in Australia and the Negritos into the mountain fastnesses. In response to further influx of still different peoples, some of the Oceanic Blacks moved down along the chain of continental islands, now known as Melanesia, lying southeast of New Guinea. Those who remained became the Papuans and those who moved on became the Melanesians.

Apparently the Melanesians reached Fiji only after the Polynesians had moved on from Fiji to the Pacific islands.

Hawaiian myths tell of a race of dwarfs, the Menehune, who were already present when the Polynesians arrived, but the myths seem to have no substance. Supposedly the Menehune had no plants that were not native to Hawaii, and no colonizing people would have come without plants. Sir Peter Buck, the great authority on the Polynesians, speculates that they could have been driven by storm from the Gilberts and that they retreated to Kauai when the later immigrants came. The trouble with this argument is that if they had been on a fishing trip or some such on which they would not have taken plants, they would not have had women along either. Other speculation is that the Menehune came from the Society Islands, which were peopled by an early group called the Manahune. But the only basis for this idea is the similarity of the names. So the same objections apply, and it seems most likely that the Menehune are a product of the Hawaiian imagination.

Polynesians and Micronesians are different, but both are of Southeast Asian descent. They both have large bodies and strong musculature, which is unusual for people in tropical latitudes. Since large bodied individuals have a crucial advantage in maintaining body temperature, the hypothesis is that these traits developed in island Melanesia from the selective pressure of cold and exposure in a marine environment.

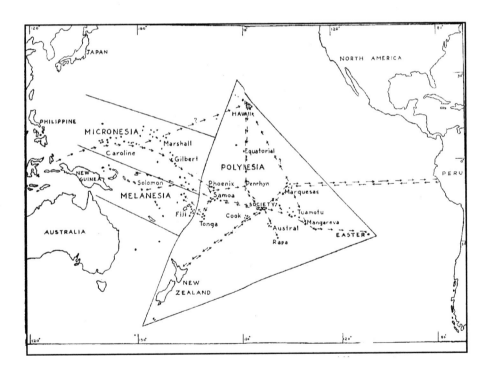

Route

One possible route for the Polynesians would have been the southern course. It goes through the closely set islands of Indonesia, passes the northern coast of New Guinea, and skirts the eastern fringe of the Melanesian chain to Fiji, which was thought to be the rallying place for the Polynesians.

The largest island of the Samoan group is Savai'i. Because the name is the dialectical equivalent of Hawaiki, the traditional homeland of the Polynesians, many observers think that Samoa was the first place they reached after leaving Fiji.

They settled in the Society Islands, and it was from this center that the rest of Polynesia was discovered and settled.

From Havai'i the Polynesians followed Orion's belt for 2,400 miles to Hawaii. Hawaiian tradition is that around the beginning of the twelfth century (1100 A.D.) a number of leaders and their followers voyaged from Tahiti to Hawaii. According to tradition, the last of these was Paao, who came about 1275 A.D.

According to Sir Peter Buck, Polynesian myths attribute the discovery of New Zealand, the Land of the Long White Cloud, to Kupe one thousand years ago in the tenth century. However carbon dating of the earliest New Zealand sites put them at 800 years ago. Also according to Buck, some time later another ancestor named Toi came in search of his grandson, who had been blown away by an offshore wind. In Toi's absence, his grandson returned and then went in search of the grandfather. Both ended up in New Zealand. They had taken with them neither plants nor wives, so they took wives from the previous settlers and became ancestors of mixed tribes.

Tahiti, because of its large size and fertility, came to support the largest population and so the political power passed from Havai'i to Tahiti.

Genealogy

In New Zealand, when reciting the list of ancestors a Maori expert would use a beautifully carved, notched stick to help his memory, touching the various notches as he went. In the Marquesas, it was a knotted braid of coconut fibers. These techniques served both as mnemonic devices and as chronologies of historical events.

Most islands have associated genealogies going back about 500 years, some 20 generations. Names before that refer to ancestors in Hawaiki, Tahiti, Vavau, and so on. The genealogies in Rarotangan go back for 92 generations. At 25 years per generation that would be 2,300 years; at 20 years it would be 1,840 years.

Canoes

The dugout canoe was deep enough to resist sailing sideways—with a big assist from the steering oar. The tendency to capsize was overcome by an outrigger and even better by a double hull. It was the double hull canoe that was used by the Polynesians for voyages in the open ocean. These canoes and those that went out to sea in search of bonito and deep-sea fish were also given an extra free board plank. All the sea-going canoes were large, fast, and safe.

The double hull canoes were often 70 to 80 feet long, and they could hold a lot of people and provisions. Some of the war canoes of Tahiti held as many as 100 men. On voyages of settlement, a double-hull canoe could carry sixty or more passengers, their supplies, and plants to start their agriculture all over again. Sixty passengers would be enough to populate a new island, but we know from traditions that there was almost always more than one such trip.

When Europeans arrived, they saw canoes over 30 meters long, built of planks tied together and with keels of solid logs. They could average 100 to 150 sea miles in 24 hours, and they could carry provisions for two to three months. Water was carried in hollow sections of bamboo. They also collected rainwater in sail-like contraptions. In a month-long voyage they could go thousands of miles. The main limitation was that they could not sail closer than 75 degrees to the wind.

Food

The coconut palm, the banana, and the breadfruit were brought from Southeast Asia to the Polynesian islands by humankind.

The sweet potato is native to South America. The Polynesians must have reached Peru and taken the plant back with them. The Peruvian name for sweet potato is kumar, and the Polynesian name is kumara. Sir Peter Buck speculates that a voyage from Mangareva missed Easter Island, landed in Peru, and returned with the sweet potato. The voyage would have taken three weeks to get to Peru, which is conceivable, but it was not a voyage that would be ventured more than once.

The sweet potato was brought to Polynesia between 1,000 and 1,500 years ago, but it did not arrive in Hawaii and New Zealand until 750 years ago.

When the Polynesians first arrived in New Zealand 800 years ago, they found a population of large, flightless birds, the Moa, consisting of 11 species and about 160,000 individuals. Some Moa were about the size of turkeys, but others were as big as ostriches, standing 10 feet tall and weighing 500 pounds. Skeletons show that they were remarkably similar to some dinosaurs. When the Polynesians arrived the birds had no fear. A man armed with a club could walk up to one and kill it at will. By the time Captain Cook arrived in 1769, none was left.

Moa were long-lived and slow to breed. They laid only one or two eggs at a time and raised perhaps one chick a year. So even a low rate of killing meant that they would not have been able to keep up. Dr. Richard N. Holdaway, chief author of a study on the Moa appearing in the journal *Science*, estimates that the extinction took no more than 160 years and probably much less. In any case, examination of the dismembered remains of the Moa indicates that none was killed after the fourteenth century.

As we saw in Chapter 16, many scientists believe that the mammoths, mastodons, camels, ground sloths, and giant beavers of North America were exterminated by Indians 13,000 years ago. Others think that diseases carried by the Indians and their dogs contributed to the extinction, and still others think that a climate change may have played a critical role. Dr. Ross MacPhee, an expert on mammals at the American Museum of Natural History in New York City, thinks that the Moa extinction also had several causes. He agrees that hunting was the prime cause. But he believes that long before the smaller Moa living in hard-to-reach places became extinct, the Polynesians must have turned to seals and seafood, which were plentiful. So he thinks that disease must have played a big role. The fact that the Kiwi, a small, hard-to-find bird that also has a low reproduction rate did survive is evidence to support his view.

But sea mammals, particularly seals, were abundant. In any case the Polynesians found the living was easy. It was a land that was ideal for hunting, fishing, and gathering.

The New Zealand climate was not suitable for coconut, breadfruit, or banana. The pig and fowl the Polynesians brought with them did not survive, probably because the land had such a wealth of fish and amazing wild-fowl that they were neglected.

The food for a voyage was usually cooked. In atoll areas, the reserve food consisted of ripe pandanus fruit grated into a coarse flour, cooked, dried, and packed in cylindrical bundles with an outer wrapping of pandanus leaves. From volcanic islands, the voyagers carried cooked breadfruit in large baskets. Maoris say that for their voyages, which were later, they also had sweet potatoes. Shellfish were dried. Fowl were carried alive, fed dried coconut meat, and killed when food was needed. For cooking the big canoes had a fireplace laid on a bed of sand and a supply of wood for fuel.

Deep-sea fish, including sharks, were caught. Fresh water was carried in coconut shells, gourds, or lengths of bamboo. Tradition says that crews were also trained in self-restraint. It was not difficult to provide rations for three to four weeks, a long enough period to cross the widest ocean spaces between island groups.

Weapons

The Polynesian weapon was the sling and stones, some of which were specially shaped. The Maori preferred hand-to-hand fighting with clubs.

Language

Vowel sounds are the same as in English. Consonants are always followed by a vowel. Dialects developed through changes in consonant sounds. R and V are used in central and eastern Polynesia, and L and V are used in Western. Sir Peter Buck used the *hamza* (inverted comma) for consonants that have been dropped. It also denotes a glottal stop. In some dialects certain consonants are not fully sounded, and they are also represented by the hamza.

In the Society Islands the K and NG were dropped. So the name of the ancestral homeland is pronounced Havai'i rather than Havaiki. In New Zealand, W is used instead of V, so the name of the ancient homeland is Hawaiki. In the Cook Islands, the H is dropped, so it is 'Avaiki. In Hawaii, where W is used, the largest island is Hawai'i. In Samoa, S replaces H, and V is preferred to W, so it is Savai'i.

Customs

In some chiefly families brothers married sisters in what Buck calls an arrogant assertion that no one else was noble enough.

The Hawaiians had so many taboos they appointed an executioner to make sure that justice was done to those the gods overlooked.

The Maori are grouped into tribes, and each tribe takes its name from ancestors who came in the fourteenth century migration.

Tools

Early on, the Hawaiians discovered obsidian, which is a particularly hard stone and therefore good for cutting tools. It seems to have been traded from tribe to tribe at the tribal borders as amber and jade were traded elsewhere.

The high islands had basalt, which is very hard and makes much better tools than shells.

Jade was found in some places. It was made into war clubs, and also into chisels and adzes that took an edge almost as sharp as steel.

Navigation

At first colonization was upwind—only later was it across and down the wind. The ease of sailing west on the return is what made sailing east possible.

The double canoe had enough range to cover the whole Pacific, although fresh drinking water could be a problem. It was undoubtedly a double canoe that got to South America and brought back the sweet potato.

Cross wind voyages are easier and safer if a course is followed around a triangular course rather than out and back. A triangular Marquesas-Hawaii-Tahiti track is the one most likely for the settlement of Hawaii.

Migrating Birds

The Polynesians undoubtedly noted bird migrations and used such knowledge in their navigation. The long-tailed cuckoo flies from tropical Polynesia to New Zealand in September. Shearwaters fly south in October. In its annual migration, the Golden Plover flies from Alaska to Hawaii—

about 3,500 miles. It arrives exhausted, collapses, and finally gains enough strength to drink, eat, and recover for the next stage south, a much shorter leg. On its return journey, it flies from Tahiti northward to Hawaii, so the Polynesians could infer that land lay in that direction.

Since most stars change their bearing as they rise, they can be used for steering only for about one hour after they rise. But then another star can be chosen. Stars that rise on one's own latitude keep a constant bearing. Typical star paths might have ten in a series. Different star paths are needed for different times of the year. Polaris can be a guide in the northern hemisphere. In the southern hemisphere, the Southern Cross rises inclined on one side, is vertical when it is south of the observer, and leans the other way when it sets. At dawn and sunset, one can use the Sun.

The Polynesians also steered by swells, which are more enduring than waves. The equatorial current was well known and understood. Estimating leeway is usually no more difficult that looking aft toward the wake and comparing it with the line of the hull.

Other signs:
1. Clouds form over islands, both high islands and low islands. If the bottom of a cloud has a green tinge, it is the reflection of a lagoon.
2. Swells are reflected and refracted showing the presence and bearing of land.
3. Swells die down in the lee of the land.
4. Birds that roost on land but feed at sea fly out at dawn and back at dusk.
5. Flotsam indicates land up-wind or up current.
6. It is possible to smell reefs, which is a protection at night.
7. Deep reefs change the color of the sea and shallow reefs affect the waves.
8. Water phosphorescence flashes backwards and forwards in the di rection of the land.

The size of the island screens compensated for a lot of error in dead reckoning. On the traditional route from the Carolines to the Marianas, which lie in a north-south line and present a small target from the south, canoes would steer to the windward (east) of the Marianas, allowing for westerly current and leeway. When they reached the latitude of the target, they turned to a more westerly course, bringing the wind around to the stern, so the canoe could run downwind to cross the island screen obliquely.

On the return journey to the Carolines, most of whom are low-lying, the breadth of the east-west screen makes the landfall secure. The navigators heaved to at night or in bad visibility to avoid missing the low-lying islands. A 30-mile sighting radius makes finding even an atoll practicable.

If one moves east or west, the pattern of stars in the sky looks the same but time changes the aspect because the Earth revolves. But if one goes north one degree of latitude (60 miles) stars will rise one degree higher in angle above the horizon at their maximum.

A star will appear to climb quickly until it nears its zenith, then it will appear to move more slowly and to hover for four or five minutes before its starts to descend. At this point the star is always either due north or south of the observer or directly overhead as it crosses the meridian of longitude of the observer. This meridian passage is a direct indicator of latitude.

If anyone knows what the sky looks like from one place they can tell whether another place lies north or south of it and within the limits of their measuring system by how much. So for anyone who knows the sky, controlling latitude is simple.

Since the Polynesians could not control longitude, they developed a system that let them do without it. The position of an island can be fixed by a method that combines both astronomical knowledge and geographical knowledge. Prehistoric explorers entered the unknown ocean under a largely familiar sky. Afterwards they acquired knowledge of the unknown ocean's geography.

The position of an island could be first learned by dead reckoning from some prior place. A fairly precise estimate of latitude is available in the configuration of the sky. Once a new island is found, the directions to and from it can be known by the whole gamut of course finders, such as horizon, stars, and so on, while the distance is given by the speed and elapsed time of the voyage.

Since most voyages were two-way, the return voyage would help fix the position of the new discovery. So the position of an island can be based on astronomy and the rest by an extension of geographic knowledge by dead reckoning. So longitude was not necessary.

In 1966, as a modern check on what was known of ancient sailing methods, a catamaran (which is relatively steady) sailed from Hawaii to New Zealand using nothing but native methods. The skipper sighted up the mast to measure zenith angle. He could not do better than a degree if the star was more than 5 degrees from the vertical. His error at landfall was 26 miles. At 26 miles experienced Pacific sailors can still conventionally detect land by various sea-signs.

Like the Vikings, the Polynesians used latitude sailing. In latitude sailing, even if you lose track of your position by dead reckoning, you can still get safely home. First, go to the latitude of the home island while still upwind of it. Then run with the wind along that latitude.

Experiment shows that the error in estimating latitude from the stars is matched by the ability to detect land from offshore.

Reaching Hawaii required going across the wind. Reaching New Zealand required going across the wind and then downwind.

A traditional concept widespread in Oceania was "compasses" directed toward stars, the Sun, winds, and swells. The star compass for the Carolines has 32 named points directed toward most islands and marked by the rising and setting positions of stars. Altair, the Big Bird constellation, is the cardinal point. It has celestial latitude of 8.5 degrees N and passes through the zenith of the Carolines. There is also a north-south axis through the Pole Star to the upright Southern Cross.

Navigators knew the star courses to many other islands. But the requirements on memory were great. For example, one set of informants had to know the courses radiating out from 18 islands, typically up to a dozen named islands in each case.

Caroline navigators were taught to recognize eight sea waves—one from each octet of the compass. The most important were the swells from the north, northeast, and east in the northern winter trade-wind season. In the voyaging season, south and southeasterly swells mark the southern winter trade winds, while in late summer, when there are westerly winds, swells come from that quarter.

Commonly two or more swells run across each other and sailors orient themselves by the way the waves interact and how the canoe is felt to move as it passes through them.

In the Carolines, the traditional system of orientation and dead reckoning is called *etak*. Tupaia, the Society islander who traveled with Captain Cook, was able to point the direction of his home island from wherever he traveled with Cook. It is not known just how he was able to do it, but surely etak had something to do with it. In etak, the canoe is visualized as being stationary while the islands move under the stars around it. Etak is a system that integrates all of the known information of rate, time, geography, and astronomy.

Currents can be detected out of sight of land in the pattern of ripples on the surface and with more breezes in the way that whitecaps fall.

Traditional Polynesian navigation systems required memorizing vast amounts of information and then applying it at sea. Much of the lore was embedded in chants. Various birds, fish, turtles, whales, and so on with known idiosyncrasies might be seen occasionally or searched for when one is lost.

Chapter 19

The Indonesians and Filipinos

In Indonesia wet rice cultivation was used in Java and in Bali very early. Because wet rice cultivation is highly productive and because it requires a well-organized and fairly stable society, it is no accident that the people of Java and Bali developed a more elaborate civilization before other parts of Indonesia.

From very early times, trade was a dominant influence on Indonesia, since the peoples of both India and China sought its products. Even the Romans knew about the Spice Islands, as Ptolemy wrote in the second century A.D.

Nutmeg and cloves were the most prized of the spices. The major source were some tiny islands, the Moluccas, now Moluku. In the days before refrigeration spices not only gave meat an exotic taste, but also helped to preserve it—or at least to mask the taste of decomposition! The spices were also used for perfumes and incense and for medicines.

Sumatra had gold, pepper, and benzoic, an aromatic gum treasured by the Chinese. Other Indonesian products were ivory, tortoise, rhinoceros horn, which is still used by the Chinese as a medicine, cardamom, ebony, camphor wood, aloes, pearls, coral, amber, and the semi-precious stone cornelian.

In the seventh century A.D., several Hindu-Buddhist kingdoms arose in Sumatra. The most powerful was the *Srivijaya*, a commercial sea power, controlling the straits between Sumatra and Malaya. In Java, at about the same time, kingdoms arose that depended on agriculture rather than trade. An example is Mataram, which encompassed the present-day Yogyakarta and Surakarta.

By the end of the tenth century, East Java became more prominent, culminating in the Majapahit kingdom. The Javanese culture that developed was a syncretism of Hinduism and Buddhism and spread to Bali.

Other than Marco Polo and a few other adventurers, the first Europeans to come to Indonesia were the Portuguese. With the spice trade and the Moluccas clearly in their minds, they rounded the Cape of Good Hope in 1498, and captured Goa in India in 1510, which provided them a base. The next year they arrived in Moluccas and built a fort.

The Portuguese hold was tenuous—a series of stepping-stones largely for trade went from Portugal to Angola on one side of Africa, to Mozambique on the other, to Goa in India, Moluccas in Indonesia, and Macao in China. Eventually, of course, Indonesia became a Dutch colony and gained its independence only after World War II.

The major spice in the spice trade was nutmeg. In the eighteenth century, Connecticut came to be known as the nutmeg state—not because Connecticut grew nutmegs or even because it had much of a role in the nutmeg trade but because its people carved fake nutmegs from wood!

The Philippines

The first people to arrive in the Philippines were the Negritos, although the exact date remains a mystery. After 3000 B.C. groups of Indonesians and Malayans arrived. Arab missionaries arrived after the 1300s and 1400s, and converted the Moros of Mindanao and the Sulu islands to Islam, the Moslem religion.

The first white men to arrive were Europeans under Ferdinand Magellan. They anchored in what was Cebu harbor in 1521, during the first round the world voyage in history. Magellan was killed while helping one Filipino group fight another, and his fleet sailed soon after.

In 1543, Roy Lopez de Villalobos visited and named the islands Las Filipinas in honor of the Prince who became King Philip II of Spain.

The first permanent Spanish colony was established on Cebu in 1565. The founder, a Spanish general, Miguel Lopez de Legaspi established Manila in 1571. None of the Filipinos, except the Moros, offered any serious opposition to the Spanish.

The Spanish catholic priests, friars, were the most powerful of the Spanish, and they converted the people to Catholicism. They built many churches and a few schools, and participated in the government. The friars worked with the village chief, who was usually a Spanish officer.

Some Filipinos tried to revolt but the Spanish put down every revolt with dispatch. Then in 1834, the Spanish opened Manila to foreign trade, which they thought would be profitable. The economy of the country improved and wealthy Filipinos began sending their children to school in Manila and Europe. When these students returned home, they tried to make the Spanish improve social and political conditions. One of the early leaders was Jose Rizal. He worked for reform until 1896, when the Spanish arrested him. He was arrested by the Spanish in 1896, charged with trying to start a revolution, and executed at the age of thirty-five.

Emilio Aguinaldo, a Filipino municipal officer, led a revolt in 1896. In 1897, the Spanish promised to limit the power of the friars and the Spanish village officers if Aguinaldo would end the revolt and leave the country. Aguinaldo agreed and departed for Shanghai.

In 1898 a rebellion in Cuba resulted in a stalemate between the Spanish rulers and the Cubans fighting for independence. The "yellow press" Hearst and Joseph Pulitzer carried seriously exaggerated reports and agitated for intervention. Pro-Spanish riots took place in Havana and an American battleship, the Maine, was sent to Havana. An explosion on February 15 blew up the ship, killing 260 Americans. "Remember the Maine" became a popular slogan, and on April 25, the United States declared war against Spain.

The first important battle fought was between the Spanish and the Americans was when George Dewey sailed from Hong Kong with the six ships of the Asiatic Squadron. He attacked the Spanish fleet of ten vessels whose guns could not reach the Americans and sank all ten without suffering any casualties. He then blockaded Manila harbor while he waited for United States troops to arrive.

Two weeks later, Aguinaldo returned to the Philippines, and formed a Filipino army, since the Spanish had not kept their promises to him. His forces fought beside the Americans.

On June 12, 1898, the Filipinos declared independence from Spain. On June 23, Aguinaldo was declared President of the Philippines.

The United States and Spain signed a treaty in Paris by which Spain ceded the Philippines to the United States. Aguinaldo was angry. He declared the Philippine Republic established on January 23, 1899 and his troops began fighting the Americans on February 4.

Aguinaldo was captured in March 1901, and he signed an oath of allegiance to the United States. The United States was divided about the solution and announced that it would work toward independence.

William Howard Taft, who later, became president of the United States, was appointed to head the Philippines as the first American governor. Because of the divided opinion in the United States, progress was made in developing toward independence, and it was scheduled for 1946. But World War II intervened.

The United States kept its air station at Clark Air Base and its naval station at Subic Bay, and in spite of much opposition among Filipinos it would have continued. But Mount Pinatubo intervened. In 1994 it erupted, covering Clark Air Base, which was only ten miles away, with several feet of volcanic ash. The United States decided that Clark was not worth the cost of shoveling the ash away and opted to abandon it entirely. It wanted to keep the naval base at Subic Bay, but the Philippine Senate voted 12 to 11 to reject the treaty.

The United States handed over the base on September 30, 1992, and the Philippines turned it into a special economic zone.

Chapter 20

The Flood

Beginning in the eighteenth century A.D. and reaching a peak in the nineteenth, Western religious scholars worked to harmonize science and religion. As described in Chapter 7, Archbishop Ussher of Ireland calculated from the genealogies in the Bible that the world had been created the eve of Sunday, October 23, 4004 B.C., that Noah had entered the Ark on Sunday, December 7, 2349 B.C., and that he left it on Wednesday, May 6, the following year.

William Buckland, another of these religious scholars, visualized a series of catastrophes, of which the Flood was only the most recent. He believed that the evidence for a flood was the drift deposits of boulders. These "Sarsen stones" are found scattered in the Salisbury plain, and their name was derived from *Saracen*, the Greek and Roman word for a nomadic people of the Arabian desert—i.e., wanderers.

Still another of these scholars, Charles Lyell, thought melting icebergs set afloat by the Flood dropped the stones. James Hutton, a geologist, published his monumental *Theory of the Earth* in the late eighteenth century in which he was the first to argue that Earth had a multi-billion-year history and that humans arrived only in the most recent period, long after fish, amphibians, reptiles, birds, and mammals. But he did not mention a flood.

In 1837 Louis Agassiz confessed that he had been converted to a new theory that vast oceans of ice had once covered Europe and Asia as far south as the Caspian Sea. This was a more logical explanation of the Sarsen stones.

When it was established that the Mediterranean had been a valley below sea level until Gibraltar broke through, it was at first thought that the biblical Flood referred to that event. But it was soon shown that Gibraltar had broken through about 5 million years ago, long before *Homo sapiens sapiens* was present to witness it, much less to construct an Ark. After that the Flood came to be thought of as one of the "imaginative but mistaken ventures" that accompanied the rise of the Earth sciences, one that was no longer accepted by anyone except the Christian Fundamentalists and members of the Creationist Movement.

In 1970, an article was published on the sedimentary history of the Black Sea reporting that it had been a salt sea, that it had turned into the world's largest freshwater lake, and that it had then turned back again into a salt sea. What was most startling was the article's conclusion that this last change had happened as recently as the end of the last ice age, when modern man was in the vicinity to see it happen. Since this was a flood that humankind had been present to witness, it seemed possible that the biblical account was based on fact after all. A book by William Ryan and Walter Pitman, on which most of this chapter is based, entitled *Noah's Flood, The New Scientific Discoveries About the Event That Changed History*, (New York: Simon and Schuster, 1998) gives a detailed account of the voyages of the deep-sea drilling ship, the *Glomar Challenger*, and the historical research that proved the case.

The Black Sea is a huge basin more than 6,000 feet deep. It receives more water from rain and river discharge than it loses by surface evaporation. The excess is expelled through the Straits of the Bosporus and the Sea of Marmora into the Dardanelles and the Mediterranean. In some parts the velocity exceeds five knots (six miles an hour).

But from the time of Jason and his search for the Golden Fleece, the ancients knew that another current at the bottom of the straits flowed in the opposite direction, from the Mediterranean to the Black Sea. As early as 800 B.C. mariners lowered stone-laden baskets to the bottom of the straits to use the current from the Mediterranean to the Black Sea to drag their boats northward against the swift-flowing outflow at the surface. In 1680, an Italian tied white-painted corks to a lead-weighted line and watched the corks stream north as the weights neared the bottom. The Bosporus channel continues far out into the Black Sea.

The Mediterranean went from a salt sea to a desert far below sea level when Gibraltar became a dam, and back to a salt sea when the dam broke through. The Black Sea, on the other hand, went from a salt sea to a fresh-water lake (the largest in the world) when the Bosporus became a dam, and then back to a salt sea when the dam broke. This last event happened 7,600 years ago in 5,600 B.C. within the memory, as we said, of humankind. In Roman times, for example, Pliny the Elder described the Black Sea as having swallowed up a large area of land in its path.

For a long time the newly formed Black Sea was felt to be so dangerous that humankind did not dare to venture into it. Historical records date the foundation of the earliest seaports on the Black Sea at about 800 B.C.

Much of the total ice cap melting occurred in two brief and rapid spurts separated by a thousand years during which the climate returned to ice-age conditions. The first pulse of melt water from the vast ice sheet covering northern Europe and Asia began 14,500 years ago. It fed dozens of huge lakes (like the Great Lakes of North America) that no longer exist. These lakes filled the sag in the Earth's crust caused by the weight of the great ice dome. They were dammed at their southern margin by the temporary bulge where the enormous weight of the ice sheets had pushed the softer Earth. These lakes swelled until one by one they breached the dam and spilled one into the other like the Great Lakes in America.

The second melt water spike occurred 11,400 years ago. But this melt water did not reach the Black Sea. The bulge in the Earth prevented it, and the water flowed away from the Black Sea north and west over what is now Berlin to the North Sea.

The world oceans continued to rise, but the Black Sea evaporated too rapidly for rain and the rivers flowing into it to keep pace. By 12,000 years ago the external ocean had risen well above the level of the Black Sea. By 7,600 years ago, the Black Sea shoreline was 350 below the top of the Bosporus dam. The beaches of the Black Sea were 400 feet below today's sea level. It was then, when the world's oceans were still 50 feet below today's level, that the trickle of salt water began to flow through the Bosporus into the basin of the Black sea and rapidly became a torrent.

The flow was astonishing. Its speed was 50 miles an hour. The level of the Black Sea rose half a foot every day! To flee, villagers had to move with their belongings and livestock from one-half to one mile a day, day after day. One's village would disappear in a matter of weeks.

A study done in Barbados of coral, which grows only in shallow water, showed that when the ice caps melted the level of the world's ocean never rose faster than six feet a *century*. The Black Sea rose six feet or more *every week!*

The story of the Flood appears not only in the Bible but also in Mesopotamia. The earliest written account of the legend is a Sumerian copy found at Nippur. Having created humans and animals, some of the gods decided to destroy them with a Flood. However others of the gods were unhappy with this decision and instructed Ziusudra, the Sumerian Noah, to build a huge boat. The storm raged seven days and seven nights and the boat was driven by ferocious gales. The text says that Ziusudra was deified for saving humankind.

The story of the Flood also appears in the epic of Gilgamesh. Gilgamesh was an historical figure, the king of the Sumerian city of Uruk (Erech in the Bible), in the period historians of Mesopotamia call Early Dynastic II, from 2,700 B.C. to 2,500 B.C. The epic is the story of his quest to find the secret of eternal life. In his search Gilgamesh visits and hears the story of the Flood from Utnapishtim, the Mesopotamian Noah and his wife to whom the gods had granted eternal life for saving the lives of so many creatures. The Gilgamesh epic was probably composed and re-composed by singing bards over a span of 2,000 years. It was finally committed to writing in cuneiform glyphs on clay tablets about 2000 years after Gilgamesh lived.

One of the languages used to tell the story of the Flood was Sumerian, which has no known roots and no known descendants, but which is the language of the first known writing of any kind. The second language was Akkadian, one of the ancient tongues of the Semitic language to which both Hebrew and Arabic belong. Scholars studying linguistics have tied the peoples who spoke these languages to each other, to speakers of other languages at the time of the Flood, and to the region of the Black Sea.

It was during a relatively warm period that *Homo sapiens sapiens* came out of Africa. Somewhat later, 25,000 years ago, the ice age began. It was followed 15,000 years later, about 10,000 years ago, by a warm period. The warm period was interrupted by a sudden, brief shift back to near-glacial conditions in Europe called the Younger Dryas. The word Dryas comes from the name of an Arctic plant, a member of the rose family, that appeared across northern Europe at the onset of the abrupt cooling. The continental ice sheets ceased melting and in some places such as Scotland and Norway once again began to expand. The cold, dry climate of the Younger Dryas produced a drastic slowdown in the rise of the sea level around the globe. It spanned the period from 12,500 years ago to 11,400 years ago.

In 1971, a dig on the banks of the Euphrates revealed the remains of two villages, one on top of the other. Carbon 14 dating put the lower and earlier village at from 13,000 to 11,500 years ago. So it began in the era of post-glacial warming and lasted until near the end of the Younger Dryas.

This lower village was primitive. It had begun as a seasonal camp with huts of reed. It was occupied by hunter-gatherers that archeologists call Natufian. They lived at this village site for most of the year, but each year for a few weeks they traveled to open prairie land to hunt for gazelle. They drove herds of these into narrow cul-de-sacs where they selectively slaughtered the young males, a conclusion that was deduced from the bones and teeth that were left. The implication is that the Natufian were sensitive to the benefits of keeping the breeding stock intact, to ensure large herds in future years.

Using salt and Sun drying, they preserved the meat for future use. They also gathered a large variety of edible plants, which they carbonized by heat for preservation. There is evidence that grain was stored in bins hollowed out from the limestone. There also remain large quantities of fish bones and mollusk shells.

The Natufians used sickles of carved deer antler studded with flakes of flint to harvest the natural; wild stands of native wheat and rye. They reaped wild barley, lentil, and vetch, the fruits of the hackberry, plum, pear, and fig trees, as well as the caper bush. The diet was stressful to their teeth and required backbreaking labor with grinding stones, mortars and pestles, but it was more than adequate for subsistence.

As the climate of the Younger Dryas grew harsher, the Natufian diet changed drastically and abruptly. The retreat of the fruit trees became evident in the sharp increase of cereals, grains, and grasses in their diet. Then the cereals became sparse, and their diet depended more on hardy plants like clover that required substantial preparation to detoxify it before the pulp or flour could be eaten. River-bottom plants died out because the Euphrates no longer overflowed its banks. So the diet of the Natufians came to be almost completely fish.

As the climate became ever dryer, a new hunting tool appeared—the delicately knapped Harif point. The Natufians became almost totally dependent on hunting the gazelle, ibex, and hare. Finally the increasing dryness of the Younger Dryas forced humans to desert the entire area. People like the Natufians either migrated to more hospitable places such as the Anatolian plateau and the Jordanian Rift Valley or died out.

A people who undoubtedly saw the strategic advantage of a site in the bend in the Euphrates occupied the second and younger of the two villages, the one on top of the older one that had been abandoned. But what was startling to the archeologists was that these new occupants were already farmers! They planted genetically altered grain, they used new tools to till the soil, new materials to build their houses, had new ways of cooking, and followed different practices for burying their dead. From the evidence at the site, no one could tell for sure where they came from.

It is theorized that the genetically altered grains these people had brought with them had come about in the following way. Under the pressure of the dry climate of the Younger Dryas, wheat plants produced small seeds protected in a shell that was tough and could resist the loss of moisture. The seeds grew in rows of spikelets that were attached to the stem of the grass by a brittle hinge, called the rachis. The plant had adapted to a strategy that dropped these spikelets from the plant early and easily, perhaps by the rustling of small animals. The seeds were trampled into the ground and so gained a foothold to start germination in advance of the harsh, extremely dry summers.

The Younger Dryas accentuated this adaptive process. If people threshed the grain locally in the wild fields to get at the seeds, nothing special would happen. But if instead they took the cut stalks back to their village the agricultural revolution would begin. The crude flint sickles would shake the plants more than the small animals did. The strands that the gatherers bundled and took to their homes would be the variants with the strongest rachis. Any seeds that were unintentionally spilled around the village during threshing and grinding would produce crops like the variant—more productive and more desirable than the originals. The inadvertently disturbed soil around the village would be like a prepared seedbed. The people about to become the first farmers had merely to observe and connect cause and effect. If they harvested the ancestral wheat with their flint-studded sickles and took them to their villages to be threshed, they would inadvertently alter the genes.

In the deteriorating conditions of the Younger Dryas humans retreated to such places as the Jordan Rift Valley. The archeologist K. M. Kenyon began digging in a mound covering ten acres in a rare oasis that lay in an otherwise utterly barren landscape of the Valley, whose floor lies 1200 feet below sea level, expecting and hoping to find the walls of Jericho. As she relates in her book, *Digging Up Jericho* (New York: Praeger, 1957) she did eventually find them, but in the process she came upon the Natufians.

A second mini ice age started about 6,200 B.C. and lasted until 5,800 B.C. During this period the shores of the Black Sea Lake offered warmer temperatures and perennially flooded river valleys, benefiting the cereals and grasses no longer able to survive the cooler temperatures and dryer conditions in their previous habitat. Once again, people like the Natufians had to move to another area. This time, many ended up on the shores of the Black Sea Lake.

Since the Black Sea Lake was below the level of the external ocean, it remained warm and more hospitable than the cold mountain flanks of the Fertile Crescent, the Negev highlands, or the Anatolian plateau to which the inhabitants along the banks of the Euphrates had retreated. The Black Sea held vast volumes of fresh water when the lakes elsewhere shriveled to undrinkable salt ponds and marshes and springs like those at Jericho dried up. Streams from the Balkans, the Alps, and Caucasus mountains kept the rivers flowing into this Black Sea Lake year-round. A vast forest and woodland covered Eastern Europe right up to the edge of the Black Sea Lake.

By the time the settlements began on the shores of the Black Sea Lake it had become a giant freshwater lake and a fantastic oasis. The great oasis attracted many different peoples and saw the birth of agriculture and a settled life. As Ryan and Pitman point out, words borrowed by the Indo-Europeans from Semitic, Kartvelian, Sumerian, and even Egyptian attest to the close proximity of these peoples. The example they give, taken from the Russian plant geneticist, Nicolae Vavilòv, is the word for wine—*woi-no* in the parent proto-Indo-European; *vinograg* in Russian, *vino* in Italic, *wein* in Germanic, *wino* in Kartvelian, *wijana* in Anatolian, and *wajnu* in proto-Semitic. Residue of retsina wine found in a jar from eight thousand years ago in Iran confirms the use of wine.

In the Fertile Crescent the rains and warmth returned about 5,800 B.C. Some of the people settled around the Black Sea Lake, such as the Halaf, left the basin, returned to the Fertile Crescent, and re-occupied some of the sites that had earlier been abandoned. But most of the peoples around the Black Sea Lake remained.

Then came the breakthrough at the Bosporus. The great oasis was drowned. Like the Natufians generations earlier, these peoples packed up their belongings when confronted by the drastic change in their environment and departed to seek a new homeland where they could carry on with their acquired knowledge, tools, and culture.

People living on the northern and western edge of the Black Sea Lake escaped into Europe and Ukraine. The people called LBK, from their linear band keramik (ceramic) pottery, dashed across Europe, leapfrogging from one site to the next, pushing ahead of their frontier for reasons that have yet to be explained, and ending up in both what is now Prague and Paris. The Danilo-Hvar people went toward Greece and Albania. Others went to the Adriatic and the islands of the Aegean. The Vin retreated upstream to the enclosed valley of the Hungarian basin. Some proto-Indo-Europeans went up the Dnieper and the Don toward the Caspian. Some migrated into the heartland of Eurasia via the Don. Others used the Volga as access to the distant steppes of the southern Ural Mountains.

Those on the southern side of the Black Sea fled into Anatolia. The Semitic peoples went south into the Fertile Crescent, where the climate, as mentioned above, had again become beneficial. The Ubaids fled south to the Levant and Mesopotamia toward the Persian Gulf. The Kartvelians re-treated to the Caucasus. The Tocharian people went east between the

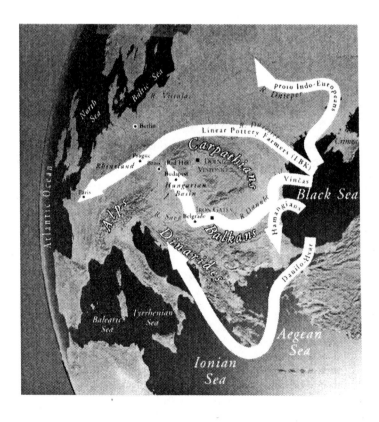

Caspian and the Urals. Other peoples went south along the coast of the Mediterranean to the Nile. The proto-Indo-Europeans ended up occupying an arc extending from the Adriatic, Western Europe and the Balkans, across Ukraine to the Caspian Sea.

The Flood continued long after the human population had fled. For 12 months the rush of water continued undiminished until the level of the lake had risen 180 feet to the lower surface of the flume. The rate of flow then began to slow down. Still, during the next 12 months the level rose another 100 feet. After two years, when the lake level had risen 330 feet, the waters reached the Kerch strait and shortly thereafter the Azov plain. It took several more years to fill the plain's basin completely, creating the Sea of Azov.

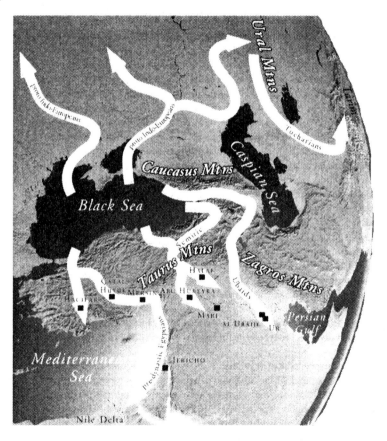

In 1997, a match was found between the DNA of the einkorn wheat from the earliest farming villages in the Black Sea area and a wild strain growing today in Anatolia. This finding caught all the experts off guard, since they had expected it to be confirmed that the cradle of agriculture was the Fertile Crescent. None could have known of the second mini ice age, which had driven humankind to the shores of the Black Sea before the agricultural revolution got fully underway. At that time scientists were only beginning to discover that there had been a mini ice age.

Homo sapiens sapiens began to experiment with agriculture at the end of the last major ice age. In the Fertile Crescent the first tentative steps in agriculture were apparently brought to a halt by the younger Dryas, which occurred 12,500 years ago to 11,400 years ago. The experiment continued and reached fruition along the shores of the Black Sea Lake. Agriculture was likely to have been invented quite independently at the Black Sea Lake, in China, and in the Americas. It may have gotten further along in the Fertile Crescent before the Younger Dryas than the archeological evidence indicates, and in Egypt it may also have gotten further along than we realize before the Black Sea Flood brought a wave of immigrants with somewhat more advanced agriculture.

When the Flood refugees arrived in any particular place, the hunter-gatherers already there were either absorbed or wiped out. In some cases, the refugees re-occupied villages that had been abandoned. In others, the refugees may have coexisted with the people of villages that were still occupied. In still others, the refugees may have taken over after destroying their inhabitants or killing the males and appropriating the females. In the Nile valley, it seems clear that there already were people who were cultivating cereals and had domesticated animals, and coexistence may have been a rather frequent outcome.

In the Black Sea area and in other parts of the Middle East the first domesticated crop was wheat. In China the first crops were millet, rice, and root crops such as taro and yam. In the Americas the first crops were maize, beans, yams, potatoes, tomatoes, and quinoa, a grain. In China agriculture may well have been independently invented not once but twice, by the Yang-shao culture of the middle Huang Ho valley and the Ta-p'en-k'eng culture of the southeastern coast, both of which appeared about 7,000 years ago or perhaps about 8,000 years ago. Slightly later, and perhaps not independently, agriculture emerged in the Ch'ing-lien-kang culture of the Huai Ho valley and the lower Yangtze.

As Ryan and Pitman point out, the humans who witnessed the Black Sea Flood and were driven from their homes had lived in the area long enough to become skilled in tilling fields, planting seeds, harvesting crops, and breeding animals. They may even have been experimenting with the diversion of streams for rudimentary irrigation. Since goods were made for both local consumption and for trade with distant communities even as far away, perhaps, as Eastern Europe, some would also have been artisans, brick-layers, carpenters, painters, sculptors, basket weavers, leather workers, jewelers, potters, and even morticians.

Archeological evidence shows that these people suffered from such diseases as malaria and arthritis. Their average life span was barely thirty years, although a few elders lived into their sixties.

In any case, the conclusion of Ryan and Pitman's book, *Noah's Flood,* is that the principle cradle of agriculture was the shores of the Black Sea Lake, not the Fertile Crescent; that it was the breakthrough of the barrier between the Mediterranean and the Black Sea that was the Flood of legend; and that it was this Flood of legend that drove the people from the Black Sea across Europe, to the Urals, to the Tarim Basin, and back to the Fertile Crescent where the climate had changed to one more favorable than it had been and where the transition from very, very dry to moist at the end of the Younger Dryas had taken only ten to fifty years.

The Language Evidence

In 1786, Sir William Jones delivered his famous discourse in Calcutta in which he said that there must have been "some common source, which perhaps no longer exists" to account for "the strong affinity, both in the roots of verbs and in the forms of grammar" between Sanskrit, Persian, Greek, Latin, Celtic, and German. "This could not possibly have been produced by accident."

Henry Creswicke Rawlinson depended upon Jones's observation of a vast interchange to help him decipher the cuneiform glyphs in the scripts of lost languages. While reading the *Hymns of the Rigveda,* the Hindu classic, Rawlinson became convinced that stories, myths, and hymns passed down in voice alone could persist with great fidelity for thousands of years. He cited the Vedic hymns as an example. There are two versions, one committed to writing very early, and the other passed on orally with remarkable accuracy for 25 centuries through monotonous recitation by countless generations of Brahmin monks, long after Sanscrit had died as a spoken tongue. At the end, the Brahmin monks did not understand very much of what they were reciting.

One of the ancestral tongues to emerge from the labors of the linguists was proto-Indo-European. The compelling questions are two: Where was its homeland, and when did the speakers of proto-Indo-European split apart?

Only a small number of the original words have been recovered, but these include the words for bear, high mountains, snow, beech tree, salmon, stream, and others that described the country of origin. A number of places were proposed. However, in 1995, a team of three Americans did a computer analysis, and it confirmed the basic conclusion that Anatolian was among the first to branch off the proto-Indo-European.

The speakers of proto-Indo-European split into the speakers of Anatolian in the south, and speakers of Celtic, Italic, and Tocharian. The Celtic speakers migrated into the interior of Europe. The Italic speakers migrated to the Mediterranean coast of Europe. The Tocharian speakers migrated to the heart of central Asia, where they arrived about 600 years after the Black Sea Flood.

A group of the Tocharians ended up in the Tarim basin at the edge of what was to become the Old Silk Road. The basin lies in the Takla-Makan Desert on the Tibetan plateau at the foot of the Tien Shan Mountains north of Kashmir. An oasis in the basin is the home of a Buddhist monastery that became a sort of Mecca for Buddhists. In 1907, Mark Stein persuaded the monks to let him examine manuscripts that had been in the monastery for 900 years. Some of the manuscripts were in both Sanscrit and an unknown language, and this enabled Stein to translate the language, to which he gave the name Tocharian after a ancient Persian tribe. Tocharian displays conspicuous similarities in vocabulary and grammar to Celtic and German. In 1985, a crew of Chinese archaeologists unearthed a naturally mummified woman who had lived a thousand years before Christ. What was surprising was her almost six-foot height, her long, narrow nose, thin lips, deep-set eyes, blond hair, and pointed skull—all unmistakable features of a European pedigree. Woven plaid textiles present in this and other graves in the area were virtually identical stylistically and technically to plaids found in Germany and Austria from roughly the same time period.

The Hairy Ainu

Still another group of Mediterranean dark-white people whose wanderings started with the Black Sea Flood in 5,600 B.C. got as far as the northernmost islands of Japan. They left cultural remains in a strip fifty miles inland along the seacoast from the Middle East, to India, Southeast Asia, China, Korea, and Japan all the way to Hokkaido and the northern islands.

There is a tiny pocket of these Mediterranean dark-white survivors of the Flood still living in the jungle between Thailand and Burma. In reference to their whitish skin, the Thai call them the "Ghost People." There is another tiny pocket of these people living in the jungles of Mindanao near Davao in the Philippines. All these people have in common a legend of the Flood, the symbol of a reverse swastika, the custom of sending the husband to bed when his wife is giving birth, and several other peculiar customs.

The Japanese call the ones who got to Japan the Hairy Ainu, since they have heavy beards and body hair. These have been mixed with Mongoloids, survivors of the ice age spent behind walls of ice in the Gobi desert, as we saw earlier. Their language, Ainu Itak, is quite obviously related to Indo-European. About 15,000 Ainu still live in Hokkaido and the northern islands.

Chapter 21

The Japanese

During the last ice age, when a large amount of water of the oceans was contained in the ice sheet, all four of the main Japanese islands were connected to each other. Kyushu in the south was connected to the Korean peninsula by a land bridge, and Hokkaido in the north was connected by another land bridge to Siberia. Around 30,000 years ago, *Homo sapiens sapiens* crossed over and occupied all of the islands. By 12,000 years ago, these people had developed a distinct culture, lasting several thousand years, that archaeologists call Jomon from the cord pattern on their pottery. The evidence is that they were a hunting, gathering, fishing people who lived in very small tribal groups. They also fashioned figurines that appear to be a female goddess.

What anthropologists call the "Incipient Jomon" lived in the period from 12,000 to 10,000 years ago. On the plain where Tokyo now stands, they left pottery fragments that appear to be the remains of very small, rounded pots. Elsewhere in the world, early man did not develop pottery until after the invention of agriculture, but these pots were made long before any people discovered agriculture, predating Mesopotamian ceramics by over two thousand years. In the following period, from 10,000 to 7,000 years ago, the Jomon used similar pots, intricately decorated with the cord-like designs to boil food.

At the end of the last ice age, about 14,500 years ago, the world began to warm. Between 7,000 and 4,500 years ago, the average global temperature was about four to six degrees Fahrenheit warmer than it is today. All over the world, *Homo sapiens sapiens* began to develop agriculture and to live in villages. Although they were cut off from the rest of humanity, the Jomon were no exception. Their culture thrived in Japan until about 3,000 to 2,300 years ago, and then came the Yayoi entering the islands from the mainland.

As mentioned earlier, following the ice age what is now the Gobi desert developed a temperate climate and became a place of lush forests, streams, and rainfall, and then a thousand years before the present era, it began to dry out, and most of the people migrated south and east. The Yayoi made their way to Korea, either pushing out or intermarrying with the original inhabitants. Subsequent waves of immigrants pushed the Yayoi into the Japanese islands beginning 2,300 years ago.

The Yayoi brought to Japan agriculture, the working of bronze and iron, and a new religion that eventually developed into Shinto. They displaced the Jomon language, culture, and religion, although this conclusion is not popular among some Japanese who would like to believe that the Jomon absorbed the Yayoi.

Although the Jomon did not absorb the Yayoi, they did interbreed with them. Both DNA and linguistic analysis suggests that modern Japanese are a mix of Yayoi and the Jomon. One Japanese scholar argues that modern Japanese are 35 percent Jomon and 65 percent Yayoi.

Westerners think of Japanese as homogenous, but this is not entirely true. Japanese in the northern prefectures have more of the Jomon characteristics—rounder eyes, more body hair, and wider faces. DNA analysis suggests they are as much as 60 to 80 percent Jomon, while those from western and southern Japan are 40 percent or less Jomon and 60 or more percent Yayoi.

South Koreans argue that it was Koreans who founded the Japanese imperial family. The Chinese say it was Xu Fu, an envoy from China sent to Japan about 2,300 years ago and that he became the first emperor, Jimmu. In any case, although the assumption has been that the culture came from Korea and China, the evidence is that the influence was back and forth. Japanese scientists, for example, no think buckwheat farming, lacquer ware making, and several other innovations originated in Japan and made their way back to Korea and China.

Japan is dotted with burial mounds of the Jomon period, from about 7,000 years ago to about 2,300 years ago. Recently, serious archeological excavations were begun of the mounds in Aomori, in the northern part of the main island of Japan, which are 5,000 years old. These will take another 15 years to complete, and work is also proceeding on 13,000 other archeological sites in Japan.

The Aomori site has six enormous holes containing the remains of wooden pillars, the base for a huge structure. The sites testify to more technology than had been supposed. One site was a settled village with separate cemeteries for adults and children. The people had dabbled in agriculture—chestnuts and millet and other domesticated plants. There is also evidence of trade—jade form 400 miles south, and obsidian from the northern island of Hokkaido.

However, the analysis of the Jomon skeletons shows that they did not look like modern Japanese. In the museum, the only visitor who looked like a Jomon was an American. The Jomon apparently looked more like Caucasians, but this must not be taken literally.

The Jomon were alone in Japan until about 2,300 years ago, when the first waves of immigrants arrived from Korea. Recent DNA studies show a close genetic relationship between Japanese and Koreans. But many of the immigrants had originated in China several generations earlier. In any case, they brought rice paddy cultivation with them and ushered in the Yayoi period. The Yayoi had the slant eyes, the so-called Mongolian flap, of Koreans, Chinese, and Mongolians.

One puzzle is the so-called Hairy Ainu. As already mentioned, these people began their journey 7,600 years ago when the Black Sea flooded. They were a white people, as we already saw; they stayed close to the sea throughout their long journey; they had a series of peculiar customs; and very small remnants of them survived in an isolated band in the jungles lying between Burma and Indonesia, and in the jungles of Mindanao. They must have made their way to the northern island of Japan when it was still empty and settled there.

Chapter 22

The Celts

As we have seen, *Homo sapiens sapiens* left Africa some 40,000 years ago. About 30,000 years ago the climate turned mild, and the people drifted north. Some of them got to the far north. There they evolved a white skin as a result of living where the Sun was seen for only six months of the year and a tolerance for milk as a result of living on the reindeer.

These white-skinned people ranged widely over what is now Scandinavia and northern Europe, gathering food, hunting, fowling, and fishing. Here and there they left their mark on a flint or an antler that they used as tools. What archeologists call the Fosna folk lived along the west coast of what is now Norway facing the Atlantic, while the Komsa folk lived along the northern coasts of Norway and Russia facing the Arctic ocean. Other white-skinned tribes whose traces have not yet been found undoubtedly also lived in the area.

All these peoples eventually came to know the bow and arrow, as well as flint knives, scrapers, harpoons, and spears. They buried their dead in shallow graves close to where they were living at the time. They developed boats made of skin stretched around a framework of flexible poles much like the Irish tub-shaped coracle and the somewhat larger curragh that we see today. They also domesticated two wolf-like dogs, the Maglemose and Svaerdborg. This way of life filled 10,000 years of pre-history.

Trade also began during this long period. As we have seen, the beginnings were by exchanges at the border between two tribes. In this way such things as amber and flint moved great distances, while the people who were doing the trading stayed in their home areas. Amber, for example, moved from the Baltic to the Mediterranean. Much later, traders themselves traveled with the goods to be traded. When the ice age began about 25,000 years ago, these white-skinned people were pushed south. The ice sheet reached Jutland about 20,000 years ago where it formed its terminal moraine and remained stationary for a long period of time. When the ice began to melt some 12,000 years ago these white-skinned people were to be found in what is now Spain, Italy, and Greece. Some had reached the Fertile Crescent, some the Ukraine, some the Caucasus, and some, a people whose descendants have been called proto-Indo-European, settled along the northern shores of the large fresh-water lake that later became the Black Sea.

Then 7,600 years ago the Black Sea flood started these white-skinned proto-Indo-Europeans on a migration that led them into Western Europe as far as Paris and into Eastern Europe and the shores of the Baltic. Among the other peoples who had lived along the shores of the Black Sea Lake and fled into both Western and Eastern Europe were some who were not proto-Indo-European and whose origins were in the Middle East.

In any case, all the refugees from the Black Sea flood had more advanced technologies, including agriculture and most likely weapons, than the peoples occupying the areas they invaded. For the time being these new arrivals must have been an impossible obstacle to the southward pressure from their white-skinned cousins who had remained in the area.

As we saw, one group of the proto-Indo-Europeans who fled from the Black Sea flood 7,600 years ago in 5600 B.C., made their way to the area east of the Carpathian mountains and were well settled there about 5,000 years ago. Eventually, the Greeks came to call these people Keltoi and the Germans to call them Kelten, while the French softened it to Celtes.

According to Merle Severy, on whose article "The Celts" in the *National Geographic* of May, 1977, the following draws, the Celts never formed a unified tribe or empire, but they had a common tongue and a distinctive material culture. Their priestly caste were the Druids, and their gods demanded human sacrifice. An example is pictured on the Gundestrup caldron that was found in Jutland. Two feet in diameter and elaborately carved, the bowl was fashioned of silver 2,000 years ago and shows a priestess mounted on a ladder cutting the throat of a man suspended over a bowl so that his blood would flow into it.

250

The Scythians, nomads from the Russian steppes, domesticated the horse about 5,000 years ago. Some time later their neighbors, the Celts, acquired horses and developed two-wheeled chariots pulled by two horses. They undoubtedly also rode horses, but since the stirrup was not yet known, they could not wield a sword from horseback without falling off. If a rider charged into an enemy gripping a spear, as did the armored knights of later years, he would end up on the ground behind his horse. However, a rider could cast a spear straight ahead if he held tight to the horse's mane with his other hand. From the back of a horse, he could also shoot an arrow with a bow. But he could fight effectively with sword or spear from a chariot, and he could probably shoot an arrow from a bow more efficiently from a chariot than from the back of a horse without stirrups.

The Celts emerged as a distinct people 2,800 years ago. When techniques for working iron had developed sufficiently to spark the beginning of the iron age, about 2,500 years ago, both their weapons and their tools dramatically improved. They were among the first to shoe horses and to make iron rims for the wheels of their chariots. The peak of their culture was 2,300 years ago.

Shortly after emerging as a distinct people, they began to move north and west. Just before the beginning of the iron age 2,500 years ago they occupied the area north of the Alps that is now Austria. This is what archeologists call the Hallstatt period of Celtic culture, dating from 2,800 years ago to 2,500 years ago. They mined for salt at the present-day Salzberg (Salt Mountain) where salt has continued to be mined ever since. What archeologists call the La Tène period, from a nearby town in Switzerland, flourished from the beginning of the Iron Age 2,500 years ago to 2,050 years ago. During the Hallstatt and La Tène periods Celtic tribes settled all across Europe. The name Paris stems from the Celtic Parisii tribe. Rheims from the Remi. Helvetia from the Helvetii. Belgium from the Belgae. Bologna from the Boii. Chartres from the Carnutes.

Just below the terminal moraine in Jutland are bowl-shaped burial mounds dating from 3,000 to 4,000 years ago, the funeral monuments of the "corded ware," or "battle axe," bronze age people of proto-Indo-European stock who appeared in eastern and central Europe about 4,300 years ago. The date suggests that their ancestors may have started their migrations as refugees from the Black Sea flood, but it is not known for certain that they were Celts.

By the Bronze Age, beginning about 3,500 years ago, trade was brisk all over Europe. Amber from Jutland was highly valued everywhere. Tin and copper from mines in what is now Austria was needed to make bronze. It was not long before the smiths and artists in northern Europe equaled the southern pioneers in working bronze.

Over the succeeding years, these peoples were well placed to meet the demand from peoples living south of them for furs and slaves. But they turned their hand to any salable commodity—grain, fish, timber, hides, salt, wine, glass, glue, horses, cattle, white bears, falcons, walrus ivory, seal oil, honey, wax, malt, silks, woolens, hazel nuts, soapstone dishes, basalt millstones, wrought weapons, ornaments, and silver. To carry the goods, they built ships, established market towns, developed trade routes, maintained spheres of influence and augmented mercantile profits with piracy and conquest abroad. They made a living by trade, piracy, and seizing land.

The Bronze Age came to an end about 2,500 years ago with a gradual transition to the use of iron.

The life style of the Celts is probably best described in their surviving sagas. One is the Irish oral saga, *The Cattle Raid of Cooley*, but the most famous is *Beowulf*, a saga of the wars between Celtic tribes for mastery. It was composed between the middle of the seventh and the end of the tenth century in Anglo-Saxon (Old English).

A recent translation by Seamus Heaney was published early in 2000 with the Anglo-Saxon text on one page and the English translation on the facing page (New York: Farrar, Straus & Giroux, 2000).

The poem was written in England, but the events took place in Scandinavia in an earlier time ruled by the laws of the blood feud, when the kin of a slain person must kill the killer or receive satisfaction in the form of *wergild*, the man-price. Beowulf's home was the land of the Geats, in what is now southern Sweden. Beowulf crosses the sea to the land of the Danes to help them defeat a man-eating monster named Grendel. After Grendel is slain, his mother rampages, and Beowulf must also destroy her. Beowulf returns to his homeland to rule for fifty years. But then, in his age, a dragon begins to terrorize the countryside. Beowulf manages to slay the dragon, but meets his own death in doing so.

The manuscript of the poem came down to us in only one copy. This barely survived a fire in the eighteenth century before it was copied and transcribed. It is now housed in the British museum. The poem contains a number of formulaic phrases that are the stock in trade of oral bards, as described in the chapters below on the *Iliad* and the *Odyssey*, and like those two epic poems it is a work of genius. The Oxford scholar J. R. R. Tolkien in 1936 published an epoch-making paper on the poem. This showed that the author was an imaginative poet. He had transformed the inherited material of fabulous elements and the traditional accounts of the past into a unity and balance. Tolkien's work changed the way the poem had been treated and initiated a new era in which it became a central piece in the study of English literature.

The following account of the history of the Celts is drawn from Gerhard Herm, *The Celts. The People Who Came Out of the Darkness* (New York, St. Martin's Press, 1975). In 387 B.C. the Celts, whom the Romans called Gauls, sacked Rome. In the year 279 B.C., they pillaged the oracle at Delphi.

The Celts were larger in stature than most of their contemporaries. The average male Celt was almost six feet tall. One whose remains were recently unearthed was six feet, five inches. Females frequently fought beside the men, and were apparently just as fierce. Queen Boadicca, of the Iceni, burned Roman London. The highest ranks in the society were warriors, armed with a two-edged, iron sword. The military in turn were based on the peasant with his plough and sickle, also made of iron. They had both wagons and chariots pulled by horses. From grain and honey they made mead.

The Romans who came to know and fear them as blond giants, handsome and strong, described the Celts. A historian of the time quoted by Gerhard Herm (p. 3) wrote that

> Their aspect is terrifying.... They are very tall in stature, with rippling muscles under clear white skin. Their hair is blond, but not naturally so: they bleach it ... washing it in lime and combing it back from their foreheads. They look like wood-demons, their hair thick and shaggy like a horse's mane.

Some Celts, he went on to say, wore bronze helmets often adorned with horns, so they looked even taller. Some wore armor made of chain mail, but many went into battle naked. Horns were sounded, weapons were beaten rhythmically against shields, and there was a chorus of shouting. Rage and war lust were systematically whipped up.

The Celts populated what is now Scandinavia, Germany, and Eastern Europe, and later they made their way to England and Ireland. In the territories they occupied in Europe there were other peoples who were smaller and darker. Some were probably direct descendants of the original *Homo sapiens sapiens* of Europe as the Basques are presumed to be. Others were probably refugees from the Black Sea flood who were not themselves proto-Indo-European. In any case, the tall, fair-haired, blue-eyed Celt met, conquered, and inbred with people who were neither tall, nor fair-haired, nor blue-eyed.

The Celts were also not the first *Homo sapiens sapiens* in the British Isles. A handful of "little dark people" had preceded them, apparently making their way on foot before the English Channel formed. Their original homeland seems to have been on the shore of the Mediterranean in southern France and northern Spain. Many of the Irish are fairly tall and red-headed, but occasionally, they are short and dark, and it is speculated that these are throwbacks to those original inhabitants.

The Celts who reached England early on created an unusual kind of monument made by cutting through several feet of turf down to the chalk layer lying below. A few of these have survived, of which the most spectacular are the Running Horse at Uffington, the Long Man of Kent, and the Cerne Abbas Giant in Dorset. The reason these survived is that very early on they became associated with May Day celebrations, and any trash or growth that accumulated in the trenches during the year was cleaned out by the local villagers as part of the celebration.

The Running Horse is 360 feet long and commands the site of a Celtic fort. What is striking is that it is highly stylized. It looks impressionistic, something that Picasso might have executed. The only other picture of a horse in this same genre appears on a bronze Celtic urn in the museum in Lincolnshire. Why these horses were so stylized is not known.

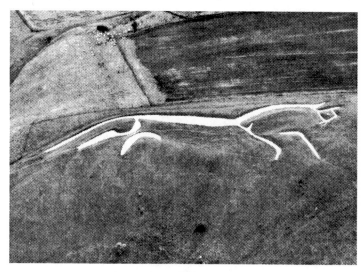

The Long Man of Kent is standing between two posts or poles, one in each hand. No one has offered any plausible explanation of what he is doing or what the carving signifies. As for the Cerne Abbas Giant the meaning is not hard to fathom, since he sports a huge erect penis, a phallus.

The Iron Age Bog People

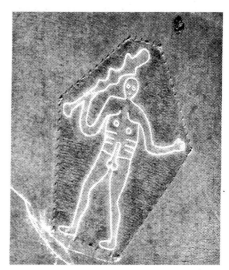

The bodies of about 700 Celts who died 2,000 years ago have been found in the bogs of northwestern Europe. Their bodies are remarkably well preserved due to the tanning action of the bog water. Most of them show signs of a violent death. A number were strangled with ropes made of twisted leather thongs, while some had the back of their skulls bashed in. People at the time had an alcoholic drink made of barley, cranberry, and bog myrtle plus honey that was halfway between a beer and a fruit wine. They ate meat as often as they could get it, and almost certainly they ate it on ceremonial occasions. But the stomach contents of the preserved bodies were grains, no meat whatsoever and apparently no wine, all eaten between 12 and 24 hours before their death. As P. V. Glob says in his book *The Bog People, Iron-Age Man Preserved* (Ithaca, N.Y.: Cornell University Press, 1969) from which this account is drawn, the execution death of these people was obviously ceremonial, and the hypothesis is that they were sacrifices intended to bring about a successful spring planting.

The executions probably occurred at the time of the mid-winter celebration whose purpose was to hasten the coming of spring. The man chosen for sacrifice was given a special meal, made of the seeds of wild and cultivated plants, and then consecrated by death to the deities who controlled the Earth's increase. The man chosen would carry the image of a goddess of fertility, a sort of Mother Earth, around the villages of the district. He would then be sacrificed and his body put in the bog to ensure that the cycle of nature would go forward.

Many of the dead had their hair tied in the so-called Swabian knot. The hair was gathered on the right side into a skillfully contrived knot, needing neither pin nor band to hold it. Such knots appear in Roman sculptures of Gauls in both the Rhine and Danube regions and are described by Tacitus.

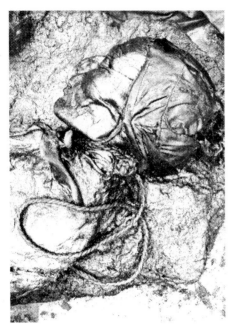
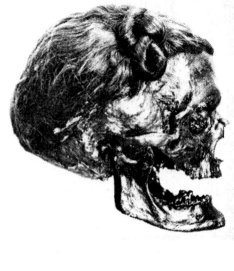

The clothing of women is demonstrated by two found at Hulde Fen. One set consisted of a skin cape, a woven scarf, and a woven skirt. The skirt was woven so that it was gathered slightly at one side where there were leather laces. A neat, squared pattern was obtained by alternating a natural wool yarn of golden brown and another of very dark brown. The scarf apparently covered the upper part of the body. The other woman has a dress that covers her whole body and a cape. In both cases a brooch, the safety pin of the time, fastened the cape.

The male costume consisted of a cap, cape, coat, leggings, and shoes. Only towards the end of the period and then only in the great deposits of war gear do trousers and sleeved shirts or tunics appear. Caesar says that the Gauls went into battle with a short garment of skin but were otherwise naked. Tacitus says that the universal male garment was a cape fastened by a brooch and that men would spend the whole day by the hearth wearing no other garment.

By 300 B.C., Rome had embarked on its conquest of Celtic lands and fought the Celts continuously for the next three centuries. In the year 52 B.C., a Celtic leader named Vercingetorix raised the countryside of what is now central France in revolt against Rome. He adopted a scorched Earth strategy to prevent the Romans from living off the land, and used guerrilla tactics. This was contrary to the Celtic tradition, which was for one big, dramatic battle, and the tribes did not give Vercingetorix their full support. The Romans finally cornered Vercingetorix and 80,000 of his supporters in Alesia, a fortified town on a rocky hill near what is now Dijon. Caesar had only 40,000 men, but they were well-trained, battle-hardened Roman legionaries. Caesar ringed the town with nine-and-a-half miles of fortifications. Vercingetorix sent out his cavalry to summon relief from the tribes, and Caesar, anticipating their attack, dug a new set of fortifications facing outward 14 miles around. So the Romans ended up defending a doughnut, with Vercingetorix and 80,000 Celts inside and 250,000 Celts from more than 20 tribes outside. But the methodical Romans were more effective than the headstrong and disorganized Celts. After a long and bloody siege, Vercingetorix finally emerged alone from the gates of Alesia, resplendent in silver and enameled armor. He rode down the hill, made a ritual circle around the dais where Caesar was seated, dismounted, threw down his arms, and sat down in silent surrender. Caesar sent him to Rome in chains; six years later paraded him through Rome in triumph, and then had him strangled.

Chapter 23

The Vikings

Viking society had three classes. An Icelandic poem describes them as serfs, free peasants, and warrior-chieftains. The serfs, according to the poem, were black-haired, and ugly, the skin of their hands wrinkled and rough with lumpy knuckles and thick fingers, their backs gnarled, their heels long—the image of toilers on the land. The free peasants were ruddy-faced with sparkling eyes. The warrior-chieftains were the Nordic dream—skin as white as new fallen snow, bright brows, blond hair, bright cheeks, and glowing eyes.

Poetry aside, two main types have long been recognized in Scandinavia. One is indeed tall, fair or ruddy complexion, light-haired, blue-eyed, long of face and skull. The other is shorter, dark-complexioned, brown or dark-haired, brown-eyed, broad-faced, and round of skull. It seems likely that the first is a description of the more or less direct descendants of the people who had first come to the far north and evolved white skins, and the second is a description of later comers who were conquered by the white-skinned people when they moved south and who were enslaved by them. But the white-skinned conquerors also interbred with the shorter, darker people.

In any case, the Vikings dealt in slaves, acquired by both trade and conquest. One source of slaves was Britain. But most came from among the Slavonic peoples on the shores of the Baltic. They were kept like cattle in the pens of Magdeburg, ready for their transfer west. Other pens were at a big clearing house at Regensburg on the Danube and at Edeby in southern Jutland. In Lyons, in Spain, and in the remoter Muslim world, the demand for slaves was insatiable—men for labor, women for both labor and lust, and eunuchs for sad service.

The local demand for slaves among the Scandinavians was also large. The term for the laborer was *thrall*. Three thralls were needed for a farm of twelve cows. A lord's estate might require thirty or more.

The Viking Ship

As Gwyn Jones says in his book, *A History of the Vikings* (London: Oxford University Press, 1984) from which the following is drawn, the Scandinavians spent centuries developing and perfecting their sailing ships and skills. This was done in the fjords of Norway, the belts, sounds, and sandy entries of the Danish mainland and island-archipelago, the lakes and rivers of Sweden, the Skaggerak and Kattegat, and Baltic Sea, and Baltic gulfs. Eventually, both their ships and their sailing skills were good enough for them to brave the open sea and raid lands to the south. The Vikings reached this point about the middle of the eighth century A.D.

The Gokstad ship, built in the mid-ninth century, survives. It is 76 1/2 feet long, with a beam of 17 1/2 feet, and a little over 6 feet 4 inches from the bottom of the keel to the top of the gunwale amidships. It has a keel of 57 feet 9 inches, made from a single oak timber. It is clinker-built of strakes of differing but carefully calculated thickness. The waterline strake is 1 3/4 inches thick. The 9 underwater strakes and the 3 immediately above the waterline are precisely 1 inch thick. Above this is the oar strake, 1 1/4 inches thick, and the two top most strakes are just 7/8 inches thick. The gunwale is big, 4 1/4 inches by 3 1/2 inches. The strakes are joined together by round-headed iron rivets driven through from the outside and secured inside by means of small, square iron plates. The caulking was either tarred animal hair or wool. The hull was kept in shape by nineteen frames and cross beams. The decking was pine. In the Gokstad ship it was laid loosely over the cross beams so that the space beneath could be used for storage.

The strakes below the waterline are tied to the frames with spruce root lashings, a device which contributed much to the ship's flexibility. This flexibility was still further increased by a carefully systematized trenailing of the above-water strakes to wooden knees and crossbeams. The elasticity of this part of the ship was such that in a replica that was sailed across the

Atlantic in 1893, the gunwale twisted out of true by as much as 6 inches, yet the ship was safe, fast, and watertight.

What also made these ships such a good raiders was that with a draft rarely exceeding 3 1/2 feet, they could penetrate all but the shallowest rivers. They were the masters of shelving beaches where there were no harbors, and they made it easy for men to disembark rapidly at the point of attack. And by turning into the wind and making off by oar, they were almost immune to pursuit by the clumsier sailing ships of the lands on which they preyed.

The Gokstad ship had sixteen oars of pine, so regulated in length that they struck the water in unison. They were operated not by oarlocks, but by holes in the fourteenth strake that could be closed.

The mast was of pine, 26 to 35 feet tall, with a rectangular sail, 23 by 36 feet, made of strips of heavy, woolen cloth strengthened by a rope network and hoisted on a yardarm some 37 feet long.

The apparatus for bearing and supporting the mast was massive. First there was the keelson, called the "old woman." It was a prostrate block of solid oak resting on the keel over a span of four frames, with a cunningly designed socket to take the foot of the mast and assist its raising and lowering. Above the "old woman" was another big block of solid oak, the mast partner. It was supported by the "old woman" and no less than six cross beams. Its forward section was massive and closed, so it could take on three sides the pressure of the raised mast when the ship was running under sail and transmit the wind's power to the hull. Its rear was grooved to facilitate the mast's lowering. When the mast was raised, this groove was fitted with an oak block or wedge.

From surviving drawings, it appears that the sail could be shortened by the use of reefing lines, and recent opinion is that the ship could be sailed across or even near the wind. This was largely due to the use of a removable pole or tacking boom, whose heavy end was seated in a socket abeam of the mast while the lighter end was fitted to the forward leech of the sail to keep it taut and drawing when the ship was sailing on the wind.

The ship was steered by a side rudder fastened to the starboard quarter. The skipper of the replica that crossed the Atlantic in 1893 found it superior to a rudder mounted on the sternpost, easily managed by a single member of the crew. The ship was also equipped with a ship's boat, either stowed on board or towed behind.

Finally, it should be emphasized that the ship that carried the Norsemen to Britain, the Frankish empire, Iceland, and beyond was a *sailing* ship. The oars were auxiliary power, for use when the ship was becalmed, when it was in some state of emergency, or when it was maneuvering in narrow waters, fjords, or rivers.

The ship of all work, the true ocean-goer was similar to the Gokstad ship, but broader in the beam, deeper in the water, and with a higher freeboard.

In their great voyages of discovery in the ninth and tenth centuries, the Vikings had neither compass nor chart. How did they find their way from Bergen to L'Anse aux Meadows in Newfoundland? The answer was latitude sailing. This was not as haphazard as it appears. To begin, the skipper would sail thirty miles or so north of Bergen to the landmark

Stad was at the same degree of latitude as his landfall in Greenland, so if he now sailed due west, he would find himself after the right number of days passing north of the Shetlands and thereafter south of the Faeroes and at a recognizable and prescribed distance from them.

On the same course the skipper would traverse the ocean well south of Iceland and know where he was by observing the birds and sea creatures associated with those islands. On a good passage in clear weather with a following wind, this part of the voyage would take him about seven days.

It would take the skipper almost as long again to sight the east coast of Greenland, about 80 miles north of Cape Farewell. Now he must head southwest and reach the west coast of Greenland either by rounding the Cape or by threading Prins Christians sund. From there on he would be following a well-described coastal route until he reached Herjolfsnes (the modern Ikigait), with its Norse farms and haven. Ahead lay the landmark of Hvarf, and thereafter many ports of call. From here we assume the skipper would continue north by the familiar route to the northern hunting grounds, to the modern Holsteingsborg, or to the huge island of Disco.

From Disco to make the shortest practicable ocean passage and use the clearest landmarks, the skipper would turn southwest for the eastern coast of Canada. He would next reach the southern coast of Baffin Island and know what kind of coast to expect. He must now follow the land south for an estimated number of days, passing the big inlet of Frobisher Bay and the entrance to Hudson's Bay until he sighted the forest land of Labrador, south of modern Nain. South of Hamilton Inlet he would be looking for the white beaches of the Strand and the distinctive, keel-shaped Cape Porcupine (the Furdustrandir and Kjalarnes of the sagas), and so down past Battle Harbour until he sighted Belle Island and thereafter the northernmost tip of New-foundland and Cape Bauld. From here to Epaves Bay and the Norse houses by Black Duck Brook was a defined route without navigational problems. In a good day's sailing of 24 hours, he could cover 120 miles and more.

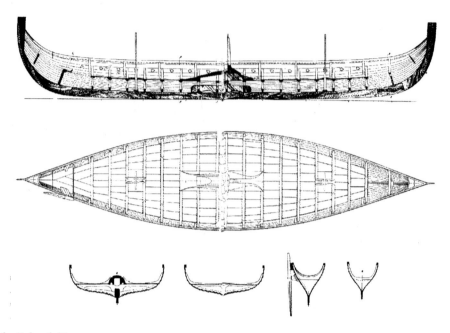

The Gokstad ship.

All this meant that the skipper had to carry a lot of knowledge in his head. He also had to know cloud formations, the color of the water at various places, marine creatures and birds, currents, the Sun and the stars, the arts of rough and dead reckoning and the use of a line to search the ocean's bottom. Most importantly, for the long Atlantic voyages he had to fix his latitude. We know that he could do this, but exactly what method he used is uncertain.

There survives a set of tables from the end of the tenth century, which gives the Sun's mid-day latitude week by week throughout the year as it is observed from northern Iceland. Any observation of the noonday Sun or the Pole Star by even so crude a method as measuring a shadow cast at noon or calculating the Pole Star's height above the horizon expressed in terms of one's own arm, hand, or thumb was a fair guide to latitude. And latitude was much more important to the Vikings than longitude because if a mariner driven off course by a storm could get back to the proper latitude and sail in the right direction, he would, barring accident, reach the place he wanted to go.

The Vikings were casual when they spoke of navigation. There is good evidence that the Vikings knew how to use the qualities of calcite or Iceland spar, which they called solarsteinn (sunstone), and this would explain their casual attitude. Calcite polarizes light and so makes it possible to locate the Sun even when clouds obscure it. We know that the Vikings possessed calcite, and anyone handling a piece of calcite would sooner or later, if only by accident, hold it up to the light and discover its qualities. The evidence is that they did. As mentioned by Tre Tryckare in his book *The Viking* (Time-Life Books, p. 14) one of the sagas relates that the Holy King Olaf and his chief, Sigurd, were sailing in a fog when it was also snowing heavily. "The king asked a man to take a look outside and the sky was cloud covered. He then asked Sigurd to tell him where the Sun could be and he [Sigurd] told him. Then the king picked up the 'sunstone' and he then saw how the stone was radiating and out of that he made the conclusion that Sigurd was right."

The Years of Raiding

In 793 the Vikings raided the monastery at Lindisfarne on the east coast of Northumbria and in the next few years, Jarrow in Northumberland, Morganwg in South Wales, Lambey island north of Dublin, the Isle of Man, the sacred island of Iona, and various islands off Aquitane in France.

In the 830s Vikings from Norway came to Ireland with conquest and settlement in mind, not raids. Then in 850 came Vikings from Denmark with the same idea. St. Patrick favored the Danes, and there was a slaughter of Norwegians at Dublin and Carlingford. The Danes rewarded St. Patrick with gold and silver.

The year 842 saw attacks on both England and France. In France, Charles the Bald was king, but the rebel Count Lambert was anxious to secure Nantes for himself. He invited the Vikings to come, and French pilots led them through the sandbanks and shallows. It was St John's Day, June 24, 842, and the town was filled with celebrants. The Norwegian Vikings attacked with unsurpassed brutality—killing everyone in sight, including the Bishop.

They wintered on an island, Noirmoutier. This is the first we hear of the Vikings using a winter base.

The Vikings attacked Seville in 844 and held everything but the citadel for a week. They carried off much treasure and took the women and children prisoner. However, the Moors struck back massively. Finally a deal was made. In exchange for the prisoners, the Vikings were given supplies of food and a truce was declared that enabled them to depart without further fighting.

After raiding France, Spain, and even Italy, a new stage of conquest and settlement began in 865. The first settlements were in the Shetland and Orkneys and then the Hebrides. They seem to have been without significant fighting, carried out by men looking not for plunder but land to settle on.

The legend is that Ragnar, after plundering up the Seine, came to England and was defeated by King Ella of Northumbria, who had him thrown into a pit and stung to death by snakes. The next year his sons—Ivar the Boneless, Ubbi, and Halfdan—came from Scandinavia and Ireland to avenge the death of their father. They captured York. In 869, Ivar and Ubbi moved south into East Anglia, where they captured and cruelly executed King Edmund. His martyrdom brought him sainthood, and his remains lie in the town of Bury St. Edmund.

In 870, Halfdan led the Danes against Wessex and seized and fortified the town of Reading. In 876, Halfdan shared out the lands of Northumbria, and the Danes engaged in plowing and making a peaceful living for themselves. The area partitioned was approximately that of modern Yorkshire.

Another Danish distribution of English territory came in 877. The end result was that the shires of Yorkshire, Nottingham, Lincoln, Derby, and Leicester had ceased to be part of England.

There were two kinds of settlement and neither involved displacement of the English. One was a military settlement as a result of conquest of inhabited lands. The other consisted of immigrants from Denmark who settled on virgin land along the lesser streams in districts of sandy or gravelly soil reminiscent of their Danish homeland.

The many villages in the northern part of England, whose names end in "by," such as Ashby, date from this period of Danish settlement. In Danish the "by" indicates a clearing in the forest.

Norwegians settled the coast along the Irish Sea from Scotland to Wales. The Danes settled on the coast facing Europe and the Channel.

The area in which Danish rather than English law and custom prevailed was later called the Danelaw. It comprised the eventual Danish conquests and settlements in Northumbria, East Anglia, and the southeast Midlands, and the Five Boroughs of Stamford, Leicester, Derby, Nottingham, and Lincoln.

In 886, King Alfred negotiated a treaty with Guthrum the Dane whereby a system of wergelds, payments in gold, bought the safety of the English who lived in areas controlled by the Danes. Although the Danelaw's political independence lasted only fifty years, its separate, i.e., Scandinavian, quality was recognized not only by Alfred and his English successors but also by the laws of Knut in the early eleventh century and by the Norman lawgivers after the conquest.

Returning to our story, in 878 King Alfred attacked the Danes and Guthrum accepted baptism, took the name Athelstan, and became a Christian (although it is doubtful that he gave up any of his other gods). In 879 he was back in East Anglia. The shires of Northampton, Huntingdon, Cambridge, and Bedford along with Norfolk, Suffolk, and Essex became part of the Danelaw.

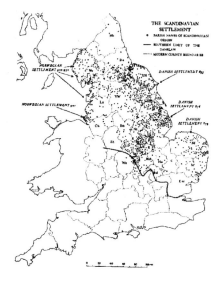

In Ireland, the Norsemen—both Danes and Norwegians—established important trading towns in the southern half of the island – Dublin, Waterford, Cork, and Limerick.

In France, the Danes founded the dukedom of Normandy in 911 A.D. The Danish leader, Rollo, did homage to King Charles the Simple and promised to defend the land enfeoffed to him. In 912 he was baptized.

From the beginning Norman society had a feudal character lacking in the Danelaw. The settlers held on to their language for a generation or two, but everything was against its survival. One count of Normandy is supposed to have sent his son from his court at Rouen to Bayeux to learn the tongue of his ancestors. But Normandy was moving farther from its Norse origins rapidly. The Norman conquests of England and Sicily in the eleventh century were not a continuation of the Viking conquests, but essentially Norman. They belong to the history not of northern Europe but of western and southern Europe. The years 910–911 saw Rollo's transition from a Viking chieftain to the overlordship of Normandy.

The Viking Movement East

The founders of the city-states of Novgorod and Kiev were men of Scandinavian stock.

There had been a steady process of assimilation of the Rus to the native population of Slavs for 200 years. Concubinage, intermarriage, a change of language and religion, and the adoption of Slavonic customs had quietly eroded the Norseness of the Rus. And the massive influence of Byzantium carried the process even farther.

It is difficult to tell at what point in time Kiev ceased to be anything but marginal to Viking history. A hard answer might set it back to the ninth century. An even harder might say that it had never been anything but marginal.

Iceland

In both the Faroes and Iceland the first people to arrive were Irish religious hermits, reaching the Faroes soon after the year 700. The Vikings followed about 100 years later, and displaced the Irish.

One Viking bent on settlement in a new land took three ravens along. Several days out, he loosed one, and it flew home. Some days later he released another, and it returned to the ship. Still later he loosed the third, and it flew straight ahead, giving them the bearing for Iceland.

In another decade the age of settlement had begun. Ingolf was the founding father, settling in what is now Reykjavik.

The lakes and rivers were full of trout and salmon. The surrounding seas were full of fish, seals, and whales. There were innumerable seafowls. And all these were easy to kill, since none had had any experience with humankind and did not know enough to flee.

By 930, all suitable land in Iceland had been occupied. The majority of settlers had come from Norway direct but some by way of Scotland. Some were Christian.

This was a time when the Viking armies all over the West had suffered heavy reverses—defeated in Brittany, pounded in Wessex and Mercia, thrown out of Dublin, Andlesey, and the Hebrides, and deprived of their leaders in Scotland and the Orkneys. So they had good reason to seek new lands. Icelandic tradition also holds that another reason they sought new land was the tyranny of King Harald at home in Norway.

But the number of people that Iceland could take was limited. Its population at no time exceeded 60,000.

The names of some four hundred settlement men are recorded in the Icelandic records. Roughly one-seventh had a Celtic connection, which usually means Irish. There were also many Celtic slaves and concubines.

In 982, Erik the Red was outlawed from Norway for manslaughter, and he was later given a three-year sentence of banishment from Iceland for the same reason. He decided to sail west and explore a new land that had been sighted by a storm-tossed Norwegian fifty years earlier. He came upon Greenland. He spent three years exploring this land, which was devoid of inhabitants but rich in animals, fowl, and pastures.

In Iceland, all the suitable land had been taken up. So Erik's description of a land that was green made it easy to gather enough people to fill 25 ships to come with him for settlement in 986 A.D. Of these, fourteen ships arrived safely. The colonization of Greenland began with perhaps 450 people and eventually would number 3,000.

Erik's son, Leif, made the first landing on the North American continent. A map purportedly drawn up in the early fifteenth century showing that the Vikings charted North America long before Columbus is almost certainly a fake. But archeologists agree that a site at L'Anse aux Meadows in Newfoundland is without doubt Norse. Excavations beginning in 1960 showed a base camp of eight houses, three were dwellings that each housed 25 to 30 people. The rest were workhouses. The buildings were in the Icelandic style, six feet thick with two layers of sod with a layer of gravel in between for drainage, with roofs made of turf laid over a timber frame. Radiocarbon analysis gave dates between 980 and 1020, the time of Leif Erikson's and subsequent visits. Other artifacts were found that could have come only from the Greenland settlements. A spindle and whorl attested to work with textiles, and since among Vikings this was a woman's skill, the find supports the testimony in the sagas that at least some of the expeditions included women. The sagas relate that a later expedition stayed three years and that the leader and his wife, Gudrid, had a son born, Snorri, who takes the honor of being the first European born in America away from Virginia Dare.

From the base camp they explored the coast, looking for a suitable site for colonization. The "Vinland" where they reported wild grapes growing was probably Nova Scotia, since it is about as far north as grapes grow. Proof that the Vikings got that far south was the fact that butternuts, a white walnut that has the same range, were found in the ruins at L'Anse aux Meadows. The Vikings were discouraged by several bloody encounters with the natives. The Vikings called these people Skraelings (a Norse word meaning wretch), although they were probably Indians rather than Eskimo, whom the Vikings met in Greenland and also called Skraelings. The spears and axes with which the Vikings were armed gave them no advantage over the bows and arrows of the natives, who also greatly outnumbered them. In any case the Viking voyages were over and done with by year 1020 A.D.

After the year 1200 the climate grew colder, and by the middle of the fifteenth century it was very cold indeed. Over much of Europe the glaciers were advancing and the tree line fell lower. The northern coast of Iceland was increasingly beleaguered by drift ice. Off Greenland the sea temperatures sank. By 1250, the ice was forbidding. By 1350, the old sailing route had been abandoned. The Skraelings, who were undoubtedly Eskimos this time, appeared in the area and by 1340 they had reached the western settlement.

Also the increased fur trade out of Russia and cloth out of England and the Netherlands worked against Greenland woolens. The European workshops also came to prefer elephant ivory to walrus tusks. But the Skraelings proved to be the last, unbearable burden, and they had both time and the climate on their side.

Chapter 24

The Norman Conquest of England

J ust prior to the Norman Conquest, the king of England was Ethelred the Unready. He was married to Emma, the daughter of Richard I, Duke of Normandy, and their only son to grow to manhood was Edward, to whom the Church later gave the title "the Confessor." Ethelred died in 1016 while the Danish warrior Canute was on his way with a fleet to attack London. Ethelred's son, Edmund Ironside, fought gallantly but was defeated and died toward the end of 1016. The Witan, the Great Council of England composed of the lay and clerical leaders of the kingdom, chose Canute as king, but this did not give his sons a hereditary claim to the throne. Canute served as king from 1016 to 1035.

As Peter Poyntz Wright says in his *The Battle of Hastings* (England: Michael Russell Publishing, 1986) on which this account is based, Canute put away his first wife and married Ethelred's widow, Emma, probably as insurance. After three years Canute became king of Denmark on the death of his brother, and by war and trickery he seized the throne of Norway. All this meant that he was not able to spend much time in England, and in his absence the earls of Wessex, Mercia, and Northumbria ruled. When Canute died his sons by his first wife were kept very busy trying to consolidate their position in Denmark and Norway. Harthacanute, the son of Canute and Emma, had a legitimate claim to the throne of England through Emma, and he became king in 1040. But he died only two years later, in 1042, and before his body was in its grave, the English restored the old West Saxon line by acclaiming Edward king.

Edward had spent his life in Normandy; he was half Norman by blood and entirely Norman in speech and feeling. To protect his position, he quickly married the daughter of the most powerful of the earls, Godwin of Essex. In 1051, a foreign guest of King Edward was involved in a brawl in Dover, which was in Godwin's feoffdom. The king ordered Godwin to punish the town, but Godwin refused and proceeded to raise an army. The other two earls supported Edward, and Godwin backed down. Edward exiled Godwin and his truculent sons, and sent Godwin's daughter, the Queen, to a nunnery. Edward then called over his Norman friends and gave them land and high-church offices. To William the Bastard, duke of Normandy, Edward promised the throne of England upon his death.

Godwin in the meantime had been collecting a fleet. He sailed up the Thames, and it was King Edward's turn to back down. All of Godwin's lands were restored, and his daughter returned from the convent to continue the bullying King Edward so hated. In 1053, Godwin died, and his son, Harold, inherited his lands and position. Harold then proceeded to make himself indispensable to King Edward. Harold put down a rebellion in Wales, among other things. For his part, Edward took little interest in politics and devoted his time and energy to his life's work, building the great abbey at Westminster.

It was obvious to everyone that Edward would die childless. Edgar the Atheling was Edmund Ironside's grandson and Ethelred's great-grandson, and so he had a legitimate claim. But he was only ten years old, and in such unsettled times when the country was under a number of threats, it was unlikely that the English would choose him to succeed. When Edward died Edgar's supporters did not even attempt to lodge a claim.

Canute, as noted, did not have a hereditary claim, and as a consequence neither did his two sons by his first wife. One son was Harald Sigurdsson, known as Hardraade, King of Norway. The other was Sweyn, King of Denmark, who made no attempt to lodge a claim. Hardraade, however, claimed that he and Harthacanute had made an agreement that if either one died childless, the other would inherit his kingdom. Whether or not there was any truth to this, Hardraade raised an army to invade England and seize the throne.

William of Normandy's claim was complicated, and somewhat tainted because he was a bastard. He was the son of Robert I, Duke of Normandy and the daughter of a tanner of the town of Falaise. His grandfather, Richard II of Normandy, and Emma were brother and sister, the children of Richard I, Duke of Normandy. So William did have a hereditary claim through

Emma, although a rather tenuous one. His principal claim was that Edward had promised him the throne in 1051. William also maintained that Harold had sworn an oath to support William's claim.

Of several versions of how that oath came about, Peter Wright believes that the most plausible is that Harold took a ship to go further up the coast of England, that he was blown off course by a storm, and that he landed by accident in Normandy. He was arrested by one of William's vassals, and to obtain custody William paid the captor money and granted him land. So the oath was obtained while Harold was in William's custody, circumstances that gave Harold little choice. Also, William sneaked into the reliquary on which the oath was taken on the bones of two British saints, Ravennus and Rasiphus. When the covering was removed after the oath and Harold saw on whose bones he had sworn, he was visibly shaken. But although the oath was taken under duress, Harold did nothing to gain dispensation from it. However, it should also be said that at the time of the battle of Hastings, Harold's two brothers were still troubled by the oath. They tried to persuade Harold to stay out of the battle and let them fight it in his name, but he refused. In any case, the oath was the pope's justification for supporting William, and the pope's support gained William some valuable allies and enormously sustained the morale of his troops.

Harold Godwinson, the Earl of Wessex, did not have a hereditary claim. But he had been Edward's closest associate, and for the last two years of Edward's life he had been acting as king. Edward on his deathbed probably said he wanted Harold to be king. In any case, the Witan confirmed Harold, and the Archbishop of York crowned him on January 6, 1066.

Harald Hardraade, King of Norway, launched a fleet to invade England and seize the throne from Harold, and Harold's brother, Tostig, joined him. Edward the Confessor had appointed Tostig to be Earl of Northumberland. But his rule had been harsh, there was an uprising against him, and King Edward deposed him. Most people believed that Tostig had been deposed as a result of Harold's advice. In any case, Harold's brother Tostig was now his enemy and joined forces with Harald Hardraade. The idea was to make Harald Hardraade king of England and to restore Tostig as Earl of Northumberland.

Harald Hardraade and Tostig sailed up the Humber with 300 ships to Riccall on the River Ouse, disembarked and marched toward York, ten miles away. Barring their way was Edwin, Earl of Mercia, and Morcar, Earl of Northumbria, who had taken up a position at Gate Fulford on the Ouse, two miles south of York. Here they gave battle on September 20, 1066. It was hard fought for most of the day, but the English finally broke after suffering losses that would affect the issue at Hastings, as Peter Wright says. But the Norwegians also suffered heavy losses, and this would affect the battle with Harold at Stamford Bridge a few days later.

Harald Hardraade did not treat York as hostile. He took hostages and food for his troops, but he offered the citizens of York a treaty whereby they would become his allies and march south with him to conquer the realm. But custom, habit, and caution demanded that he secure hostages from all over the shire, and it was probably to obtain these that he marched the main body of his force to Stamford Bridge on the Derwent, 12 miles from his ships at Riccall and 8 miles northeast of York. Harald Hardraade then camped at Stamford Bridge to rest his troops.

But Harald Hardraade underestimated Harold of England, who was riding north from London as fast as he could with his housecarls. They made the 180 miles in just four days. Harold spent the night of September 24 at Tadcaster. The next day he moved rapidly through the undefended city of York, and at the end of a 17-mile march came upon the unsuspecting Norwegians at Stamford Bridge.

In numbers and arms, the two armies were well matched. For both of them the stakes were very, very high. They fought on foot, with the English having the advantage of surprise and preparedness.

Wright estimates that Harald Hardraade probably had about 18,000 men when he first landed. His forces suffered some casualties at York, and he had to leave some men to guard the ships. So he probably had 7 to 8,000 men when the battle was joined. Hardraade was one of the greatest military figures of the eleventh century, but Harold caught his forces off guard. Hardraade himself was struck in the throat by an arrow, Tostig was also killed, and there can have been few survivors among their bodyguards. Their frightfully punished army took flight, and the survivors were harried over a dozen bloody miles to Riccall. Harold was confident that this sorry remnant would not be able to disrupt his rear when he turned to meet the Normans in the south, so he stayed his hand, and gave them quarter. Only 24 of the 300 ships that brought the attacking force were needed to carry the survivors home.

When William learned that Harold had been crowned, he was irate, apparently feeling that he had been insulted, since everyone knew about the oath and William's pretensions to the crown. He consulted his two half brothers, Bishop Odo of Bayeux and Robert de Mortain, and then sent an emissary to Harold demanding that he surrender the crown. The demand was rejected.

William then called a council of war of his vassals. They were not obliged to support an overseas expedition and turned him down. But William was clever. From the age of eight he had been under the guidance of experts at political intrigue, and he had learned his lessons well. He met with his vassals one by one, and by threat and promises won them over. But this gained him only about 1,200 armored cavalrymen. It might be said parenthetically that one of these was Preudirlegast (Pride of Le Gast, a village in Normandy) whose name in the next generation or two was corrupted to Prendergast and whose descendant four or five generations later was Maurice Prendergast. Maurice was one of the principal lieutenants of Richard de Clare, Earl of Pembroke called Strongbow, in the Norman conquest of Ireland, and the ancestor of the many Americans named Prendergast.

William then appealed to Pope Alexander. The fact that five successive popes had excommunicated the Archbishop of Canterbury probably made it easier for the pope to give William his blessing. He did so and also sent him a consecrated banner to carry into the battle. With the pope's support, it was easier for William to gain allies. The Germans promised help and so did Sweyn of Denmark. A large number of armored cavalrymen with their vassals joined from Brittany and Flanders.

Harold had his housecarls, mounted infantry who were the best-trained troops in all of Europe. He also called out the Fyrd, a sort of National Guard of territorials instituted in the reign of King Alfred that was required of every village. These forces were put to guard the coast.

William had about 500 ships built. Believe it or not, he also built three portable castles! These were made of wood, knocked down, and ready for assembly as soon as a proper earthen mound or motte could be found or made! Once in place they would serve as keeps.

William and his fleet were ready to sail by August 12. But the winds were against them, and food supplies were getting low. On September 12 the wind changed enough to permit the fleet to move to the mouth of the Somme, where food was more plentiful. The move also provided experience in transporting horses in the rather small ships, which was new to the Normans.

The winds finally turned favorable for the passage to England on September 27. The invading army loaded the ships and sailed the next day for

Pevensy. The coastline has changed a lot since then, and the harbor was much more favorable for a landing than it appears today. Only two ships were lost on the way over, one of which was carrying William's soothsayer who had failed to predict his own demise.

Harold had dismissed the Fyrd, whose term of service was limited to the summer, and Harold himself was away fighting Harald Hardraade's attack in the north. So the landing was unopposed. One of the portable castles was erected within the Roman fort at Pevensy, and patrols of 25 or so of the armored cavalrymen were sent out in all directions. William then moved his troops to Hastings, and the other two portable castles were erected there, possibly in the old Roman fort.

William wanted to provoke Harold into an early fight, since the longer the delay the more trouble William would have feeding his men and the more of the Fyrd Harold would be able to call back. Living off the country was the only way William could feed his troops, but he also adopted a deliberate policy of devastation and terror to frighten the people into submission. Since the area around Hastings was home ground for Harold and the parishes of Crowhurst and Whatlington were part of his personal estates before he became Earl of Wessex, William's decision to devastate the area was also intended to provoke Harold into acting before his forces were completely ready.

William's army consisted of about 5,000 combatants and another 2,500 boat crews and supply personnel. The combatants consisted of about 1,200 Norman armored cavalrymen, with another 800 from adjoining and supporting countries. There were also 800 archers and 3,000 infantry.

As for Harold's army, his housecarls normally numbered 3,000, but after the losses at Stamford Bridge, probably only 2,000 remained fit for the battle at Hastings. Harold's brothers Leofwin and Gyrth probably had 1,000 housecarls each. Also about 4,000 of the Fyrd had also arrived. Some Danes from Northumberland or thereabouts also joined Harold's force.

William had relatively mobile cavalry, although the horses lacked armor of any kind. Harold had only infantry, but they were, as we said, among the best in Europe. So in terms of numbers, training, and equipment the two sides were rather evenly matched. But for both sides, this was to be a new kind of battle with which neither had any experience, a battle in which William's relative mobile cavalry was to be pitted against Harold's static infantry.

In choosing to defend the ridge at Senlac, Harold was forcing William's troops to advance uphill. Harold's front was 680 yards. The men were very close together, probably facing sideways so their shields would overlap in most cases. Harold's line was defended by about 1,000 men and behind each man was another seven or eight waiting to take his place if required. In the words of one participant, the Saxons were "so tightly packed that not even the dead could fall."

William's division of Bretons took up position opposite Harold's right flank. They faced rather boggy ground, which made for heavy going, and beyond that a rather shallow slope uphill. The Franco-Flemish forces took up position opposite Harold's left flank, which was firmer ground but had a steeper slope. The Normans were the largest of the three divisions, and they occupied the center on a contour 50 feet lower than Harold's front line and about 150 yards distant from it, just out of range of the few archers that Harold had.

William's archers were placed in front, the infantry behind them, and the cavalry at the rear. William positioned himself a little behind the formation so he could supervise the deployment and the first shock of the battle. With him were a small number of headquarters staff and messengers to carry instructions to the divisional commanders. There was thin cloud cover, and no threat of rain.

Morale must have been high on both sides. The Normans had the papal sanction, and had successfully completed the channel crossing, perhaps one of the most difficult parts of the venture. If they won, they would receive grants of land and many riches. But if they lost, such a small band of invaders with the sea at their back must inevitably die. William made some sort of speech to those around him, and this was the gist of what he said, that they were fighting not merely for victory but for their lives.

For their part, the Saxons had defeated Harald Hardraade and were defending their homeland. Harold was 44 years old and William 38. Harold's standard was the "Wyvern of Essex," a dragon, and his personal standard was some sort of warrior, probably based on the Cerne Abbas Giant.

When William donned his armor, he got it on back to front. This could have been seen as a bad omen in such superstitious times, but William laughed it off. He also hung around his neck the relics of the British saints, Ravennus and Rasiphus, on whose bones Harold had taken his oath.

As the Norman troops advanced the archers fired their arrows. They were shooting uphill, and their arrows either stuck in the Saxons' shields or went harmlessly over their heads. Since the Saxons had only a handful of archers, there were few arrows for the Normans to pick up. So the archers ran out of arrows, and their attack almost certainly stopped before William had intended it to stop and before the Saxon line had been weakened.

The infantry advanced between the archers. To climb 50 feet uphill in heavy armor only to find that the Saxon line had not been weakened must have been a blow to Norman morale. And the Norman shields were not very effective against the death-dealing weight of what the Saxons threw at them—spears, javelins, axes, and stones fastened to pieces of wood. Although one of the Normans said that they managed to "rain death and wounds on the Saxons," this claim may have been little more than whistling in the dark.

The Bretons on the left reached the top of the hill before the others, and the Saxons hurled everything they had at them. The Bretons turned and fled, leaving the Norman left flank exposed.

Many members of the Saxon Fyrd left their position to pursue the fleeing Bretons, almost certainly against Harold's wishes. Unable to see the whole field of battle, they may have thought it was the entire Norman force that was in retreat. William's response was swift. He ordered some of the cavalry on the left of the Norman division who had not yet gained the ridge to wheel left and attack the Saxon pursuers. The Saxons tried to make a stand on a little hillock, but they lacked body armor and were quickly wiped out.

William then pulled back the entire Norman and Franco-Flemish forces to regroup. The Bayeux tapestry shows the Normans taking the chain-mail hauberks off the dead so the living could use them. During the 30-minute lull in the battle, according to Peter Wright, William was self-possessed, controlling his anger at the Bretons, and demonstrating a capacity for leadership. As a result, he reversed what might well have been a rout.

The second attack was more closely coordinated. It seems to have lasted two hours, with one charge after another being thrown back by the Saxon wall. The churned-up slopes in front of the Saxon line became slippery. The horses had no armor, so if a knight got close enough to use his sword, he was likely to lose his horse and this would leave him very vulnerable indeed. Many were killed on both sides, and dead and wounded men and horses piled up, hindering the Normans.

Then the Franco-Flemish forces on the right broke, apparently precipitated by a rumor that William had been killed. In any case, the Bayeux tapestry shows William throwing back his helmet so he could be recognized, and Eustace of Boulogne, who commanded the Franco-Flemish division, holding out both arms to stop the retreat, with the papal banner in one hand.

The Norman attack continued at the center, but William again pulled back the entire force to regroup. He reorganized the whole force into a single division, and he personally took command of it.

William himself lost a total of three horses from under him during the battle, and at some stage fought on foot. By this time William had probably lost about one-fourth of his men and a much higher proportion of the horses, which without armor were very vulnerable to the Saxon battle-axes. As Peter Wright makes clear, William obviously and correctly believed that defeat meant certain death.

The final assault started about three o'clock. The Normans advanced slowly and carefully, with the Saxons shouting abuse at their every step. In what turned out to be a brilliant stroke, William ordered the archers to shoot with a high trajectory so the arrows would come down on the Saxons from above. This made the arrows much more effective than they had been in the first attack, and the fact that they came from above distracted the Saxons' attention.

The Saxon line weakened here and there, and the Normans began to force their way through and split the line into sections. Fighting was hand-to-hand, with everyone on both sides in danger of being trampled by injured and panicked horses. William ordered Eustace of Boulogne to lead a combined Norman and Franco-Flemish attack on Harold's left flank. Although the accounts conflict, Harold's brothers, Leofwin and Gyrth, seem to have made their way to his side since their bodies were apparently found together.

Legend has it that Harold was hit in the eye by an arrow. This interpretation was based on the impression that the tapestry portrayed Harold twice at this point, once with arrow in eye and once on ground after being cut down by a knight with a sword. Later opinion is that Harold appears only once, lying on the ground. Also, on close examination of the tapestry the arrow was not in the knight's eye, but just above his helmet. He remains standing, whereas a person with an arrow in his eye could certainly not. Furthermore, this knight is armed with a spear and a shield, while the fallen Harold, which is Harold beyond dispute, is armed with an axe.

Eustace of Boulogne, commander of the Franco-Flemish division, and three others from that division cut down Harold. One of these four, probably Ivo of Ponthieu, grossly mutilated Harold's body, cutting off both of his hands among other things. In fact, Harold's body was so badly mutilated that they had to summon his mistress, Edith Swanneck, to identify it by marks on his body that only she would have seen.

Picture from the tapestry showing a knight with an arrow in the eye and the fallen King Harold From the Peter Wright book and the Bayeux tapestry.

Many of the housecarls fought on until they were killed. Others fled into the forest. Bands of Norman cavalry pursued them, showing no mercy and cutting down any that failed to find a hiding place.

As Peter Wright makes clear, the Normans had no doubt about the rightness of their cause. Harold had broken his oath to support William's claim to the throne. The pope had excommunicated Harold and given William the papal edict and the papal standard. The Normans were bitter about the broken oath and inflamed by the loss of so many of their comrades. So they were without pity for either Harold or those who fought with him.

Harold had apparently picked an overgrown and steep-sided ravine named Malfosse behind the line at Hastings to be the rallying point for a rearguard action if needed. It may be that before the battle ended it had been lined with Saxons, and it may also be that fleeing Saxons deliberately led the pursuing Normans into the ravine as a trap. In any case, Eustace led about 50 of the Norman armored cavalrymen in pursuit of the Saxons who made for Malfosse. It was almost six in the afternoon, the light was fading, and the Normans rode headlong into the gully where the waiting Saxons cut them down. Eustace stopped at the edge, dismounted, to investigate, and then ordered a retreat.

At that moment William himself appeared. Apparently thinking that Saxon reinforcements may have arrived, he canceled the order to retreat. At that moment in the dimming light a Saxon struck Eustace between the shoulders from behind and blood gushed from his mouth and nose. His men carried him from the field. William took charge, and in a feat of great bravery helped beat off a Saxon attack with a broken lance. Peter Wright believes that Eustace's order to withdraw from Malfosse coming on top of the two times when the Franco-Flemish division under his command had broken was beginning to cast doubt in William's mind on Eustace's ability and determination.

At dawn the next day, there were about 2,000 Norman dead on the field and 4,000 Saxons, as well as 600 to 700 dead horses. So there were about six human bodies and one dead horse for every yard of the hill. The Normans had suffered about 30 percent casualties, killed and wounded. The Saxon losses, of course, were almost total. William permitted relatives to remove the Saxon bodies, rather than have them devoured by wild animals.

As Peter Wright points out, it was very unusual in those times for a battle to last as long as this one did. It was also the first major engagement pitting armored cavalrymen against infantry. As it turned out, William's decision to bring horses, in spite of the difficulties transporting them in such small ships proved to be decisive. William was also lucky that Harold had to meet the threat posed by Harald Hardraade and Tostig in the north. Harold had manned the shoreline all summer, and if he had still been doing so and William had faced an opposed landing, things might very well have gone the other way.

William moved cautiously after the victory. The garrison at Dover surrendered, and William made a wide sweep around London to cut off its food supply. The Witan elected Edgar the Atheling as Harold's successor, but the young man had the good sense to go to William and submit. Since no help was forthcoming from the northern earls, London opened its gates. William was crowned King of England in Westminister Abbey on Christmas day, 1066.

To calm English fears, William promised to introduce no foreign law. At the same time he began building the tower of London, and each of the Normans who was granted land was instructed to built a motte and bailey castle to secure his feoffdom. A motte and bailey castle consisted of a keep, a tower of stone on top of a mound or hill, with a courtyard below surrounded by a wall. The whole castle would be defended, but if the bailey was overwhelmed the defenders would retreat to the motte to make their stand. Every town in England that was the seat of a Norman lord has the ruins of a motte and bailey castle.

William ordered a census and survey of all the land, people, livestock, and goods in the kingdom. Called the *Domesday Book*, it was the most exhaustive survey made anywhere in Europe before William's time and for many centuries thereafter. As the Domesday Book documents, more than 84 percent of the rural population were unfree serfs, 13 percent were freeman or small landholders. The rest, one man in thirty, were the feudal aristocracy of greater and lesser vassals and high Church officials. The only people not included were some of the few townsmen and the lower clergy.

When the Anglo-Saxons conquered England six centuries earlier, they had almost completely displaced the earlier peoples, whereas the Normans were a minority of only a few thousand ruling over a million Anglo-Saxons. William reserved vast forests for his own pleasure of the hunt. He introduced the political feudal system, in which the king gave land to the highest feudal lords in exchange for the obligation of military service and these higher lords in turn gave portions of it out to lesser lords also in exchange for the obligation of military service. William claimed that his victory gave him title to all the estates held by Anglo-Saxons. Some of the earls and thanes who had not opposed the Normans at Hastings were given back part of their lands, at least temporarily. But those who were at Hastings or the subsequent rebellions lost everything. In dividing this land among the Normans, William obtained the services of about five thousand men at arms like those who had won the battle at Hastings.

Although William was technically a vassal of the king of France, he had honored the obligation solely in the breach. He was determined to have no such independence among his own vassals. One way he accomplished this was to make sure that no vassal of his had very much land in any one place, and he broke up the old earldoms so none wielded the power that Godwin had in Wessex. Gradually the lower vassals came to owe their loyalty not to their immediate overlord but to the king. He also kept the old Saxon Fyrd as a check on the Norman barons. When some of the barons rebelled in 1075, William put them down with the help of the Fyrd and the conquered English.

Still other measures instituted by William were to tighten and centralize royal power. Although local government was left as it had been; William normalized the Church, separated it more definitely from secular affairs.

The upper class Anglo-Saxons and high churchmen lost their lands and powers, but the peasants merely changed one master for another.

The military feudal system in England was a Norman innovation, but the economic feudal system, the manorial system, was already in place, although William strengthened it. All the fighting aristocracy kept land for their own use and support, and on that land they were lords of the manor. A bailiff usually managed the estate, and the serfs were bound to the land. They owed the lord several days each week of work. They also owed him a portion of the produce from their own land, as well as extras on occasions such as Christmas. The serf also had to use the lord's mill, ovens, and bridges and to pay a fee for doing so.

There were a certain number of freemen, later known as yeomen. They held their land from the lord, but they paid rent for it, rather than servile labor. They could move to another manor if they saw fit. They were liable for service in the Fyrd. Only the lords could afford the expensive cavalry equipment, but the yeomen formed a tough infantry. In later centuries with their longbows they would defeat whole French armies.

In the spring of 1067, William returned to the continent to see to things in Normandy. No sooner had he done so than revolts broke out in England, the more serious in the north, and continued until 1072. Danish fighters came over to aid in an uprising in the old Danelaw. To put it down William and his barons laid waste to the north country so thoroughly that a famine ensued in which, in the words of one of the old chroniclers, people "ate the flesh of human beings, horses, dogs, and cats." Between York and Durham not a single inhabited village was left. The last of the rebellions was in the swampy fens around Ely, near Cambridge. William confiscated the rebels' lands and gave them to his followers. He was sparing in death sentences, but he had a lot of hands cut off and a lot of eyes gouged out. With the massacre of its inhabitants, the old Danelaw disappeared as a distinct region and northern and southern England were at last welded into one.

Part Five:

Circles of Stone, Religions, Myths, and Legends

Chapter 25

Stonehenge and Avebury

Stonehenge and Avebury are located on the Salisbury plain in England. Of the approximately 500 stone circles in Britain, these two are the most spectacular.

For thousands of years up to about 6,000 years ago, scattered bands of roving hunter-gatherers living on game, fish, and wild plants roamed the area. They grew no crops and had no domesticated animals. For tools and weapons they used flint, bone, and deer antler. They built huts and probably had tents of animal skin. The landscape was dense woodland, with hardly any open grassland. Probably no more than one or two small bands of people lived in the Stonehenge and Avebury areas at any one time.

Then came the Neolithic age. Beginning about 6,000 years ago waves of farmers crossed over to the British Isles from Europe in skin boats, which were probably very much like the Irish coracle. They brought with them seeds of a primitive wheat and small numbers of cattle, sheep, goats, and pigs. They cleared small irregular plots by felling trees with flint axes and burning the brushwood. They used digging sticks and a primitive wooden plow to till the ground. Their weapons were also flint. Their clothes were leather, similar to suede. Their clay pots were baggy-looking as if they were clay imitations of leather vessels. They buried their dead in long barrows.

These were the so-called Windmill Hill people. They constructed large hilltop enclosures, which are Britain's oldest large structures, made by digging circular ditches around a knoll. The name comes from the one on Windmill Hill near Stonehenge. Cattle breeding eventually became their main occupation. They also kept sheep, goats, pigs, and dogs. And they grew wheat.

Because they could build up a store of food in the form of grain and meat on the hoof, these people increased in numbers rather rapidly. The forests gave way to grassland as a result of clearing, burning, and grazing and by goats stripping the bark from trees. By about 5,000 years ago the area began to look like it does today—a grassy plain. Also, the population and the food supply had grown so large that people could be spared for "public works."

Soon after 4,500 years ago new groups came over from Europe—the Beaker folk, so called because of the pottery drinking vessels in their graves. They knew how to work copper, as well as gold. The main source of both the copper and the gold was Ireland, and the Beaker folk opened trade routes from Ireland to Wessex and other parts of Britain, particularly Cornwall where tin was found. So they laid the foundations for a British industry that combined copper and tin into bronze that was to last for 2,000 years.

From this time, 4,500 years ago to about 3,500 years ago, the Beaker folk buried their important dead in round barrows. The Beaker folk interbred with the earlier Neolithic people living in the area and gradually lost their identity just as the Norman invaders later did. The Beaker folk may have been the ones to introduce the British language, which persisted until the coming of the Saxons. The descendants of the British language survive today as Welsh, Cornish, and Erse.

By about 4,000 years ago, the use of bronze for tools and weapons, made by alloying copper from the west of Britain and Ireland with tin from Cornwall led to the rise of a population apparently dominated by a number of ruling families—the Wessex people of the early Bronze age. Their wealth came from farming and cattle raising and also from their position on one of the trade routes between Ireland and the nearer parts of Europe. The best guess is that they did not migrate to the Stonehenge area, but were the more advanced descendants of the Beaker folk.

At the end of the early Bronze age, about 3,500 years ago, this rich community suffered a rapid decline. The worsening of the climate may have been one cause. Grain, mainly barley, began to be grown on fields with permanent boundaries and crop rotation and manure were used to restore the fertility of soils that had been depleted. This required more labor, reducing the amount available to build monuments. After 3,500 years ago,

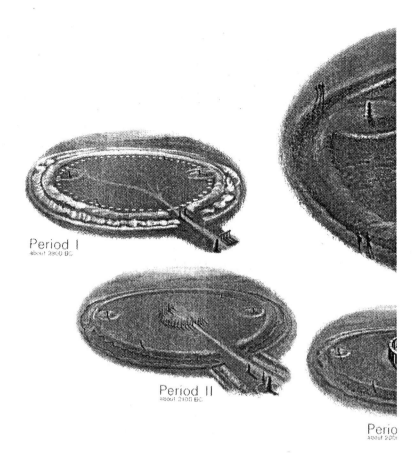

Period I
About 2800 BC

Period II
About 2100 BC

Perio
about 200

Stonehenge began to lose the special importance it had enjoyed for two thousand years as a center of religion and political power.

Stonehenge was built between 4,800 years ago and 3,100 years ago—a span of 17 centuries, almost as long as the Christian era, a thousand years or so after the pyramids of Egypt were built and a few hundred years before the fall of Troy. The building of Stonehenge took place in several periods.

Period I.

The first period had its beginning about 4,800 years ago. The tools used to construct it were picks made of red deer antlers and scoops made of the shoulder blades of oxen. There was an outer bank that formed a fairly true circle, 380 feet in diameter. Then came a ditch that apparently had no significance, since it was used as a dump for rubble. Then came an inner circle some 320 feet in diameter and six feet high. It was glaring white chalk,

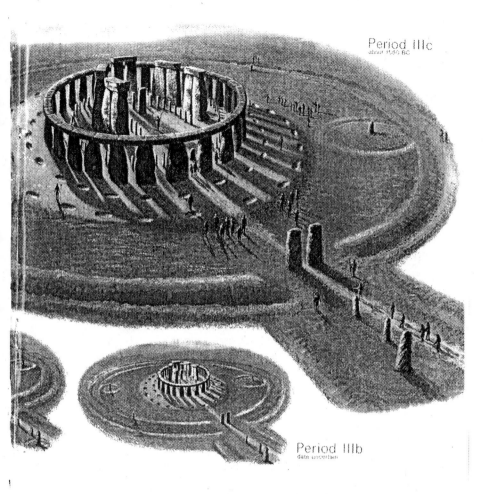

Period IIIc
about 1550 BC

Period IIIb
date uncertain

and must have been awe-inspiring.

Inside of the bank was a ring 284 feet in diameter of 56 holes. These are called the Aubrey Holes, named for a sixteenth century investigator. Each hole is one meter in diameter and one meter deep.

One hundred feet outside of the circle was what has been called the heel stone. A pair of small stones without a lintel stood in the middle of the entrance forming a sort of gateway.

The passageway through the two banks is 35 feet wide. If a person stands in the center of the circle and looks out through the entrance on the midsummer morning he will see the Sun rise over the heel stone.

The Aubrey Holes seem to have been filled in very soon after they were dug. Later, cremated human bones were buried in smaller holes made in the chalk filling of some of the Aubrey Holes, but there is no reason to believe that the Aubrey Holes were made as graves in the first place or that they ever held posts or uprights. They probably were used in some kind of magical or religious ceremony. The four station stones may or may not have belonged to this period.

The number of Aubrey Holes presents a puzzle. If the number system of the people who dug them were on the base 10, derived from 10 fingers, then 50 holes or 60 holes would be understandable. Even 64 holes would be understandable—8 times 8. But 56?

Period II.

Around 4,100 years ago, seven hundred years later (about 28 generations!), Stonehenge was radically remodeled by the newly arrived Beaker folk. Eighty bluestones weighing up to four tons each were set up to form two circles with an entrance pointing toward the rising sun at the summer solstice. For some unknown reason, the work was not completed and a number of the bluestones were never set upright. It appears as if a decision was made to replace the planned work with something much larger.

Period III a.

This new structure was started about 4,000 years ago. It was a circle and horseshoe of large Sarsen stones with lintels on top. As explained in an earlier chapter, the word Sarsen is applied to stones found scattered seemingly at random in the Salisbury plain. The word derives from Saracen, the Greek and Roman word for a nomadic people of the Arabian Desert—i.e., wanderers. This extraordinary structure shows a number of refinements that cannot be found in any of the other stone rings in Europe. First, all the stones have been squared or dressed to shape by pounding with heavy stone hammers. Second, the lintels are held in place by mortise-and-tenon joints, familiar to wood workers, wrought into the solid stone.

Vertical tongue-and-groove joints lock the lintels of the outer circle end to end. Third, the lintels are not straight-sided but have their sides shaped to the curves of the circle on which they are erected. Finally, the pillars are tapered.

The joints are undoubtedly derived from woodworking. At Woodhenge and Durrington Walls, there were huge timber structures in much the same circular form. The upward taper may have imitated the taper of tree trunks. Or it may have been an attempt to increase the apparent height by an optical illusion.

Period III b.

After the Sarsen stones had been set up, more than 20 of the blue-stones that had been dismantled at the end of Period II were selected, dressed to shape, and erected in an oval setting on the line of the later bluestone horseshoe. For some unknown reason, this project was also abandoned and the oval setting of bluestones was demolished.

Period III c.

The final reconstruction of Stonehenge probably followed almost at once. The original number of stones in the bluestone circle was probably about 60, set quite close together, but most have since been broken up, removed, or survive as broken stumps below ground level. In the middle ages the local people found them an easy-to-use building material. The largest bluestone of all, called the Altar Stone by nineteenth century observers, probably stood as a tall pillar on the axial line inside the central and highest Sarsen trilithic and has since fallen down. There is no reason to believe that either its horizontal position or its name is anything but accidental.

Period IV.

About 3,200 years ago, the avenue was extended from Stonehenge Bottom to pass over the hill to the east, and from there southeast to the River Avon. This must mean that Stonehenge was in use at that date and presumably for some time afterwards.

The bluestones, weighing about five tons each, came from the Prescelly Mountains. For the first few miles of the trip, they were probably put on sleds, and pulled over rollers. Tests show that 25 men could pull such a load up a 4-degree slope. In this way they traveled the 10 to 20 miles to Milford Haven.

If put on a raft at Milford Haven, a bluestone could be poled along the coast by a crew of four. The route was up the Bristol Channel, past Bristol, and up the Avon River. Then it went by land for a short distance and then down the Wylye River to Amesbury and Stonehenge.

The larger Sarsen stones, with the average weighing 30 tons and the larger as much as 50 tons, came from much closer—Marlborough Downs. At the rate of 16 men per ton, it must have taken 800 men to pull such stones with as many as 200 more to move the rollers, clear the brush, and guide the sledge. The task of moving the Sarsen stones from Avebury to Stonehenge would have kept a thousand men busy for seven full years.

Egypt's Cheops pyramid was made of 2,300,000 blocks of stone averaging 2 1/2 tons, with the heaviest weighing 15 tons. The pyramid was 481 feet high and covered 13 acres. It was erected in a few years by tens of thousands, perhaps hundreds of thousands of laborers. Stonehenge, less massive but quite as cunningly contrived, was built over a period of three centuries by hundreds or perhaps thousands of workers. It has been estimated that Stonehenge III took 1.5 million man-days of labor.

More than 350 long barrows have been found within a few miles of Stonehenge. The guess is that they were so placed as graveyards are placed near modern churches. The Windmill Hill people built the oldest of these long barrows, which was constructed well before 5,000 years ago. After that came the round barrows of the Beaker folk.

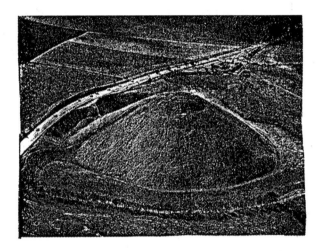

Silbury Hill

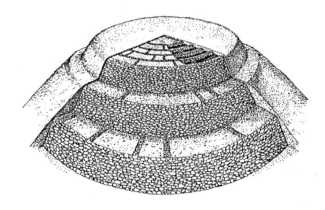

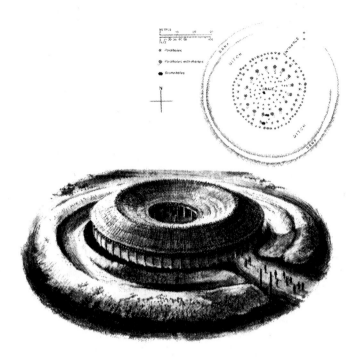

The wooden Basilica.

Avebury Circle is some 17 miles north of Stonehenge. A village was built on top of it in medieval times and the villagers scavenged most of its stones. Avebury was built in two phases and was contemporaneous with Stonehenge.

Finally, in the same area with Stonehenge and Avebury is Silbury Hill. It is the largest artificial mound in Europe. Its base is a circle more than 200 yards in diameter and it rises to a height of 130 feet. Nearly half a million cubic yards of chalk had to be dug and hand-carried to make this vast mound, which means it probably took two million man-days of work.

In 1777, a shaft was dug from the top to the underlying chalk and nothing was found. In 1849, another shaft was dug in from the south side to meet the vertical shaft and again, nothing was found. Both the date and the purpose of Silbury Hill remain a mystery.

The purpose of Stonehenge has been much debated. Ancient temples and modern churches had and have some sort of an altar, and the congregation faces inward at it. Stonehenge clearly faced outward. Its orientation leaves no doubt that from *inside* the circle the sun could be seen rising exactly over the heel stone on midsummer's day.

What was the meaning and purpose of all the other stones and stone rings, the 56 Aubrey Holes, and the rest? No one really knows, except that it obviously did have both meaning and purpose. We know that people visited it from quite far away. The remnants of a very ancient footpath can still be seen leading from the channel to Canterbury and on to Stonehenge. The English have called it the Pilgrim's Way from the dawn of their history.

Gerald S. Hawkins, an astronomer who puzzled over Stonehenge for many years, came to believe that the whole complex worked as a sort of ancient computer to predict eclipses, which he surmises had some religious significance. By moving stones at specified intervals of time about among the filled-in Aubrey Holes, he has shown that the complex can be used to predict eclipses. All that can be said is that it is easily conceivable that he is right, that the religion of the Stonehenge people may have put great emphasis on eclipses and that the priests did in fact develop a method of predicting them. But no one will ever know.

Chapter 26

Hinduism and Buddhism

The ancestors of the Bengali and the Madrassi, as already mentioned, must have been among the earliest of *Homo sapiens sapiens* to reach India. But before coming they must have spent a number of generations in the Middle East, for their gods were from Mesopotamia and Iran. The phallus and female fertility gods were both items of worship. The Bull and the Ram were also part of it. Human sacrifice was, too. Their descendants were the Dravidians, who were the ancestors of the present-day Bengali and Madrassi.

About 3,500 years ago a new wave of conquerors came down from the northwest, the Aryans. They dominated India for a thousand years, until about 2,600 years ago. They were light-skinned and looked down on the dark-skinned Dravidians. They had horses, chariots, and swords, so it was a relatively easy conquest.

The gods of these Aryan conquerors were not the gods of an agricultural people but those of nomads—the Vedic gods of Earth, sky, wind, storm (Indra), and fire (Agni). Interestingly, *soma* – a milky fermented liquor that produces hallucinations—was an integral part of the Vedic sacrifices.

Then came a time of flux, the rise of the Brahmins as a priestly caste and the first phase of Hinduism. Hinduism is not identified with a particular person, as Christianity is with Christ, Buddhism with Buddha, Islam with Mohammed, and Confucianism with Confucius. The reason is probably that it existed much earlier than the others. It is in fact the only one of the very early religions to survive, and so it is the only major religion existing today that worships many gods. It is as if westerners were still worshiping Zeus, Apollo, and Athena. The other major religions were all monotheistic, although many people would regard some branches of Buddhism as exceptions. In any event, in the case of Buddhism, Christianity, and Islam a reformer came along whose theology came to replace the earlier pantheon of gods, many of whom had displayed the all-too-human characteristics of hate, vengeance, sexual appetite, and even a thirst for blood. In India, Buddha's teachings were adopted by the elite, but were never embraced by the mass of the people. So when new invaders replaced the elite, the people's religion, Hinduism, reasserted itself.

Even in modern times, Hinduism has a remarkable hold on a significant percentage of highly educated Indians. My wife and I, for example, once stayed at the home of an Indian husband and wife both of whom were graduates of Oxford. Their son had an American Ph.D., and the British king had knighted the wife's father. While we were there the wife's mother came each morning to the family shrine to put a food offering at the feet of Ganesh, the Elephant-headed god.

Buddha was born a Hindu 2,500 year ago. What he espoused was not really a rival religion to Hinduism but a system of ethics. Buddhism spread rapidly among the rulers and the elite in India, but among the masses the belief in the old gods of Hinduism continued.

In the fifth century A.D., there was a revival of Hinduism among the elite. It was at that time that the *Mahabarata*, the basic book of Hinduism, took its final form. Today, Buddhism is almost unknown in India—it is a foreign religion.

In the first phase of Hinduism, the Brahmins gained in power because of the increased importance of ritual and of sacrifice. Their role was not so much to worship the gods, as to try to influence and manipulate them. Sacrifice was needed to maintain the strength of the gods as well as to please them.

Another theme in Hinduism is gaining knowledge and practicing austerities—the self-denial of the monk. In Hinduism, time is conceived as a cycle, and the idea of reincarnation looms large. A central notion is *Karma*, which is intimately related to the idea of rebirth—it is the destiny you created by what you did in a former life. *Karma* means "action." Cause leads to effect.

The caste system arose out of the racial differences between the Aryan conquerors and the Dravidians. The word for caste, *Varna*, derives from the word for color. But the caste system also had origins in the division of labor.

The basic castes are as follows:*Brahmin*, the priests; *Kshatriyas*, the warriors and rulers; *Vaisyas*, artisans and farmers; *Shudras*, the unskilled laborers.

Each of these four has hundreds of subcastes. The first three are the twice-born. The untouchables are outside the caste system.

The principal gods of Hinduism are three:

The first is *Brahma*—the creator. The second is *Shiva*—the destroyer, but he is also a creator, for by destroying he makes way for the new. The third is *Vishnu*—the preserver.

In India today, people tend to worship either Shiva or Vishnu, and there are separate temples for each. If there is a temple in India dedicated exclusively to Brahma, I have not heard of it. Perhaps this is because Brahma's role was to create the world, and although he has to recreate it every few million years, he has little if any role in the lives of humans.

However, this is not true in Bali. The oldest and one of the holiest temple complexes in Bali is *Besakih*. It was built in 1,007 A.D. on top of a mountain and has about 30 temples dedicated to almost every god in Hinduism. But the principal temple is dedicated to all three of the top gods, Brahma, Shiva, and Vishnu.

Non-believers are not allowed in that temple, but you can peek through a gate on one side, and watch the worshipers scatter flowers at the feet of the three gods, who are lined up side by side.

Brahma has four faces, one for each direction.

Shiva is sometimes portrayed with four arms and sometimes eight. He has a third eye, which destroys enemies by fire when he opens it. Each hand holds a weapon or other symbol—a trident, an hour-glass drum, a noose, a club with a skull at the operational end of it, a deer, and so on.

Shiva's wife is Parvati. Another wife is Devi. Two other wives are Uma and Durga—as well as the consort, Kali. However, some devotees regard Devi, Durga, Uma, and Kali as different manifestations of Parvati. Shiva's throat is colored blue. The reason is that Devi once choked *Shiva* to keep him from swallowing poison. Another version is that Shiva swallowed the poison and is holding it in his throat forever, since it would otherwise poison all of humankind.

Shiva's steed is the bull. At his temples, the bull is usually in a separate, small building with a roof but no walls and is usually portrayed lying down with his head held high, as if chewing his cud.

Shiva's symbol is the *lingam*, that is, a phallus—an erect penis. The center of a Shiva temple is never a statue but always the lingam.

Shiva's wife, Parvati, is represented in many of his temples by the female sexual organ—the yoni. It is usually carved as the stone base enclosing the shaft of the lingam.

In India, the most familiar portrayal of Shiva in places other than temples is as *Nataraj*—Lord of the Universe or Lord of the Dance. In this portrayal he is dancing on the body of a demon, and over his head is the arch of the heavens.

Ganesh, the elephant-headed god, is Shiva's son. Shiva was away from home for a long period, and when he returned he found a young man in Parvati's bedroom. Not recognizing his own son because he had grown so much, Shiva lopped off the fellow's head. Parvati raised hell and made Shiva promise to supply Ganesh with a new head. The first creature to come along was an elephant, so Ganesh has the head of an elephant.

Ganesh's steed is a mouse, and you will see the mouse crouched at Ganesh's feet in most portrayals. I have often wondered if the

The Lord Brahma

ancients who developed the pantheon of Indian gods might have been impishly playing with their followers. A god with the head of an elephant riding a mouse?

For reasons that I have never been able to discover, Ganesh is the favorite god in Bombay, and the subject of a festival.

Kali, Shiva's consort, saved Shiva when he was battling a demon with magical qualities. Every time a drop of the demon's blood hit the Earth, a thousand new demons sprang up. Kali saved the day by positioning herself below the battle and gobbling up every drop

The Lord Shiva

of the demon's blood before it could reach the Earth. So Kali is portrayed with blood dripping from her teeth and mouth.

In another myth, Kali was cut into thousands of pieces. One small piece of her fell on what is now Calcutta. The literal meaning of Calcutta is "Kali's big toe"—*Kali Kuta*. She was miraculously reassembled, and she is Calcutta's principal deity.

There is a temple devoted to Kali in Calcutta. Whether deliberately or by happenstance, right next door to the temple is Sister Theresa's refuge for the destitute, who are picked up from the streets each day by truck and brought to the refuge to die in some comfort. Prevented from sacrificing humans, the priests of the temple sacrifice endangered animals. When my wife and I were there a few years ago several priests were jailed for sacrificing two rare deer.

The Lord Vishnu

Ganesh

The priests of the Kali temple give today's authorities a lot of trouble. In Calcutta for weeks before a festival in which Kali is honored, striking papier-mâché statues of Kali with blood dripping from her teeth and mouth are constructed all over Calcutta. Then on the appointed day they are all carried—by hand, truck, and donkey—to the holy Ganges River where they are set afloat.

Both alcohol and hashish—a very ancient and very potent form of marijuana—are consumed in great quantities, and hundreds of happy, friendly, and totally stoned people gather around a Western visitor offering him a drink of whatever it is they are having.

Vishnu is dark; he is always portrayed as blue in color. Vishnu had 10 different avatars—incarnations—as follows: 1, fish; 2, tortoise; 3, hog; 4, man-lion; 5, dwarf; 6, *Rama* of the battle-axe; 7, *Rama* of the *Ramayana*; 8, *Krishna*; 9, *Buddha*—yes, Buddha, most Hindus believe that Buddha was really a manifestation of Krishna. Krishna's tenth and final avatar is still to come. He will some day return as a White Horse to destroy the foreign barbarians in India and restore order.

The most famous are the seventh avatar, Rama in the Ramayana and the eighth avatar, Krishna.

In statues, Vishnu usually has four arms and his hands hold a conch shell, a discus, a mace, and a lotus (sometimes a bow).

Vishnu's steed is a magical giant bird, *Garuda*, which Indonesia chose as the name of its airline.

Vishnu is often portrayed reclining on a coiled serpent floating on the waters (*Narayana*—"moving in the waters"). Vishnu does this after each destruction of the universe and *Brahma* arises from a lotus growing from Vishnu's navel, in order to create the universe anew.

Having a total of ten avatars, or mani-festations, Vishnu has a larger share than any of the other gods of wives, consorts, or what-ever. But some Hindus believe that each of the different goddesses is actually *Lakshmi*, his wife, in a different guise. So when Vishnu is Rama, his wife is really Lakshmi born again as Sita.

Hinduism is *not* a proselyting religion. It was not spread by either organized missionary societies or by the sword.

Khajuraho

There is one church at Khajuraho that the population is sufficient to support, three that were abandoned and are now maintained by the state, and two churches that are still supported by a population.

The three churches that are maintained by the state are similar to those elsewhere.

The lingam, the symbol of Shiva in temples, an erect penis.

297

There are three parts, ranging from a higher one in which the lingam is contained, a lower one that is open providing an area for the dancers, and one that is slightly lower still also open that is an area for the musicians.

Nataraj, Shiva as god of the dance.

Christian churches have an altar. So does a Mithra church. The audience faces the altar and ceremonies are performed. In a Confucian temple there was no ceremony. At Stonehenge, the congregation was presumably inside, but looked out. In Hindu temples at Khajuraho, there was no place for a congregation. The dancers performed solely for the god. In the inner circle, the highest portion, there was no light. In the dark of the inner sanctum stood the lingam, surrounded at its base by the yoni. Around the shrine surrounded by a wall was a simple walkway wide enough for only one person.

One step down was a space open on the sides and roofed lower than the preceding, which was where the dancing girls performed.

Another step down at a still lower level was another space open on both sides and roofed lower still where the orchestra sat and played.

Around the higher tower were exquisite statues of the dancers, done

The yoni, the symbol of the female god, a cunt, surrounding the lingham

with careful attention to their poses, position, and decorations.

In the center of each of the three walls was a larger picture, composed of a male and three females engaged in a ritual copulation.

Below the level of the temple on one side the ground fell away requiring a step, which was filled with carvings that were less formal and fancy than the ones on the main temple. These included a man with a huge, erect penis assaulting a horse.

Bhuvaneshwar

Bhuvaneshwar is a great temple modeled after a huge vehicle headed toward the sea. It is situated on the sea, in the south, below the entrance of the Ganges.

This was also a temple where huge wagons that were pulled by hundreds of people were kept in the street outside. Every year people were killed who tripped and fell beneath the grinding wheels.

One of the more interesting sights was an elaborate design made of different colors of chalk that served a purpose known only to the participants.

The Great Books of Hinduism

The great books of Hinduism are the *Veda*, the *Mahabharata*, the *Ramayana*, and the *Bhagavad-Gita*.

The *Veda* contains the religion of the Aryan conquerors. It is a collection of hymns, technical texts for rituals, spells and incantations, and so on, culminating in the *Upanishad* which deals with the symbolic meanings of the old rituals.

The *Mahabharata*, like the *Odyssey* and the *Iliad*, is based on the story of an actual historical battle. As already mentioned, it was fought at about the same time as the siege of Troy near what is now Delhi between two branches of a royal family for control of the kingdom.

The *Mahabharata* was the product of many minds, and was passed down orally by bards for centuries before it was committed to writing. However, unlike the *Odyssey* and the *Iliad*, the *Mahabharata* is to people living today a holy book, like the Bible.

The *Ramayana* is quite separate from the *Mahabharata*. Unlike the others, a real person, the sage Valmiki in the third century A.D, supposedly wrote the Ramayana. But if there was such a person, he may have been a poet who collected and gave form to myths and stories that had existed for centuries. The *Ramayana* was probably first put into writing during the first century A.D., and material was added up to about 400 A.D.

The *Ramayana* is an epic poem telling the story of a prince, Rama; his breathtakingly beautiful and heartbreakingly faithful wife, Sita, and their struggle with a demon, Ravanna. It is almost impossible to travel in Bali, where Hinduism is the religion, without seeing a *Wayang* puppet show that does not include parts of the *Ramayana*!

It is a marvelous adventure story, but an adventure story with a purpose. The purpose is to elevate Vishnu to rank with Brahma and Shiva. In brief outline, the story is as follows. In a rash moment, *Shiva* grants a boon to the demon Ravanna, whose domain is the island of Ceylon. Ingeniously, Ravanna claims as his boon that a god cannot kill him.

Ravanna then begins to throw his weight around, becoming a real nuisance to the gods themselves. The gods talk it over and realize that the boon did not mention a man. So they decide that Vishnu, in his avatar as Krishna, should take a man's form in order to eliminate the demon. So Krishna is born as Rama, the son of a king.

Rama has a happy childhood and young manhood. One charming episode—and a favorite of painters—is Rama's adventure with the cowgirls, the gopi. Rama sits unseen in a tree and spies on the cowgirls bathing. One, Radha, is an exceptional beauty. Rama steals her sari, so she has to remain after the others leave. Rama and Radha have an affair—an affair that has inspired many Indian love poems.

Later, Rama wins Sita, the daughter of a neighboring king, in an archery contest. Rama's stepmother cons his father into sending Rama into exile for fourteen years, so her son, Bharata, can become king. The father dies shortly afterwards, and Bharata goes to Rama and offers him the throne. Rama chooses to continue to obey his father's command and stay in exile.

Later the demon Ravanna kidnaps Sita and takes her to Ceylon. Rama makes an ally of the monkey king who lends him the monkey general, Hanumān, who incidentally has the power of flight. They build a bridge from India to Ceylon, so the monkey army can cross.

Rama kills Ravanna. But Rama receives Sita coolly because he is suspicious that she has lost her honor. Anxious to prove her purity, Sita agrees to take the fire

Hanuman

test. But no one is able to light the fire. It seems that Agni, the ancient god of fire, knows that Sita is innocent and so keeps the fire from igniting. So Agni delivers Sita to Rama's arms.

The *Bhagavad-Gita*

There is nothing comparable to the *Bhagavad-Gita* in the Western world.

It is really a book of theology, not an epic at all. It was composed much later than either the *Mahabharata* or the *Ramayana*, probably around 100 A.D. It was then inserted in the middle of the *Mahabharata*.

The *Gita* is written as a dialogue between the greatest warrior in the *Mahabharata* battle, Prince Arjuna, and his chariot driver, who is actually Krishna in disguise.

The two great armies are lined up for the decisive battle in a civil war. On the eve of the battle, Prince Arjuna, shrinks from the thought that on the morrow he must kill his fellow humans, including relatives, teachers, and friends.

The Lord Krishna, disguised as Arjuna's chariot driver, explains why he must fight with all his strength—making the central point of Hinduism that what is evil depends upon one's caste and role in life, and since it is a warrior's role to fight, the act of killing is not an evil but a duty.

Suddenly, Krishna reveals himself to Arjuna in all his dazzling radiance, as both the creator and the destroyer of all things.

J. Robert Oppenheimer, the father of the atomic bomb, who was something of a mystic, learned Sanskrit in order to read the *Bhagavad-Gita* in the original. Writing about the test explosion of the atomic bomb at Alamogordo, Oppenheimer relates that when the bomb went off, he was in a dreamy reverie—induced in part by physical exhaustion. He remembers wondering if Krishna, the center of all things, was also in the center of the bomb's inferno.

Oppenheimer later wrote that as he became conscious of those around him again, "There floated through my mind a line from the *Bhagavad-Gita*:

'I am become death, the shatterer of worlds.' I think we all had this feeling more or less."

Parenthetically, let me say that I have looked at a dozen or more translations of the *Bhagavad-Gita* and found that not one gives this exact wording of the line. Most render it in some variation of either "I am death, the destroyer of worlds," or "I have become death, the destroyer of worlds." On one occasion, a taping for a TV documentary, Oppenheimer also used this more conventional translation. All this leads me to believe that the "shatterer of worlds" was Oppenheimer's own translation. For my part, I think that "shatterer" of worlds is a vast improvement!

In Bali today, as mentioned above, Brahma, Shiva, and Vishnu are worshiped in the same temple. But in India one or another god will be favored in a particular locality, Ganesh around Bombay, Kali in Calcutta, and so on.

As the great German sociologist Max Weber pointed out in his awesome study of the world's religions, each major religion tries to explain why there is evil in the world. Zoroastrianism says it is because light and dark, good and evil co-exist in a never-ending struggle. Luther explained it by the concept of *Deus Abscondidus*—God created the world and then departed, i.e. absconded. Evil then crept in.

Even the atheistic early socialists wrestled with the problem. At their conference in Brussels at the beginning of the twentieth century, the Socialists addressed the question of how socialism would explain the death of a child in a streetcar accident. Their considered reply was that in the perfect socialist country there would be no accidents!

The way Hinduism explains the existence of evil in the world is unique. There is no evil as such. What is evil to one caste is not to another. It is not evil for warriors to kill, but their sacred duty, while it is evil for other castes to kill.

This is what Krishna explains to Arjuna—that it is his duty to kill in the coming battle, even though some of those on the other side are cousins, uncles, teachers, and friends whom he has loved.

In addition to laying out the religious basis of the caste system, the *Bhagavad-Gita* ordains that the goal of a human being is to fuze with the universal spirit. There are three ways to do this: 1. austerities (or yoga); 2. sacrifices; and 3. *Bhakti*, devotion to Krishna. The first is for holy men, law now forbids the second, and so the third is the only practical way for ordinary human beings.

Hinduism made its way from India to Cambodia and even to the Chams in Vietnam. And it also made its way to Java and Bali.

Indonesian and Hindu traders must have carried Hinduism to Indonesia. There was a lot of trade between what are now the Tamils in India and the Javanese and Balinesians. Indonesian princes also invited Brahmin priests to join their courts, and they brought knowledge of Sanscrit along with them.

Buddhism

By the year 2500 B.C., the Aryans had pushed beyond the Punjab into the plains and valley of the Ganges. One kingdom of these Aryans was about 100 miles northeast of Benares and about 30 miles south of the Himalayas. The family name of the Rajah was Gautama, and to them was born a boy in 563 B.C. who became Buddha. The boy grew up, married, and lived happily until his twenty-ninth year, ten years after his marriage. He then had four visions—of age, illness, death, and of dignified retreat from the world. These visions starkly set the problem of human suffering before him. That same night his son was born, and that same night he turned to the life of a mendicant wanderer seeking truth and a solution to the problem of suffering.

For several years he wandered, attaching himself to various holy men. He earned a reputation as a holy man himself, and disciples gathered around him. But he found no satisfaction in it. So he abandoned the ascetic life and began eating regular food again. His disciples left him.

One day in his wanderings, Buddha rested beneath a Bo tree. Suddenly, enlightenment came. He saw that desire was the root of all evil, worry, anger, and violence. At the same time, he saw that love of all creatures was central. Desire makes us want to live again after death. As a result, a person who cannot control his desires goes through an endless chain of rebirth in other forms—the wheel of life and senseless repetition. He who can suppress desire breaks out of the chain and achieves Nirvana.

At that moment, Buddha could have achieved Nirvana for himself. Instead, he chose to return to the world to save others.

Buddha established himself in the so-called deer park near Benares, where the ruins of the Buddhist stupas of his own day still stand. For the next 45 years, Buddha preached his new doctrines, finally dying in 483 B.C.

Like Hinduism, early Buddhism was not a proselyting religion. Individual Buddhist monks wandered with their begging bowls and preached to all who would listen. But that is not proselyting in the same sense as, say, the Jesuits, the Baptist missionary society, or Mohammedans, who proselyted with the sword.

Buddhism came to Indonesia by way of traders and sages invited by kings. As already mentioned, a Chinese traveler, Xuan Zang (Hsüan Tsang in Wade-Giles), visited India via the Silk Road in the years 629 A.D. to 645 A.D., when Buddhism was at its height in India, and brought copies of the sacred texts back with him to China.

Buddhism got to Japan via Japanese traders going to China and a few wandering Chinese monks. Buddhism got to Burma with Burmese traders who brought it back from trips to India. The great Shwedagon pagoda in Rangoon with its dome sheathed in tons of dazzling gold leaf contains a hair from Buddha's beard that he was supposed to have given the traders who brought it back to Burma. Buddhism got to Sri Lanka (Ceylon) the same way. The great Pagoda in Kandy, Sri Lanka, contains one of Buddha's teeth.

Societies with a low literacy rate reduce great thoughts to a set of numbered truths so they can be more easily remembered. In the case of Buddhism it is called the Eightfold Path.

In the years following Buddha's death, Buddhism broke into two groups, the *Hinayana* or "small vehicle" Buddhism and the *Mahayana* or "great vehicle." Hinayana Buddhism retains the simple rules of discipline laid down by Buddha. It is followed in Burma, Cambodia, Ceylon, Thailand, and Vietnam. Mahayana Buddhism adds many other Buddhas and saints. It envisions a heaven and a hell and salvation by faith and grace. It has many different subdivisions, from sects emphasizing pageantry to the austere Zen in Japan. It is followed in China, Japan, Korea, and Mongolia. A peculiar form of it is practiced in Tibet. In Indonesia, Buddhist influence melded with Hindu.

Chapter 27

Mithraism, Confucianism, Christianity, and Islam

The worship of Mithras had its origins in what is now Iran. Later, Mithras became the god of the Roman legions and Mithraism a mystic cult popular throughout the Roman Empire. At an early date, Mithraism spread from Iran to India, and Mithras appears in the Veda as Mitra. As M. J. Vermaseren says in his book *Mithras, The Secret God* (New York: Barnes and Noble, 1963) on which the following account is mainly based, Mithraism later spread to Asia Minor and in the first century B.C. crossed into Europe.

In Iran, Mithras first appears as an attendant minor god of the good and righteous Ahura Mazda, the deity of light identified with the Sun and opposed by Ahriman the god of darkness. Later Mithras was portrayed as the slayer of the bull, for which he is best known. In the most common altarpiece, Mithras has forced the bull down with his knee. He holds up the bull's head by one horn, and he thrusts his dagger deep into the bull's heart. The earliest recorded mention of Mithras is as Mitra among the Hittites in the Anatolian plateau in the fourteenth century B.C.—3,400 years ago. The last known reference is to the Roman Mithras in the fifth century A.D., 1,500 years ago. So Mithraism lasted about 2,000 years, just about as long as Christianity has been around.

Zarathustra or Zoroaster was a prophet in Eastern Iran who lived in the period between 1,000 B.C. and 600 B.C., most likely around the latter date. He was a great reformer who tried to transform the then current polytheism into monotheism with Ahura Mazda as the supreme god. He also tried to abolish both the blood sacrifice made in the bull offering of Mithraism and its ritual use of Soma, which was mixed with the blood of a sacrificed bull to bestow immortality on those who drank it. Zarathustra was murdered in a temple.

According to Plutarch, who lived in the first century A.D., the Romans became acquainted with Mithras through pirates from Cilicia, a province of Asia Minor, whom Pompey later drove from the seas.

Mithras is usually pictured wearing a Phrygian cap. His temple was supposed to be a natural cave close to a source of running water. When no cave was available, the sanctuary was given the appearance of a cave. The top of the cave is often decorated with stars, to represent heaven. There were usually no windows, so the temple was dark. Two benches at one end of a central aisle flanked the altar. Ceremonies took place in the central aisle, while initiates watched as they reclined on the benches. The altar was a niche in the wall, and in front of the niche were two fire altars. In Rome alone there were at one time more than a hundred temples devoted to Mithras.

December 25 was the day most sacred to Mithras, the day the god's birth was celebrated. His birth was another miracle—he came forth not from a woman, but from a rock. He was naked, save for his Phrygian cap, he held a dagger in one hand and a torch as the begetter of light in the other. He is also equipped with a bow and arrows.

The greatest deed that Mithras performed for humankind was killing the bull. It was a creative and beneficial act, for out of the bull's death arose fresh life.

In another famous deed, in a time of drought Mithras shot an arrow into a barren rock and miraculously water spurted forth for his thirsty followers.

Still another famous act portrayed in the temples is the hunt. Mithras rides at full gallop, his cloak flying in the wind, and brings down rabbits, deer, gazelles, and boar.

After his slaying of the bull, the miracle of the arrow shot into the rock, and the hunt, Mithras completes his stay on Earth by banqueting with Sol, the sun god, on the flesh of the bull. The divine meal is portrayed often, second only to the bull slaying. Mithraists believed that by eating the flesh of the bull and drinking its blood they would be born again. It would bring salvation to the soul and in time achieve rebirth and eternal light. After

Mithras accomplished his miraculous deeds, he was transported to heaven in a chariot.

Although Mithraism preceded Christianity by over a thousand years in the Middle East and in the Roman empire by at least 100 years, the Christians found it an abomination. In particular this was because of some of the similarities that in fact may well have been due to Christian copying. December 25 was the day of Mithras's birth, the same as Christ's. In fact, of course, it was the approximate date of the midwinter solstice, which was significant to a large number of pagan religions. Mithras brought water forth from a rock, as did Moses. But most of all the Christians abhorred the sacred meal partaken by Mithras and Sol. As one of the early Christian leaders said, it was "a devilish imitation of the Eucharist," ignoring the fact that Mithraism practiced it first. When the Christians attacked the temples of Mithras it was the depiction of the sacred meal that they destroyed even more often than the central altar depicting the slaying of the bull.

Mithraism had seven grades of initiation: the raven, the mate, the soldier, the lion, the Persian, the courier of the Sun, and the father (pater). The raven was the initiate grade and the lion grade was the most frequently achieved. By the 3rd century A.D. the worship of Mithra was widespread throughout the Roman Empire.

The battle at the Milvian Bridge on the Tiber in 312 A.D., when Constantine had a vision of Christ, was the beginning of the end for the Mithraic cult. The Emperor Julian called himself a convinced Mithraist, in spite of his Christian upbringing, leading the Christians to call him The Apostate. But he died in 363 A.D. A period of tolerance followed. Then in 382, the Emperor Gratian issued an edict removing the Mithraic altar of Victory from the Senate, and withdrawing state support for the cult. Shortly before 377 A.D. a cave of Mithras was destroyed, probably the temple at San Silvestro. An edict in 391 A.D. forbade all pagan worship in Rome. Another edict in 392 laid down severe punishment for any practice of pagan worship.

Confucianism

As a child I visited one of the many Confucian temples in China and was deeply impressed. It consisted of a simple square building. This was in a park with a variety of trees. The feeling was of serenity.

The temple itself was simple. The floor was covered with a wall-to-wall mat of fiber of some kind, two inches thick. So quiet prevailed. There was no altar. On the wall facing the entrance was a framed saying of Confucius. The two walls on each side also had a framed saying. Other than that there was nothing. No altar, no statues, no burning incense. Over all was a feeling of peace and serenity.

At that moment if someone has asked me to convert, I would have done so. It was the most mature, intelligent place of worship I have ever seen, before or since.

Unfortunately, the Communist regime has destroyed all the Confucian temples, except one that was kept as a kind of museum piece.

Christianity

Mary, the mother of Jesus, was not deified until the fourth century A.D. This fact, along with the others described below, was supplied by Marcello Craveri in his *The Life of Jesus* (translated by Charles Lam Markmann, New York: Grove Press, 1967). Joseph chose her as wife and learned only then that she was pregnant. Horrified, he threw himself on the floor. Tears streaming down her face, she sobbed, "I am pure. I have known no man!" Then an angel appeared to Joseph in a dream, declaring that Mary was indeed expecting a child of divine origin and that he should take her as wife. He did so, and Jesus was born in 4 B.C., the year of Herod's death.

The Church set the date of the birth of Jesus as December 25. This is the date of the winter solstice, and significantly marks the end of winter and the beginning of spring. It also marked the worship of Sol Invictus, the national cult of the Roman Empire, and provided another highly persuasive reason for naming that particular date. In Rome the feast day of Saturnalia, an even more ancient holiday, was dedicated to demonstrations of friendship and affection. It was simple for Christianity to replace the heathen belief in Saturn without impairing the admirable customs of the Saturnalia.

The appearance of a comet as reported by Matthew has been thoroughly investigated by modern scientists without success except for a finding that a comet could be seen in Babylonia in the year 7 B.C. sometime around the first nights of December. And it is precisely Babylonia or Persia that must be considered the home of the Magi who, according to Matthew, reached Jerusalem under the guidance of the comet. If it is unacceptable to admit that the episode of the Magi is legend, then one must assume that they were Persian or Chaldean astronomers or disciples of Zoroaster who went to Jerusalem precisely to be present at the event they had foreseen.

The Gospels declared apocryphal by the Council of Nicaea (325 A.D.), portray Jesus as a capricious, spiteful, and vindictive child whose power went to his head. He beat two children to death because they played some harmless trick on him and when their parents complained he had them stricken blind. Aside from such stories, which are dated about the fourth or fifth centuries, there is nothing about the childhood of Jesus.

The first episode is the disappearance of Jesus, found three days later engaged in a debate with a group of learned doctors. But this was not unusual. Exceptional children often engaged their elders in debate in those times, and Jesus was clearly exceptional.

In 6 A.D., when Jesus was thirteen years old, if we accept the idea that the date of his birth was 7 B.C., the year of appearance of the comet, Jerusalem was subject to much unrest. Jesus probably submitted himself to a vow of fasting, abstinence, and chastity. He was baptized by John the Baptist early, and in the years that followed proceeded to make his own name. John was imprisoned for a long time for insulting the wife of the King, Herodias, whom he constantly reproached for her adultery. The King gave a magnificent feast to celebrate his birthday. Salome, the seventeen-year-old daughter of Herodias, launched impulsively into a dance. Casting aside one silken veil after another, the girl was finally half-naked before the men, their eyes alight with desire for her marvelous body. The King promised the daughter anything she asked. Salome showed some hesitation, and asked her mother, Herodias. Her mother replied, "The head of John the Baptist." Jesus was profoundly affected. He fled.

Months later Jesus returned to Jerusalem. The priests of the temple threatened to stone him, and again he fled. Jesus was told that Lazarus was ill. He hesitated, and Lazarus died. Jesus went to the grave, and when the stone had been removed called, "Lazarus, come forth." His hands and feet still bound, Lazarus rose. "Loose him," Jesus said, "and let him go "

The priests more alarmed than ever once again debated whether they should arrest Jesus, and once more he fled.

The Last Supper of Jesus and the Apostles was served in the richly appointed house of Mary, the sister of Simon Peter. Jesus began to wash the feet of the Apostles, and then he said out of an anguished heart that one of them would betray him. He took a sop of bread, dipped it in a bowl of sauce and took it to Judas, bidding him, too quietly for the others to hear, "That thou doest, do quickly." The ceremony of the Passover dinner followed immediately.

After the dinner, Jesus fled again, pausing at Gethsemane. Here he was met by Judas, who kissed his hand in a prearranged signal to enable the soldiers to identify him.

Pontius Pilate supposedly judged Jesus innocent, but the people of Jerusalem demanded that he be crucified. Resigned to failure, Pilate sent for a basin of water, washed his hands, and declared himself innocent of the death.

Jesus was taken to Golgotha, and crucified. On the third day after burial Jesus was resurrected, and his body ascended into heaven.

Islam

Mohammed was born in Mecca about 570 A.D. Unlike Christianity and some schools of Buddhism, the faithful do not worship the founder as a god. They believe he was simply a prophet.

Mohammed began preaching in Mecca about 610 A.D. His doctrines alarmed the rich and powerful, and he fled to Medina—the flight called the *Hegira*. He returned with his by now many followers in 630 A.D., and destroyed the idols around the *Kaaba,* a holy stone black in color that is probably a meteorite.

Islam was spread by the sword—one of Mohammed's successors invented the *Jihad,* the holy war. Within 100 years, they had built an empire that stretched from Spain to India.

The god of Islam is one god, and he is a kind and just god. The Koran forbids the representation of human and animal figures, so orthodox art rarely pictures living beings. It condemns usury and games of chance, but permits a man to have four wives. There is a heaven and life after death. Life on Earth is a period of testing. The principal duties are prayers five times a day, alms-giving, fasting, principally during Ramadan, and pilgrimage. The Sabbath is Friday.

In the 600s, Islam split into two factions. The Sunni Muslims follow in a straight line from Mohammed. The Shi'ites follow Ali, Mohammed's son-in-law. Most Shi'ites live in Iran.

Islam is a proselyting religion. It was carried by the sword to various parts of Africa, to India, to what is now Malaya, and to the Southern islands of the Philippines. But it did not come to Indonesia by the sword. Many of the Indonesian petty kings adopted Islam in the early 1500s as a political weapon against the then-dominant Majapahit Empire. Adopting Islam was also a political weapon against the Christianity that the Portuguese traders were also bringing to Indonesia. In any case, Islam gradually replaced Hinduism and Buddhism in Indonesia except in Bali, which kept a form of Hinduism.

Both Christianity and Islam are proselyting religions. The two used both missionaries and the sword to spread the faith. Neither has made much headway where a major religion, such as Buddhism, was already entrenched or where the other was already established. But both have done very well among mountain and jungle tribes, whose religion was still animist.

Both Christianity and Islam also did well in Hindu areas among one group and one group only—the untouchables. The lives of untouchables were so miserable, they were easy targets. Islam got to the subcontinent first, and missionaries converted hordes of untouchables. Their descendants are the inhabitants of Bangladesh. Their cousins in India, the Bengali, are mostly still Hindu.

But Islam also used the sword, conquering whole regions of India and then offering the people a choice of converting to Islam or dying.

Christianity came late to India, and made a few converts among the remaining untouchables. But British policy by this time did not condone conversion by the sword, so Christianity by and large failed.

In the case of Indonesia, it was not the sword that spread Islam, but the spice trade. The first traces of Islam in Indonesia are in northern Sumatra, where traders from Gujarat stopped on their way to China. There were settlements of Arab traders in Indonesia in the seventh century. And Marco Polo noted converts to Islam in Sumatra in 1292.

The big advance of Islam came in the fifteenth and sixteenth centuries. But it came not by conquest, missionaries, or the spice trade but, as already mentioned, because a number of the Indonesian princelings made it a state religion and imposed it on a population still either Hindu or animist. Their motive is difficult to determine from this distance. But it seems that it might have been a way for smaller, satellite states to declare their independence from the then-dominant Majapahit Empire and to resist the Christianity brought by the Portuguese.

Indonesia's form of Islam is different from any other, principally because it retains some of the Hindu and animist elements that preceded it. Something similar happened to Catholicism in Latin America, where the influence of some of the earlier Indian notions is still noticeable.

Chapter 28

The *Iliad*

The *Iliad*, composed by the blind bard Homer along with the *Odyssey*, is an epic poem dating from the most ancient period of Greece. Laid in the ninth year of the Trojan War, it describes events during a 41-day quarrel between Agamemnon, leader of the Greek forces, and Achilles, their greatest warrior.

The excavations at Troy by Heinrich Schliemann and others established that a total of nine cities had been built on the site, each one on the ruins of the others. Archeologists finally agreed that what was designated as Troy VII a, built on the ruins of a city leveled by an earthquake, was the Troy of the *Iliad*. It had been completely destroyed by fire and plundering shortly before 1200 B.C., some 3,200 years ago. The *Mahabharata*, the epic poem of India dealt with in Chapter 26, also tells the story of another war that actually took place and at about the same time, 3,200 years ago.

The *Odyssey*, which is dealt with in the next chapter, begins after the end of the Trojan War. When Odysseus, king of Ithaca, sailed for home, some of the gods were angry with him and put seemingly endless obstacles in his way. The *Odyssey* is the story of his journey and what happened when he finally got home to find his wife besieged by several dozen suitors.

The events leading up to the 41 days recounted in the *Iliad* and the story of the subsequent conquest of Troy are described in various myths and legends familiar to generations of ordinary people living in Greece in the centuries following the war. It all began when the gods gave a banquet at Olympus to celebrate the marriage of King Peleus and the sea nymph Thetis. Eris, the evil goddess of Discord, whom the gods heartily disliked, was not invited. Angry, she threw a golden apple into the hall marked, "For The Fairest." All the goddesses wanted the prize, but the choice came down to three. One was Hera, wife of Zeus, king of the gods. A second was Pallas Athena who had sprung full-grown and in full armor from the head of Zeus. She was called the Maiden—Parthenos in Greek—and her temple is the Parthenon. The third was Aphrodite, the goddess of love and beauty. The three asked Zeus to judge who was the fairest, but he wisely refused and sent them to Paris, son of King Priam of Troy. Paris, Zeus assured them, was an excellent judge of beauty.

A soothsayer had warned King Priam that Paris would some day be the ruin of his country, so he had exiled him to herd sheep on nearby Mount Ida. It was there that the three goddesses found him—herding sheep and living with a lovely nymph named Oenone. The goddesses did not really ask Paris to say who was the fairest, but only to choose between the bribes they offered him. Hera promised to make him lord of Europe and Asia. Pallas Athena promised to see that he would lead Troy to victory against its Greek enemies and lay Greece to ruins. Aphrodite promised to give him the fairest woman in the entire world. Paris was self-indulgent, a weakling, and, as later events showed, something of a coward. He awarded the golden apple to Aphrodite.

The fairest woman in the world was Helen, daughter of Zeus and Leda. She had many powerful suitors, and her reputed Earthly father, King Tyndareus, her mother's husband, was afraid those rejected would be angered. Clever Odysseus, knowing that as king of the small island of Ithaca he had little chance to win Helen, whispered in the king's ear that to counter the anger of the rejected suitors he should make them all take an oath to champion the cause of whomever was chosen to be Helen's husband if he was ever wronged. Tyndareus did so, and Odysseus as his reward asked for and received the hand of Penelope, not so beautiful as her cousin Helen but fair enough.

Helen chose Menelaus, the brother of Agamemnon. Soon after that Tyndareus died, and Menelaus succeeded him as king of Sparta.

After Paris gave Aphrodite the apple, she led him straight to Sparta, and he gave never a thought to Oenone, left forlorn. Menelaus and Helen received him graciously. Although the bonds between guest and host were sacred in Greece, Paris proceeded to violate them. Menelaus went on a trip to Crete and when he returned Paris and Helen were gone, along with most of the Spartan treasure hoard.

Menelaus called upon the kings of Greece to honor their vows and help him recapture his wife and the stolen treasure. All but two of them obeyed. One who did not was the shrewd Odysseus. He wanted to stay with his new wife and young son, so he feigned madness to get out of having to go to Troy. But his attempted trick was exposed. The other who did not obey was Achilles. He was the son of Peleus and the sea nymph Thetis, whose marriage was mentioned above. When Achilles was still a baby, his mother held him by his heel and dipped him into the River Styx to make him immune to any hurt. Carelessly, she neglected to dip him a second time so the heel would be covered as well. So he was immune to any injury except in the "Achilles heel." Thetis learned that in spite of this protection, if Achilles went to Troy he was fated to die there. So she dressed him in women's clothes and sent him to the court of King Lycomedes.

Odysseus was then sent by the chieftains to find Achilles. Clever as usual, Odysseus disguised himself as a peddler selling luxurious ornaments the women would love but included among his wares some fine weapons. When one of the women ignored the ornaments and fingered the weapons, Odysseus knew he had found Achilles. Odysseus had no trouble persuading Achilles to join the great adventure as the commander of his father's troops, the Myrmidons.

Adverse winds shut the Greek army into the port of Aulis. A soothsayer told them that Artemis, goddess of the hunt, who like all good hunters was careful to preserve the young, was angry with them. Her reason was that one of the Greek soldiers after killing one of her wild creatures, a hare, had then gone on to kill all of the hare's young. The soothsayer said that the only way to appease the goddess and calm the winds was for Agamemnon to sacrifice his eldest daughter, Iphigenia. Reluctantly, Agamemnon did so. He had her suspended upside down, and as she piteously begged for mercy he slashed her throat. The adverse winds ceased to blow, and the great fleet sailed to Troy. But the evil price Agamemnon had paid would some day bring down an equal evil upon them all, and especially upon Agamemnon himself.

Of the Trojan warriors, the greatest was Hector, one of the fifty sons of King Priam. Both Achilles and Hector knew that they would die before

Troy was taken. As Achilles said at one point (Robert Fagles' translation, pp. 35 and 265).

> Mother tells me,
> the immortal goddess Thetis with her glistening feet,
> that two fates bear me on to the day of death.
> If I hold out here and I lay siege to Troy,
> my journey home is gone, but my glory never dies.
> If I voyage back to the fatherland I love,
> my pride, my glory dies,
> true, but the life that's left me will be long.

Achilles chose glory and early death at Troy. As for Hector, no divinity told him that he would die in the battle, but he was certain that he would. He told his wife Andromache that he knew well "in his heart and soul" that Troy would fall and that he would be killed.

One of King Priam's daughters, the lovely Cassandra also foretold the fate of Troy. The god Apollo had loved Cassandra and had given her the power of prophecy. She had refused his love. Although he could not take back his gift, since divine favors once granted could not be revoked, he decreed that no one would ever believe her prophecies. She told the Trojans on every occasion what would happen, but no one gave her words a thought.

For years victory wavered from one side to the other. Then in the ninth year a quarrel flared between Achilles and Agamemnon. The *Iliad* begins with the following words (Robert Fagles' translation):

> Rage—Goddess, sing the rage of Peleus' son Achilles,
> murderous, doomed, that cost the Achaeans countless losses.
> Begin, Muse, when the two first broke and clashed,
> Agamemnon, lord of men and brilliant Achilles.

In a raid for supplies, the Greeks had carried off the beautiful Chryseis, daughter of one of Apollo's loyal priests, and given her to Agamemnon. The father came to the Achaean camp to ransom her with rich gifts. Impressed by his gifts, all ranks of the Achaeans cried out their assent. But Agamemnon with cruel words spurned the offer, saying that the girl would die of old age in his house, slaving on the loom and forced to share his bed! "Now go," Agamemnon said to the father, "don't tempt my wrath—and you may depart alive."

Terrified, the old man left. But he prayed to Apollo, who sent down the arrows of the plague. For many days, men, cattle, and horses died, and the smoke of funeral pyres darkened the sky.

A prophet advised that to end the plague the girl had to be returned to her father. Agamemnon said that if he lost Chryseis, he must have another in her stead. "I will take Briseis, your prize," Agamemnon said to Achilles, "so you can learn just how much greater I am than you." Insulted, Achilles drew his sword, but he was also torn with doubt about killing Agamemnon. Then Athena came roaring down from the heavens and seized Achilles' fiery hair. Hera had sped her down, she told Achilles, to tell him that Hera loved both Achilles and Agamemnon, and that Achilles should check his rage, not lay hand to sword, but lash Agamemnon with words alone. One day, Athena continued, glittering gifts would lie before Achilles, and three times over Agamemnon would have to pay.

Agamemnon and Achilles continued to exchange insults, and then Achilles withdrew to his own ships drawn up on the shore. Chryseis in all her beauty was returned to her home and father. Agamemnon then sent two heralds to Achilles' tent to collect Briseis. Achilles welcomed them, saying that he had no quarrel with them but only with Agamemnon. He instructed his close and dear friend Patroclus to hand the girl over to the heralds. But Achilles then said that the heralds should bear witness to his vow that if the day should come when the Greeks needed him to save their armies from ignominious, stark defeat, he would not come.

Achilles' mother, the silver-footed, sea nymph, Thetis, was as angry as her son. She went to Zeus and asked him to inflict loss and defeat on the Achaeans so they would realize how much they really needed Achilles, and Zeus nodded his head to agree.

Apollo's temple stood on the citadel of Troy, the Trojans never forgot to make generous sacrifices to him, and so he was the city's champion. Because Paris, a Trojan, had given her the apple, Aphrodite also sided with Troy. Aphrodite's lover was Ares, the god of war, and he always stood with her. Because Paris had chosen Aphrodite, Hera and Athena hated the Trojans and sided with the Greeks. Poseidon favored the Greeks because they were a sea people. Also, long ago a Trojan king had cheated Poseidon of payment for building the walls of Troy, and he was determined to see the city destroyed. Zeus was neutral because Hera was so disagreeable when he openly opposed her. However, he could not resist Thetis to whom he was indebted for help on a previous occasion. Hera suspected, as she usually did, what Zeus was up to and objected vehemently. But Zeus was finally driven to say, as modern husbands are sometimes tempted to do, that if she did not stop talking, he would throttle her with his "irresistible hands."

Zeus sent a lying dream to Agamemnon urging him to order his longhaired Achaeans to attack and promising him victory. While Achilles sulked in his tent, a fierce battle was fought.

On the battlefield, Paris, the skin of a leopard slung across his shoulders, stepped forward to challenge any of the Greeks to fight him face to face in mortal combat. Helen's cuckolded husband Menelaus was thrilled at the sight of the adulterer Paris right before his eyes, "Now for revenge," he thought and leaped down from his chariot. But Paris cringed back into the Trojan ranks. Hector raked his brother Paris with insults. "Paris, appalling Paris! Our prince of beauty—mad for women, you lure them all to ruin!" Paris replied that he would fight Menelaus one on one between the lines, the winner to take Helen as his wife and her treasure.

The Achaean and Trojan forces both exulted, hoping that this would end the agonies of war. King Priam and Agamemnon met between the armies and sacrificed two lambs to bind their pact. The lots were cast for first blow, and Paris won.

Paris hurled his spear. It hit Menelaus's shield full center. But the shield was made of several layers of ox hide covered with a layer of bronze, and the brazen point of the spear bent back. With a prayer to Zeus for revenge against the man who had wronged him, Menelaus hurled his spear. It hit Paris's shield, and penetrated. But Paris swerved and dodged. So Menelaus drew his sword and brought it crashing down on the ridge of Paris's helmet. But the blade shattered. Menelaus lunged forward, grabbed Paris by the helmet crest, and dragged him toward the Argive lines. The braided chinstrap was choking Paris, strangling him. But Aphrodite snapped the rawhide strap and snatched Paris away in swirls of mist—easy work for a god—and set him down in his own bedroom.

Then off Aphrodite went to summon Helen, who was appalled. "Why now, oh Goddess," she responded, "because Menelaus has beaten your handsome Paris?" Helen refused to go with her, saying that it would be disgraceful to share that coward's bed once more. But Aphrodite turned on her in fury. "Don't provoke me," Aphrodite stormed, "Or in my immortal rage I may just toss you over, hate you as I adore you now—with a vengeance!" Helen was terrified.

Aphrodite led Helen to the bedroom where Paris waited. In spite of her fear of Aphrodite, Helen berated him, taunting him to go back to the fight. In his reply Paris conceded that, thanks to Athena, Menelaus had won the day but that he would bring him down on the morrow. For the moment, Paris said, he was overwhelmed with longing for Helen. So he led the way to bed, and Helen followed. While the two made love, Menelaus stalked up and down the lines like a wild beast.

Agamemnon called out to both armies that since the victory had clearly gone to Menelaus, the Trojans must surrender Helen and all her treasure— and pay the Greeks reparations.

The gods met. Hera and Athena wanted to see Troy destroyed, which amused Zeus, who mocked them. But finally he relented and said that Hera could have her way, but warned her that if in the future he was bent on destroying some city that she loved, she should not attempt to thwart his fury. So they made a deal, Troy would be destroyed, but if Zeus were ever angry with one of Hera's favorite cities—Argos, Sparta, or Mycenae—she would not rise in their defense.

Zeus ordered Athena down to see that the Trojans were the first to break the truce. She winged down, found the archer Pandarus, and fired the fool to shoot an arrow at Menelaus, saying that he would thereby win fame. But then Athena deflected the arrow so that the wound was slight. Nevertheless, dark blood gushed from the wound for all to see. The truce was broken. The battle raged.

Staunch Diomedes, son of the King of Argos, hurled his spear at Pandarus and Athena drove the shaft to split the archer's nose between the eyes, the tough bronze cracked his teeth, cut off his tongue at the roots, smashed his jaw, and came ripping out beneath his chin. He pitched from his car, and his life slipped away on the wind. His fellow Trojan, Aeneas, sprang down to straddle the body. Diomedes hefted a boulder that no two men could hoist, and it struck Aeneas thigh, smashed the socket, snapped both tendons, and tore the skin in shreds.

Aeneas would have died on the spot if Zeus's daughter, his mother Aphrodite, had not taken him in her arms and wrapped her shining robe around him protecting him from further hurt. Diomedes knew Aphrodite for the coward goddess that she was and rushed her. He thrust his sharp spear at her soft, limp wrist; and the ichor, the immortal blood of the gods, came flowing quickly. She gave a piercing shriek and dropped her son. Apollo plucked him up, swathed him in a mist, carried him to the holy place of Troy, and Artemis healed his wounds.

Aphrodite fled to Olympus, where her wound was healed instantly. Hera and Athena mocked her, and Zeus smiled broadly and said that fighting was not for her, that she should see to the works of marriage and let Athena and Ares deal with bloodshed.

The Achaeans held a war council and decided to build a wall behind a deep trench to protect their ships. The Trojans also held a war council. One captain pointed out that because their side was the one that had broken the sworn truce, they had to fight as outlaws. The wise course, he urged, was to give Helen and her treasure back. But Paris said no, straight out. He refused to give up the woman, but he did say that he would give back the treasure that he had hauled home from Argos and add to it from his own stores.

The offer was made to the Achaeans, but Diomedes stood up to say that it should be refused, that it was obvious that Troy's doom was sealed.

At the urging of the chiefs, Agamemnon sent ambassadors to Achilles to offer rich prizes if he would return to the fighting. Agamemnon offered seven tripods never touched by fire, ten bars of gold, twenty burnished cauldrons, a dozen massive stallions, seven women captured at Lesbos, and along with them the one he had taken away from Achilles, Briseis. He swore that he had never mounted her bed, never once made love with her. And, he continued, if the gods permitted them to conquer Troy, Achilles could have as much of its gold and bronze as he wished and choose for his pleasure 20 Trojan women, second only to Helen in their beauty. And if the gods permitted them to journey home, Achilles could become his son by marriage. Agamemnon had three daughters, and Achilles could lead away whichever one he liked with no bride price. And Agamemnon said he would add a dowry, a magnificent treasure the likes of which no man had ever offered with his daughter. Seven citadels he would give filled with people who would honor Achilles like a god. "Let him bow down to me!" Agamemnon said, "I am the greater king. I am the elder-born—the greater man."

A three-man delegation and two heralds were sent to give the message to Achilles. One was old Phoenix, who was in fact a member of Achilles' own household and commander of one of his regiments. A second was the giant Ajax. The third was tactful Odysseus. At Achilles's tent, they were offered and enjoyed a bountiful feast. Then Odysseus spoke, saying that everything now hung in the balance. Whether they saved their beached ships or saw them destroyed depended on whether Achilles would put his fighting power in harness. Odysseus repeated the list of treasures Agamemnon had offered, tactfully leaving out the part in which Agamemnon had said that Achilles should bow down to him, that he was the greater king, the elder-born, the greater man. But Achilles refused—saying that not for the entire world would Agamemnon win him over. Achilles recalled that from shipboard he had stormed and sacked 12 cities. From them he had dragged piles of plunder and given the lot to Agamemnon—who was always skulking behind the lines safe in his fast ships. He always took it all, left a few scraps to the other commanders, but kept the lion's share for himself. He had seized and kept the girl Achilles loved. Well, Agamemnon could bed her now—enjoy her to the hilt. Tomorrow, Achilles said, he and his ships would depart.

Phoenix was eloquent in his appeal, and Achilles agreed not to leave the next day, but promised to stay until Hector and the Trojans threatened his own ships.

The Trojans fought their way across the ditch, breached the wall, and neared the ships. Agamemnon, his brother Menelaus, Diomedes, and Odysseus were all wounded. Achilles sent his bosom friend Patroclus to find out how the battle was going, and Patroclus returned to beg Achilles to relent. Achilles said that he was a man dishonored and could not fight for those who had disgraced him. Patroclus said that Achilles should give Patroclus his armor and let him lead the Myrmidons. If the Trojans thought Achilles had come back into the fight, they might pause and so give the Greeks a breathing spell. Achilles agreed. As a result, the Trojans were thrown back. But then Hector killed Patroclus, stripped him of Achilles's armor, and put it on himself.

Achilles was devastated at Patroclus' death. Enraged at Hector, he made his peace with Agamemnon. Achilles' "lithe and lovely girl," Briseis, was returned, and she grieved over the body of Patroclus, who, she said, "was always kind."

But Achilles had no armor, so his mother, Thetis, went to the smith-god Hephaestus who made him a magnificent set. First Hephaestus made a great and massive shield, blazoned with well-wrought emblems across its surface. Next he made a breastplate "brighter than gleaming fire;" then a sturdy helmet, beautiful, burnished work, with a raised, golden crest; and finally greaves of flexing, pliant tin.

Donning the new armor, Achilles went back into the battle and slaughtered many Trojans. Achilles then met Hector, wearing Achilles' own armor. Achilles knew that armor well, since it was his own, and aimed for the one spot that lay exposed, where the collarbones lift the neck bone off the shoulders, the open throat, where the end of life comes quickest. There Achilles thrust, and the point went stabbing clean through the tender neck. But the bronze point failed to slash the windpipe, and Hector could gasp out a plea that his body not be left to be devoured by dogs but given to his father, King Priam, who would give a princely ransom. But Achilles scorned the plea, not even for Hector's weight in gold would he give Priam the body. The dogs, Achilles said, would rend Hector's body—blood and bone!

Then Achilles stripped the armor off Hector, Achilles' own armor, which Hector had taken from Patroclus. He lashed the corpse to his chariot by the feet and dragged it to his tent among the ships. His intention was to throw it to the dogs and birds of prey.

For Patroclus Achilles then held a magnificent funeral, complete with athletic contests and human sacrifices—ten captive Trojans. Whenever renewed grief overcame him, he dragged Hector's corpse, still tied by the feet to his chariot, around Patroclus's body.

But Apollo pitied Hector and, dead though he was, warded off corruption and wrapped the golden shield of storm around his body so his skin would not rip as Achilles dragged his body behind the chariot.

The gods looked down and pitied Priam's son, Hector. Apollo proposed that the gods send Hermes to steal the body. But Athena and Hera, whom Paris had so offended, were opposed. Finally, Zeus said that they must abandon that idea. He then called Thetis, Achilles' mother, to hear his decree—that Achilles must accept a ransom from King Priam and then give him Hector's body. Thetis was to take the judgment to Achilles, and Iris was sent to give the message to King Priam.

Achilles remained coldly indifferent when his mother told him that Zeus had ordered that he give up Hector's body to Priam, although he had no choice but to obey. In the middle of the night, to Achilles great surprise, Priam himself came to Achilles' tent, alone, except for one herald. Priam had himself brought the ransom, kissed Achilles' hands, and said: "I have endured what no one on earth has ever done before—/ I put to my lips the hands of the man who killed my son."

Achilles thought of his own father, fated never to see his son again, and wept. But then he went from pity for his own father to pity for King Priam. So he told Priam he could take Hector's body and promised him a truce for the 12 days it would take to bury Hector properly.

With that he clasped the old king by the wrist,
by the right hand, to free his heart from fear.
Then Priam and the herald, minds set on the journey home,
bedded down for the night within the porch's shelter.
And deep in his sturdy, well-built lodge Achilles slept
with Briseis in all her beauty sleeping by his side.

(Fagles, page 610)

There followed the 12 days of mourning and preparation for the funeral. At last they carried gallant Hector forth, placed his corpse upon the pyre's crest, flung a torch and set it all aflame. Then they shared a splendid funeral feast in Hector's honor, held in the House of Priam, king by will of Zeus.

The *Iliad* then ends with a single line: "And so the Trojans buried Hector breaker of horses."

The Fall of Troy

With Hector dead, Achilles knew that he did not have long to live. But one more feat of arms was left to him. Prince Memnon of Ethiopia, son of the Goddess of the Dawn, came with a large army to help the Trojans. In glorious combat, Achilles killed Memnon. Then Paris shot an arrow at Achilles and Apollo guided it to his one vulnerable spot, the heel. Odysseus held back the Trojans and Ajax carried Achilles' body to the ships on his huge shield, seven layers of bull's hide covered with a plate of bronze. Achilles' body was burned on a funeral pyre and his ashes, in accordance with his wish, were placed in the same urn with those of Patroclus.

An assembly of the Greek warriors decided that Ajax and Odysseus were the two heroes who best-deserved Achilles' marvelous arms wrought by the god Hephaestus. A secret vote awarded them to Odysseus, and Ajax felt himself dishonored. He believed that Agamemnon and Menelaus had turned the vote against him. At nightfall he went to their quarters to kill them, but Athena struck him mad. He thought the Greeks' flocks of sheep and herds of cattle were the army and rushed to kill them. Finally, he dragged a huge ram that he thought was Odysseus to his tent, bound the animal to the tent pole, and beat it savagely.

Then his mind cleared and he realized that his shame in not winning Achilles' arms was a shadow compared with the shame his own deeds would bring upon him. "The poor cattle" he said to himself, "killed to no purpose by my hand. In such a state, only a coward clings to life. If a man cannot live nobly, he can die nobly." He drew his sword and killed himself.

The Greeks held that a suicide should not be honored with a funeral pyre and urn burial. So Ajax was buried in an earthen grave.

With Achilles dead, there was no one to lead the Myrmidons, so Agamemnon sent for Achilles' young son, Neoptolemus. Although still a boy, he had inherited his father's courage and much of his battle skill. Odysseus gave him his father's arms, the arms wrought by Hephaestus that Odysseus had been awarded.

Shortly afterwards, Paris was wounded. He remembered that his former lover, Oenone, had a magic drug that could cure any ailment, and he begged the gods to carry him to her. They did, and he pleaded for his life. But Oenone refused. He had deserted and long neglected her, which could not be forgiven in a moment. She watched Paris die, and then killed herself.

The truth is that Paris was no great loss. Troy endured; indeed, its walls had never been touched in all the years of fighting. The Greeks learned that there was a most sacred image of Pallas Athena in the city, called the Palladium, and that as long as the Trojans had that image Troy could not be taken. In the dead of night, Diomedes climbed the wall with Odysseus's help and bore the image off to the Greek camp.

Then the wily Odysseus planned out a stratagem. He had a skilled worker in wood make a huge horse, hollow and so big it would hold several men. Odysseus and a band of Greeks concealed themselves inside. The Greek fleet sailed away, as if for home, but hid behind a nearby island. Odysseus also left behind a single Greek in the deserted camp to tell the Trojans a tale calculated to make them draw the horse into the city.

When the day came, the Trojans were astounded to see the huge wooden horse outside their walls, the Greek camp deserted, and the Greek fleet gone. The Trojans exulted, flocked to visit the deserted camp, and marveled to see it empty. When they returned to puzzle over the wooden horse, Sinon, the Greek who had been left behind, discovered himself to them. Weeping and protesting that he no longer wished to be Greek, he was seized and dragged before King Priam. Sinon's story was one of Odysseus's masterpieces, and he was a most plausible liar. Pallas Athena, Sinon said, had been furious at the theft of the Palladium. The oracle, he went on, reminded the Greeks that they calmed the winds when first they came to Troy with blood and the maiden Iphigenia slain and that with blood and a Greek life they must expiate that act. Sinon went on to say that he was the one the Greeks had chosen to be sacrificed. The night before the awful rite was to be carried out, Sinon escaped to the swamp where he had hidden.

The Trojans believed Sinon's story, pitied him, and assured him that henceforth he could live among them as one of themselves. But Sinon did not forget to relate the second part of his story. The wooden horse, he said, was a votive offering to Athena. The reason for its great size was to discourage the Trojans from taking it inside their walls. What the Greeks hoped for was that the Trojans would destroy it and so draw down the wrath of Athena. Placed in the city it would turn her favor to the Trojans and away from the Greeks.

The story was clever enough to have had the desired effect all by itself. But Poseidon, the most bitter of all the gods against Troy, contrived an addition that made the result certain. When the horse was first discovered, the Trojan priest Laocoön and his two sons were the only doubters. They heard the story with suspicion, and Laocoön said that they must beware Greeks bearing gifts. Poseidon then sent two fearful serpents out of the sea. They glided straight to Laocoön and his two sons, wrapped their coils around them, and crushed out their lives. The horrified Trojans thought that Laocoön and his sons had been punished for opposing the entry of the horse into Troy. They opened a gate, tore down enough of the adjoining wall to permit passage of the horse, and dragged it into the city.

In the middle of the night, the Greeks hiding inside the horse let themselves down and quietly opened the rest of the gates. Silently, the Greeks started fires throughout the city. When the Trojans awoke and struggled to put on their armor, the city was already burning. They rushed into the streets where bands of Greeks were waiting to strike each man down before he could band together with others. The quickest-witted Trojans tore off their armor and donned that of fallen Greeks, and in the more distant parts of the city, some of the Trojans were able to band together. But too many Trojans had been slaughtered in the first surprise.

Achilles' son, Neoptolemus, struck down King Priam before the eyes of his wife and daughters. By morning all the Trojan leaders were dead except Aphrodite's son Aeneas. He fought on as long as he could find a living Trojan to fight beside him. But then he thought of his home and the helpless people he had left there. He hurried to them—his old father, his little son, and his wife. His mother Aphrodite appeared and urged him on, keeping him safe from the flames and from the Greeks. But even with the help of the goddess, he could not save his wife. She was separated from him and was killed. But with his father on his shoulders and leading his young son, he made his way with Aphrodite's help through the enemy and out into the countryside. Aeneas lived, made his way to Italy, and his descendants became the Etruscans.

Aphrodite also helped Helen, got her out of the city, and took her to Menelaus. Menelaus received her gladly, and when he sailed for Sparta, she was with him.

King Priam's wife, Queen Hecuba; the wife of Hector, Andromache; and Hector's baby son were captured. Andromache thought that the Greeks would let her take the child with her into slavery. But a herald appeared and spoke faltering words. Pleading that she not hate him for the news he brought against his will, the herald said, "The boy must die, be thrown down from the towering wall of Troy." With the death of Hector's son, Troy's last sacrifice was made.

When the Greeks sacked the city, Cassandra, whose true prophecies were never believed, was in Athena's temple, clinging to the image of the goddess and so under her protection. The Greeks tore Cassandra from Athena's image, dragged her out of the temple, and gave her to Agamemnon as his prize. Athena was enraged at the violation of her temple and even though she had favored the Greeks, she went to Poseidon. "Help me to vengeance," she begged, "Give the Greeks a bitter homecoming. Stir up your waters." He did. Also in their haste to sail home, the Greeks failed to make proper sacrifices to the other gods, and they welcomed Athena's plea and Poseidon's great storm.

Most of the Greeks were blown to distant lands and had much trouble getting home. It took Menelaus seven years and Odysseus ten. But not Agamemnon. The gods had a worse fate in store for him. His ship came safely through the storm, and he landed triumphant, the proud conqueror of Troy. The elders of the city gathered to meet him, but as they waited they talked in low tones of the past. The elders knew of the curse that hung over Agamemnon and the House of Atreus, the curse that their ancestor Tantalus had brought upon them in his defiance of the gods. They recalled that Tantalus' son, Pelops, had two sons, Atreus and Thyestes on whom the inheritance of evil fell full force. Thyestes fell in love with his brother's wife and made her false to her marriage vows. Atreus found out and in vengeance killed his brother's two little children, had them cut limb from limb, boiled, and served to their father to eat. Atreus was king. Thyestes had no power. So the atrocious crime was not avenged in Atreus' lifetime. But the curse went down to Atreus' children, of whom Agamemnon was one, and his children's children. The elders recalled in particular the sacrifice of Iphigenia, lovely, innocent young thing, trusting her father utterly, and then confronted at the altar with the cruel knives, with the father she loved telling men to lift and hold her over the altar, while he slashed her throat.

The elders knew that Agamemnon's wife, Clytemnestra, had come back from Aulis where she had seen her daughter sacrificed, that she had taken a lover, and that he was still there in the palace with her.

Then Agamemnon arrived and with him was a young woman, very beautiful but very strange looking. It was Priam's daughter, Cassandra.

Clytemnestra appeared at the door to greet him. Everyone except Agamemnon knew of her infidelity, but, smiling, she spoke of the great love she bore for her husband, the agonizing grief she had suffered in his absence.

Agamemnon answered her with reserve. He pointed to the young woman in the chariot, and said that she was Cassandra, Priam's daughter, the army's gift to him and the flower of all the captive women. Let Clytemnestra see to her and treat her well. With that he and Clytemnestra entered the house and the doors closed behind them.

Cassandra turned a terrified face to the old men, asking what house was this? They answered soothingly that it was the house where Agamemnon, the son of Atreus, lived. She said that it was a house the gods hated, a house where men are killed, where the floor was red with blood, and a house where a father had feasted on his own children. Then she turned from the past to the future. She said that on that very day two more deaths would follow and that one of them would be her own. And with that she went into the palace.

A cry rang out! It was the king's voice, crying that he was struck, that it was his deathblow.

The door of the palace opened, and there stood Clytemnestra with dark red stains on her dress, her hands, and her face. It was Agamemnon's blood, and she was glad. She saw no reason to explain her act or excuse it. She was not a murderer, but an executioner. She had punished a murderer, the murderer of his own child.

Chapter 29

The *Odyssey*

T he opening line of the *Odyssey* calls on the Muse to sing of the man of twists and turns who was driven time and again off course on his way home from plundering the hallowed heights of Troy. The Muse chooses to begin the tale in the tenth year of Odysseus' long journey home, which was the seventh year of his being held captive by the bewitching nymph, Calypso. Although all the gods had in one way or another contributed to Odysseus' troubles, all except Poseidon now felt that he had suffered enough.

Poseidon had gone to visit the Ethiopians, worlds away, to accept an offering of bulls and rams by the hundreds, so the gods took advantage of his absence to meet on Olympus. Athena spoke first, saying that her heart went out to Odysseus, cursed by fate to be parted so long from his family and loved ones. There he sat day after day on a headland of Calypso's island longing to die. Why, Athena asked, was Zeus so dead set against Odysseus?

Zeus replied that Athena spoke nonsense, that it was not he who opposed Odysseus, but Poseidon, the Earth-Shaker, who hated him for blinding Poseidon's son, Polyphemus, the one-eyed Cyclops. Although Poseidon would not go so far as to kill Odysseus, Zeus went on, he kept driving him far off course from his native land. But if the gods put their heads together and worked out Odysseus' journey home, Zeus said, Poseidon would let his anger go.

So Hermes, the messenger of the gods, was dispatched to tell Calypso to free Odysseus, and Athena went to Ithaca to rouse Odysseus's son, Telemachus.

When Hermes reached the cave where Calypso made her home and told her that Zeus commanded her to release Odysseus, she shuddered and burst into a flight of indignation. But she realized that in the end she had to obey.

Athena flew to Ithaca and took the appearance of an old friend of Odysseus on his way to trade a cargo of gleaming iron for bronze. She then approached Telemachus, who treated the visitor warmly as a guest. The "old friend," who was really Athena, said that he had stopped off at Ithaca for a short visit, and he then began to question Telemachus about the suitors for Penelope's hand, of whom he had heard. Telemachus replied that there were 105 of them besieging his father's house and eating him out of house and home. The "old friend" of his father's advised him to fit out a ship and go to Pylos to ask old King Nestor about Odysseus' fate and then to Sparta to ask the same of Menelaus. If Telemachus found that Odysseus was alive and well, he should brave out one more year. If he found that Odysseus was dead, he should return, arrange the funeral rites, and give his mother to another husband. Then, if any suitors still remained in his house, Telemachus should find a way to kill them.

Heartened, Telemachus went to where the suitors were listening to a bard as he performed "The Achaeans' Journey Home From Troy." Penelope came down from her chamber, broke into tears at the song, and begged the bard to stop.

Telemachus spoke sharply to his mother, asking why she should deny the bard the chance to entertain them all. He told her to go back to her quarters and tend her loom. As for giving orders, the men would attend to that, he said—he himself most of all, since he was the one who held the reins of power in the house. Astonished at his rebellion, Penelope withdrew to her rooms.

Telemachus then berated the suitors and called for an assembly of the citizens of Ithaca to meet at dawn. The suitors bit their lips, amazed that he spoke with such daring.

At the assembly the next morning, the herald put the speaker's scepter in Telemachus' hand. Telemachus then described how the suitors were feasting at his expense; and, filled with anger, he burst into tears and dashed the speaker's scepter to the ground.

Then Antinous rose to say that it was not the suitors who deserved the blame, but Telemachus' mother, Penelope. For three years, she had played fast and loose with the suitors, building up each man's hopes. Her latest masterpiece of guile was to set up a great loom and start weaving a shroud for Odysseus' old father, Laertes. By day she would weave and by night she would unravel all she had done.

Then Mentor, whom Odysseus had left in charge, rose and berated the members of the assembly for failing to curb the suitors, who were few while they were many. One of the suitors replied, calling Mentor a rabble-rousing fool. If Odysseus returned and tried to rout the suitors from the palace, the suitor said, he would suffer a humiliating end.

The assembly adjourned, the people returned to their homes, and the suitors to the palace. Telemachus sought out his old nurse, now in charge of the storeroom, swore her to secrecy, and asked for wine and food for a voyage to Pylos and Sparta.

Pallas Athena, disguised this time as Telemachus himself, obtained the loan of a ship from one of Telemachus' friends. Then, still disguised as Telemachus, Athena roamed through town recruiting crewmen. She then hauled the ship down to the water and moored it at the harbor's mouth. Then back she went to King Odysseus' halls and showered sleep over the suitors who groped through town to find their beds. She called to Telemachus in Mentor's voice and led the way to the ship. And then she sent a following wind to hasten them over the wine-dark sea.

When the ship reached Pylos, Telemachus met with Nestor, who knew little of the fate of the others except from hearsay. Nestor then provided Telemachus with a chariot to go to Lacedaemon to see Menelaus, and sent Nestor's own son, Pisistratus, along with him as a guide. *

When they arrived in Lacedaemon, Helen greeted them and remarked on how much Telemachus looked like Odysseus. She asked if he was his son, and on learning that he was, told some tales of Troy herself. Menelaus, in answer to Telemachus' plea for news of his father, told of being marooned during the seven years it took him to get home from Troy. Finally he tricked the Old Man of the Sea into telling them how to escape. The Old Man said that if they had wanted a rapid journey home, they should have offered Zeus

---

*It has often been remarked that Homer was not familiar with much of the geography of Greece and Asia Minor, and this part of the epic confirms this observation. In those days there were no roads over the mountains of Greece from Pylos to Lacedaemon that could take a chariot.
In studying for the West Point entrance examination, aspiring cadets of my generation used mnemonic devices to remember the strange Greek names. The mnemonic for Telemachus' guide was "Pisistratus on a flat rock."

and the deathless gods a handsome sacrifice before they left Troy. Since they failed to do so, Menelaus would have to sail back to Egypt and repair the damage by making a splendid offering to the gods.

Asked about the other leaders at Troy, the Old Man of the Sea replied that Menelaus already knew the fate of those who died at Troy, such as great Ajax who died by his own hand. As for the others, two died on the way home. One was the younger Ajax. Poseidon had overheard him boasting that he had escaped the teeth of the gods and for his arrogance Poseidon plunged him into the vast, seething depths.

As for Agamemnon, Menelaus' brother, he had been ambushed and killed in his own house by Aegisthus, whom Agamemnon's wife, Clytemnestra, had taken as her lover. Hearing of the death of his brother for the first time, Menelaus was overcome by grief.

After he recovered, Menelaus asked about the third leader, the one who was still alive. The Old Man said that the third leader was Odysseus and that the nymph Calypso held him prisoner on her island home. She had offered him immortality, but he had refused, wanting to return to his wife and son. In the nights, true, he would sleep with Calypso, an unwilling lover alongside a lover all too willing. But by day he would sit on the headland and long for death. He had no way to voyage home, no ships, and no crew to ply the oars. After Hermes had told Calypso she had to let Odysseus return home and she realized she had no choice but to obey, the queenly nymph sought Odysseus out where he sat on the headland, weeping. Calypso told him that he no longer had any reason to weep, that she would help him build a raft and find his way home.

For seventeen days Odysseus sailed the raft and on the eighteenth sighted the island of the Phaeacians. But then Poseidon returning home from Ethiopia saw him. Angry that the gods had acted behind his back, Poseidon rammed the clouds together and churned the waves into chaos. A massive wave threw Odysseus from the raft and dashed it to pieces. But Ino, a mortal woman once but now a goddess living in the sea, tossed him a scarf that made him immune to both pain and death, cautioning that once he reached the shore he must throw the immortal scarf back into the sea.

Zeus's daughter Athena stopped the winds in their tracks except for the North Wind, which she whipped up to beat the breakers flat so Odysseus could reach the shore. Stroking hard, he came to a river's mouth, the perfect spot. He loosed the goddess' scarf and dropped it into the river flowing out to sea, and Ino caught it! Then he found a grove of olives and buried himself in the leaves.

Athena showered sleep on him and then made her way to where Nausicaa, the daughter of Alcinous, King of Phaecia, and two handmaids slept. Disguised as one of Nausicaa's friends, a girl her own age, Athena chided Nausicaa for letting her fine clothes lie on the floor neglected and urged her to take them to the washing pools in the river. When the maidens had washed the clothes and were waiting for them to dry, they sang and danced. It was a lovely sight, but Nausicaa, a virgin still unwed, outshone them all.

Odysseus woke, tore off a leafy branch to hide his private parts and approached the girls. They scattered in panic at the sight of such a man all crusted and caked with brine. Nausicaa alone stood her ground. Odysseus pled his case in winning words, endearing, sly, and suave, praising her beauty, her bearing, and her lithe and flowing grace. He said that he had been twenty days at sea, and he begged for a rag to cover himself and directions to make his way to the town.

Nausicaa answered staunchly, invited him to bathe himself in the river, gave him a flask of olive oil to rub his skin, and a cloak and shirt to wear. Then, she said, he should follow them to town and instructed him on what to do.

As instructed by Nausicaa, Odysseus reached the palace, bowed down before the queen, and clasped her knees. She recognized the clothes he was wearing and asked how he had come by them. Odysseus answered that he had been held for seven years on Calypsos' island, that he had voyaged on the raft for twenty days, that he had then met Nausicaa, and that she had given him the clothes. The queen was mollified, and King Alcinous promised to convoy Odysseus home!

But first the king arranged for a hero's welcome—games of every kind: boxing, wrestling, jumping, and foot racing, as well as a performance by a bard of the story of the wooden horse and the conquest of Troy, during which Odysseus could not hide his tears. After the games and singing were over, the king asked Odysseus to tell them his own story and explain why he wept when the bard had sung his story of Troy.

"I am Odysseus, son of Laertes, known to the world for every kind of craft," Odysseus began. He told how on the way home the wind had driven him and his crew to the stronghold of the Cicones. There they sacked the city, killed the men, and dragged away the wives and plunder. Odysseus then urged his men to cut and run, but there was too much wine to swill and too many sheep to slaughter. So the Cicones called for help, attacked, and broke the Greek lines, killing six men out of each ship.

From there they sailed on, but Zeus sent a howling, demonic gale. Nine whole days they were borne by the wind, finally reaching the land of the Lotus-eaters. These people had no notion of killing Odysseus and his men, but simply gave them lotus to eat. The three crewmen who ate the lotus lost all memory of going home and had to be dragged to the ship.

Then they reached the land of the mighty Cyclops, the one-eyed giants. They spotted a cave and around it big flocks of sheep and goats. Odysseus took a dozen of his finest fighters and a skin of wine made from grapes in Apollo's holy grove, a drink fit for the gods! Making their way to the cave, they rested and ate some of the cheeses the giant had stored.

Then the giant Cyclops, whose name was Polyphemus, returned, drove the sheep and goats into the cave, and hoisted a tremendous, massive slab of stone to block the entrance. When the giant finished his chores, he built a fire. Then he spotted Odysseus and his men in the cave. "Strangers!" he bellowed, and demanded to know who they were.

Answering that they were Achaeans, they asked for the warm welcome that Zeus decreed should be given to all strangers. The giant replied that Cyclops never blink at Zeus or his shield. But then he slyly asked where they had moored their ship, that he would just like to know.

But Odysseus was not taken in. He told the giant that Poseidon had smashed the ship. The giant did not reply but snatched up two of Odysseus' men, knocked out their brains, ripped them limb from limb, and bolted them down, entrails, flesh, bones, marrow, and all! And then he stretched out and went to sleep.

Odysseus thought first to draw his sword and stab the giant's chest. But then he thought, "How could he and his men roll back the massive stone that blocked the entrance?" And so for the moment he did nothing.

When the Cyclops woke, he snatched up two more men to make a meal. Well fed, he drove his fat sheep from the cave and put the huge slab of stone in place to block the entrance. Then crafty Odysseus thought of a plan. The Cyclops had left behind his great club of green olive wood, full of sap. Odysseus chopped off a fathom's length, shaved the tip to a stabbing point, and hardened it in the blazing fire.

When the Cyclops returned, he snatched up two more men for his meal. Odysseus then lifted up to him a wooden bowl full to the brim with the ruddy wine from Apollo's grove. The Cyclops tossed it off and called for more. That finished, he called for still more and asked for Odysseus' name, promising to give him a gift. Odysseus gave him a third bowl, and said that his name was "Nobody." The giant drank down the wine and said that his gift was that he would eat Nobody last.

Then he toppled over, dead drunk, and fell asleep. Odysseus got out the olive stake, and put it into the embers of the fire. When it was red hot, he and his men thrust it into the Cyclops' one eye and bored it round and round to make the boiling eyeball burst.

With a tremendous roar the Cyclops called for help from his fellow Cyclops. They came running to his cave and asked what was the trouble—was someone stealing his flocks? "Nobody!" the giant cried back. He yelled that Nobody was killing him by fraud! The other Cyclops replied that if nobody was bothering him, his trouble must be a plague sent by mighty Zeus. So for help he should pray to his father, Poseidon. Then they went away.

The giant groped around for the doorway slab, heaved it off, and sat down with his arms stretched out to catch anyone trying to sneak out

Odysseus lashed the sheep together, three abreast. Under each ram he trussed up one of his men. Odysseus then tucked himself under the bell-wether ram and hung himself there face upward. As the rams went out of the cave, the giant felt the back of each one, never guessing that the men were tucked up underneath.

Once out of the cave, Odysseus and his men loosed themselves and made their way back to their comrades at the ships, herding the sheep with them. Once off shore, Odysseus shouted stinging taunts back at the Cyclops, calling him a shameless cannibal who dared to eat his guests against the will of Zeus. If the Cyclops wanted to know the name of the man who had blinded him, he shouted, it was Odysseus, son of Laertes, who made his home in Ithaca! At that the giant bellowed out to his father, Poseidon, asking that Odysseus be made to come home late, a broken man, all shipmates lost, alone in a stranger's ship, and find a world of pain at home!

Odysseus, continuing his tale to King Alcinous and his court, related that next they reached the island of Aeolia. The king of the island hosted them a month, and when he sent them on their way he gave Odysseus a sack, the skin of a full-grown ox, binding inside the winds that howl from every quarter. And then he set the West Wind free to blow them on their way.

Nine days they sailed, until their own land, Ithaca, came in sight. But then, bone-weary from working the vessel's sheet himself all that time, Odysseus fell into an enticing sleep. But the crew had begun to mutter among themselves, sure that the bags so tightly tied contained a fabulous treasure, while they were empty-handed. They loosed the sack, and all the winds burst out, driving them back to Aeolia. Odysseus pleaded with the king to repeat his help, but the king refused, saying that it would be a crime to host a man whom the deathless gods despised so much.

Six whole days they rowed and on the seventh they raised the Laestrygonian land. The rest of his squadron sailed into the cove, but Odysseus anchored his ship outside and tied her fast to a cliff side. They sent two good men to scout the land and a third to run back news of what they found. The men entered the sumptuous palace of the king of that land and found his wife inside—a woman huge as a mountain crag that filled them with horror. She summoned the king who gave them a barbarous welcome. He snatched one of the men and tore him limb for limb for dinner. The other two sprang free and reached the ships. The king then let loose a howling and hundreds of men as large as giants swarmed from every side. From the cliffs above they flung great rocks down on the ships that had gone into the harbor. Hulls were smashed like splinters and the giants speared the Greeks like fish and took them home to make their grisly meal. Odysseus hacked through the ropes that moored his own ship outside the cove, the men put their backs to the oars, and they escaped—their ship alone of all the squadron.

From there they sailed on until they reached Circe's island. Odysseus divided the men into two platoons, and cast lots. The one commanded by Eurylochus drew the lot and went Circe's cave. She invited them in and all did so but Eurylochus, who sensed a trap. She gave them cheese, barley, and pale honey mixed in Pramnian wine, but into the brew she stirred some wicked drugs. Once they'd drained their bowls she struck with her wand and turned them into swine, with the grunts, snouts, and bodies of pigs, and only their minds remaining human. Back Eurylochus ran to their swift, black ship and told the tale.

Odysseus took his sword and went to set the men free. On the way, he met Hermes, messenger of the gods, who gave him a potent drug to take to make him immune to Circe's wicked drugs and instructions on what to do. When Circe struck at him with her wand, Odysseus followed Hermes instructions and rushed her with his sword as if to run her through. She cow-ered and coaxed him to join her in her bed. As Hermes had instructed, Odysseus did not refuse, but made her swear the binding oath of the gods that if he lay naked with her that she would never plot some new intrigue to harm him. She did so, and Odysseus mounted Circe's gorgeous bed.

She turned the swine back into men, and then feasted them for a whole year.

Then his crew complained that they wanted to be on their way home, and Odysseus called on Circe to fulfill her promise. She said she would help them home, but first Odysseus must travel to the House of Death to consult the ghost of Tiresias, the seer of Thebes, on just how to do it. She gave him detailed instructions on what he should do when he got to where the dead were confined.

When Odysseus got to the River Styx, following her instructions he dug a trench a forearm's depth and length, poured into it libations, milk and honey, mellow wine, and water, and sprinkled glistening barley over all. As Circe had told him to do, Odysseus then slaughtered a ram and a black ewe on the spot, draining their blood into the trench. Suddenly countless shades of the dead surged around him, among whom was his own mother. As instructed, Odysseus drew his sword to keep the ghosts from coming near the blood until he had questioned Tiresias on how to cross the swarming sea and reach home at last.

Tiresias said that on his way home Odysseus would be forced to take shelter at the island where Helios, God of the Sun, grazed his cattle. If they left the beasts alone, all would reach home safely. But if the cattle were harmed, his ship and men would be destroyed.

Odysseus then asked Tiresias how he might make his mother know and speak to him, and Tiresias said that anyone he let drink the blood would speak the truth to him and that anyone he refused would turn and fade away.

Odysseus let his mother drink and spoke with her. Then there came a grand array of women, and he spoke with many—the mother of Oedipus; Leda, Tyndareus's wife; the lovely Ariadne, daughter of Minos; and many more.

Then forward marched the shade of Agamemnon, who told of his sad fate. Then came the ghost of Achilles. Odysseus spoke to him with winning words, but Achilles rejected them, saying that he would rather be a slave on Earth for some tenant farmer than rule over the breathless dead. Achilles asked about his father but Odysseus could tell him nothing. But Odysseus was able to report to Achilles that his son, Neoptolemus, had fought bravely at Troy and had returned home unscathed. On hearing this, the ghost of Achilles went loping off, triumphant.

They left the House of Death and returned to Circe's island. Again she warned of the perils that lay ahead. First was the island of the Sirens whose song would transfix any who heard it. Odysseus put beeswax in the ears of the crew to keep them from hearing the song and had the crew bind him to the mast, telling them that when he begged to be freed they should bind him even faster.

Next were Scylla and Charybdis. On one cliff was a cave where Scylla lurked, with each of her six heads on six long necks to snatch up men from every ship that passed. On the other side Charybdis' awesome whirlpool gulped the dark water down, ships and all. As Circe advised, they hugged Scylla's crag and lost six men but kept their ship and escaped a much worse fate.

Next they made the island where the Sun god grazed his sheep and oxen. When their supply of food ran low, the crew, against both Circe's warning and the oath they had sworn to Odysseus, decided that rather than die of starvation they would kill and feast on the Sun god's cattle. When they sailed away, the Sun god sent a frightful storm that sank the ship. All the men except Odysseus were lost.

Odysseus clung to the mast and keel, barely escaped Charybdis and Scylla, and drifted for nine days. On the tenth he was cast up on Calypso's island, where he was held for seven years.

When Odysseus finished this tale, the Phaeacians packed a ship with handsome gifts and sailed Odysseus back to his homeland, Ithaca. When the ship arrived, Odysseus was sleeping deeply, so the crew put him ashore with his treasure.

Poseidon was angry with the Phaeacians for helping Odysseus and to teach them to cease escorting home every castaway on their shores, he proposed to Zeus that he should take vengeance on them by sinking the Phaeacian ship in the harbor when it returned and piling a looming mountain around the port. Zeus suggested a refinement, that Poseidon turn the ship and its crew of 52 young men, the "best in town," to stone at the mouth of the harbor rather than just sinking it as well as block the harbor with a mountain. And so he did.

Back at Ithaca, Odysseus awoke, Athena joined him, and together they hid the treasure in a cave. Then Athena made him appear to be an old man, in rags, and he went off to see Eumaeus, his loyal swineherd. Some time later, Telemachus came home from his trip to Pylos and Sparta and joined them.

Athena then appeared to Odysseus, told him that the time had come to reveal himself to Telemachus, and stroked him with her golden wand to make him fresh and clean. Odysseus revealed himself to Telemachus and the tears welled up in the eyes of both.

Then they began to plot how they might deal with the suitors. Odysseus cautioned that they should let no one at all hear that he had come home from Troy, not Eumaeus nor even Odysseus' father, Laertes.

At dawn, Telemachus set off to present himself to his mother, telling Eumaeus, the swineherd, to take the luckless stranger, whom Eumaeus still did not know was Odysseus, to town so he could beg his supper there.

On their way their path crossed that of the goatherd Melanthius, taking his goats to make a meal for the suitors, and he poured insults on the beggar that was Odysseus disguised. After Melanthius delivered his goats to Odysseus' house, he took his seat among the suitors and both meat and bread were set before him.

When Odysseus reached the palace, an old dog lying on the doorstep lifted up his muzzle and pricked his ears. It was Argos, whom Odysseus had trained as a puppy twenty years earlier. He thumped his tail, but then the dark shadow of death closed his eyes.

Telemachus motioned the swineherd Eumaeus over and gave him bread and meat to take to the stranger, whom Telemachus of course knew was Odysseus, and told him to suggest to the stranger that he make the rounds of the suitors and beg from each. When Odysseus, still disguised as a beggar, did so, Antinous berated him. When Odysseus answered back, Antinous seized a stool and threw it, hitting Odysseus square in the back.

When Penelope heard how Antinous had violated hospitality and struck the stranger, she cried out that Apollo should strike Antinous just as hard. And, thinking that the stranger might have news of Odysseus, she asked that he be brought to see her.

In the meantime, Odysseus instructed Telemachus to round up all the deadly weapons in the palace and stow them upstairs, leaving out enough swords and ox hide bucklers for just themselves.

When Penelope came down from her chambers, she commanded her servants to set a chair for the stranger, and began to question him. He told her a tale of falsehoods, but he gave them the ring of truth. And he ended by swearing to her that Odysseus was safe and that he would return. "If only," Penelope replied, "what you say would come to pass!" Though he was a stranger, she confided to him that she was going to announce to the suitors a contest with Odysseus' great bow. Odysseus used to line up 12 axes in a straight, unbroken arrow and then stand back and whip an arrow through the lot, and she was going to use this as a test for the suitors.*

Penelope called on her servants to bathe the stranger, make his bed, and wash his feet. But the crafty Odysseus asked her to hold off, that beds and glossy spreads were not his style. As for washing his feet, he would allow no one to touch them unless it was some old retainer, the soul of trust. Penelope replied that there was such a one, an old woman who had reared her husband Odysseus from the day his mother bore him.

When the old woman came to wash the stranger's feet, she remarked on how much he resembled Odysseus. He replied that many who had seen them both said the same. But then Odysseus thought that if she spotted the old scar above his knee made by the tusk of a wild boar when he was a boy, she would know him, and he swerved around to be in the dark.

But the old nurse felt the scar with her hands. She whispered quickly to him that yes, he was Odysseus. She turned to signal Penelope, but Athena turned Penelope's attention elsewhere, and Odysseus clutched the nurse's throat, hugged her tight, and muttered in her ear that she who had suckled him at her own breast would be his death if she told anyone, even Penelope. If she did not keep silent, when he killed the disloyal women of the house, he would not spare her, even though she was his old nurse! The shrewd old nurse said she would be as still as a rock.

The next day, Eumaeus brought three fat porkers and leaving them to root in the courtyard went to Odysseus and hailed him warmly, asking how the suitors were treating him. Just then the goatherd Melanthius sauntered up and turned on Odysseus again with cutting insults.

When the time came, Telemachus set up the axes and said that he would be the first to try. Three times he tried to string the bow and failed.

---

* Part of the test was to be able to draw the bow. The only man in Ithaca before Odysseus went to Troy who had the strength to draw the bow was Odysseus himself. But since no arrow could possibly penetrate twelve bronze and iron axes, there has been much dispute about what was supposed to happen. The most plausible explanation is that this was *not* a demonstration of the power of an arrow to penetrate bronze and iron, but of the accuracy of Odysseus's aim. The speculation is that at the top of each axe was a ring to hang it on the wall and that the test was to see if the aim were so accurate that the arrow would pass through the rings on all 12 axes.

The fourth time, he would have done it, but Odysseus stopped him with a shake of his head.

Several of the suitors then tried to bend the bow and failed. As this was going on, Odysseus, still disguised as a beggar, asked his swineherd Eumaeus and his old shepherd, Philoetius, if they would fight for Odysseus. Both said they would. Certain that they were loyal to the death, Odysseus revealed himself by showing them his scar, and the men broke into tears and threw their arms around their master.

Odysseus then instructed Eumaeus to put the bow and quiver in his hands at the first opportunity and then to go tell the serving women to lock the doors to their rooms and that if they heard the groans of men they should sit tight. And he told the shepherd, Philoetius, to lock the courtyard's outer gate.

As soon as Eumaeus gave him the bow, Odysseus scanned every inch of it, turning it over tip to tip, testing it this way and that, fearing worms had bored through the weapon's horn in his long absence. (The best bows in ancient times were laminated in three layers, wood in the two outside layers and horn in the middle. When a bow is bent, its inner edge is compressed and the outer stretched, which this arrangement facilitates, while the horn in the middle stays the same. In this way the power of the bow is maximized.) Then with virtuoso ease he strung the great bow and plucked the string to test its pitch. Zeus cracked the sky with a thunderbolt, and Odysseus rejoiced at this sign that the god supported him at last. He snatched an arrow lying on the board and still seated on his stool sent it straight and true never missing an ax from the first ax handle clean on through to the last and out. Horror swept the suitors, and their faces blanched.

Odysseus gave a warning nod, and Telemachus girded on his sharp sword, picked up a spear, and took his stand beside his father. Odysseus cast aside his rags, and poured out from the quiver his flashing arrows. Calling on Apollo to give him glory, he trained a stabbing arrow on Antinous, who was just tilting a goblet of wine to his lips. The shot hit him square in the throat, stabbing through the soft neck and out. The cup dropped from his grasp and his life's blood came spurting out his nostrils in thick red jets.

Only Eurymachus had the breath to speak, saying that if the stranger truly was Odysseus, he was right to kill Antinous, since it was Antinous who had driven them all to crime. But the others, he argued, should be spared, and they would recoup Odysseus' losses covering all they had eaten and drunk.

Odysseus told him no, not for all his father's wealth. Eurymachus spoke again, this time to the suitors, saying they would all be killed if they did not fight—that they must charge Odysseus in a pack. Eurymachus drew his sword, but Odysseus shot him down. Another rushed the king, but Telemachus stabbed the man from behind.

As Odysseus continued to fire his arrows, Telemachus ran to get shields, spears, and helmets for Eumaeus and the shepherd, Philoetius.

Telemachus brought them weapons and armor and they quickly girded themselves. Odysseus told Eumaeus to guard the side door.

Among the suitors, the goatherd Melanthius, who had taunted Odysseus on every occasion, volunteered to fetch some armor from the storeroom. He clambered up through the smoke-ducts high on the wall, bundled up a dozen shields, spears, and helmets and rushed them back to the suitors.

When Odysseus saw the suitors armed, brandishing their spears, his heart sank. The cool prince Telemachus said that it was he who was to blame for leaving the door to the storeroom ajar. He sent Eumaeus to shut the door to the storeroom and said he suspected it was Melanthius who had fetched the arms. As they talked, Melanthius climbed up to fetch more arms. Eumaeus spotted him and asked whether he should kill him. Odysseus told them not to kill him, but to bind and string him up to the rafters of the storeroom still alive.

Now Odysseus and the three others faced a larger, stronger force. Then Athena flew in to perch on the great hall's central roof beam, black with smoke. Six suitors in a single hurl launched their spears. But Athena turned the whole salvo wide of the mark. At Odysseus' command he and his three supporters let fly and the lances struck home. Dashing forward to wrench their spears from their fallen enemies, the four let fly again, with telling effect.

One suitor flung himself at Odysseus and clutched his knees, claiming that he had tried to restrain the suitors, that his hands were clean, that he was just their prophet. Odysseus replied that if he was a prophet for the suitors, a priest, he must have prayed that Odysseus' dear wife would be his own. Snatching up a sword, Odysseus struck him square across the neck and the praying head went tumbling in the dust.

The bard who had always performed for the suitors remained, still clutching his lyre. He laid it down, rushed to Odysseus, and hugged his knees. Telemachus heard the pleas and called Odysseus to hold off, that the bard was innocent, and that so was the herald Medon, who had tended him when

340

he was little. As it happened, Medon was cowering under a chair. He heard Telemachus, jumped up, and hugged Telemachus' knees. Breaking into a smile, Odysseus told the two that the prince had pulled them through and bade them go outside and wait while he did the household chores that called for his attention.

Odysseus then told Telemachus to call the old nurse. Odysseus commanded her to report on the women of the house, telling who were disloyal and who were guiltless. Of the fifty women in the household, she replied, some dozen went tramping to their shame, thumbing their noses at her and at the queen.

Odysseus directed that the guilty ones be summoned to the hall and set to work cleaning away the bodies, scrubbing down the chairs and tables, scraping smooth the packed Earth floor, and putting the entire house in order. Then the women were to be marched out to the courtyard, to be hacked by swords, their lives slashed, and blotted from their minds the joys of love they relished under the suitors' bodies, rutting on the sly!

Once the house had been cleaned and the women marched to the courtyard, Telemachus had nooses put around their necks, tied the nooses to a cable used on a dark-prowed ship, and yanked them up. They kicked their heels for a time, but not for long.

Melanthius? They hauled him into the court, lopped off his nose with a ruthless knife, tore his genitals off and cast them out for the dogs to eat raw. In manic fury they hacked off his hands and feet.

Calling for fire and brimstone, Odysseus purged the house. When it was clean, the old nurse brought the loyal women from their quarters. They flung their arms around Odysseus and hugged him. Odysseus broke down and wept. The old nurse went to wake Penelope, who at first refused to believe that Odysseus had returned. If the suitors were indeed dead, she said, it must have been a god. When Penelope came down to the great hall, she sat for a long time in silence. In one moment the man who was supposed to be Odysseus seemed to be so—then the next moment he seemed to be not the man she knew, but only a huddled mass of rags. Telemachus upbraided his mother for hesitating, but Odysseus broke into a smile and said Penelope should be allowed to test him.

Then Odysseus reminded Telemachus that if someone kills a lone man, he has to flee to escape avengers, but they had killed the best of the island's princes, and there would be many seeking vengeance. They should delay news of the death of the suitors spreading through the town. For the moment, they should have all the household dress well, the bard sing, and everyone dance so that anyone passing would think a wedding feast was underway.

Odysseus then bathed, and Athena crowned him with beauty head to foot, made him look taller and more massive. Facing Penelope, Odysseus said she was a strange woman, and asked what other wife would hold back from her husband after twenty years. He said that Penelope had a heart of iron, and he called the nurse to make him a bed, saying that he would sleep alone.

But Penelope put her husband to the test. She told the maid to move the sturdy bedstead out of their chamber, the room the master built with his own hands, and spread it with fleece. Odysseus blazed out in fury, saying that her words cut him to the core. Who could move the bed, he asked? He knew it could not be moved, for he had fashioned it himself. There had been an olive tree in their court, around it he had built the bedroom, then lopped off the crown of the tree, clean-cut the stump and shaped it to make their bed.

Penelope felt her knees go slack, her heart surrender. She dissolved in tears, rushed to Odysseus, flung her arms around him, and kissed him. Now that he had revealed the secret sign of their bed that no one had ever seen but the two of them and a single handmaid, the servant she had brought with her when she came from her father's house, he had conquered her hard heart at last.

Athena held back the dawn so they could have their fill of love and sleep. Then they rose. Snapping on his burnished armor, Odysseus said he must be off to the upland farm to see his father, Laertes. She must go to her lofty chamber with her women and sit tight there, see no one, and question no one.

Pallas Athena shrouded Odysseus, Telemachus, Eumaeus, and the shepherd Philoetius in darkness and quickly led them out of town.

At first Odysseus did not reveal himself to Laertes, but sought to test him. He spun a tale saying that he had met Odysseus five years earlier. Hearing this, Laertes wept, a black cloud of grief came over him and he clawed the ground. Odysseus' heart shuddered. He rushed forward and revealed himself. Laertes caught his breath and asked for a sign. Odysseus showed him the scar and then named the trees in the orchard Laertes had given him as a boy. Laertes threw his arms around his son.

They joined Telemachus, Eumaeus, and Philoetius for a meal, but in the meantime, news of the death of the suitors spread through the town and kinsmen came to collect the bodies. An assembly was called and Antinous' father rose to speak of the mortal blow that Odysseus had dealt their island people, first taking off their young men to war in Troy from which none had returned and now killing the best of their princes. He called on them all to pursue and kill Odysseus before he escaped across the sea. Then the two whom Odysseus had spared, Medon and the bard, appeared. Medon said that it was not without the help of the gods that Odysseus had slain the suitors, that he had seen Athena in the guise of Mentor there. At this news, terror gripped them all. Then an old and respected warrior spoke, saying that they had never listened to him nor to Mentor when they had urged them to stop their sons' senseless folly in besieging Penelope. But they should listen now, and not attack!

Some held fast to their seats, but some ran for their armor, with Antinous' father leading them. Athena appealed to Zeus to ask for peace, and Zeus said that now that Odysseus had taken his revenge, both sides should seal a pact that Odysseus should rule for life. They should be friends with peace and wealth cresting through the land. The gods would then purge their memories of the bloody slaughter.

Odysseus, Telemachus, Eumaeus, Philoetius, and Laertes put on their armor. Athena breathed enormous strength into Laertes. He cast his spear and hit Antinous' father, killing him. Odysseus and his gallant son charged and would have killed them all if Athena had not called on them to halt and make peace at once.

When Odysseus had visited the underworld, Tiresias told him that he must make his peace with Poseidon by traveling inland, carrying an oar on his shoulder, until he reached a people utterly ignorant of ships. When someone there failed to recognize an oar when they saw it and asked him why he was carrying a winnowing fan on his shoulder, he was to plant the oar in the ground and make an extraordinary sacrifice to Poseidon—a bull, a ram, and a boar. If he made this sacrifice, Odysseus would live to a ripe old age with all his people in blessed peace around him. Presumably Odysseus carried out these instructions.

In any case, as already mentioned, Athena handed down her pact of peace between both sides for all the years to come—and the *Odyssey* ends with the following words—"the daughter of Zeus whose shield is storm and thunder, yes, but the goddess still kept Mentor's build and voice."

Chapter 30

Who Wrote the *Iliad* and the *Odyssey?*

The *Iliad* tells the story of what happened, as we have seen, in a period of 41 days in the ninth year of the siege of Ilium beginning with the quarrel between Agamemnon and Achilles and ending with the burial of Hector. The *Odyssey* begins after the end of the war and tells the story of the ten years it took Odysseus to get home to the island of Ithaca. The *Iliad* consists of 15,693 lines of hexameter verse and the *Odyssey* of 12,109 lines. The versions that have come down to us appear to have been current in the late eighth century or early seventh century B.C., some 2,700 years ago, while the actual events took place 3,200 years ago, some 500 years or 20 to 25 generations before these versions were current.

In the case of the *Iliad*, there is evidence that epic poems once existed dealing with the events before and after the siege. In fact, two references to such poems are contained in the *Odyssey* itself. In one, Penelope breaks into tears when she hears a bard performing "The Achaeans' Journey Home From Troy." In another, during the welcome that the King of Phaeacia arranged for Odysseus in the tenth year of his journey home, a bard relates the story of the wooden horse and the conquest of Troy, and while listening Odysseus cannot hide his tears.

In any event, in the centuries following the siege, ordinary Greeks were familiar with the story of what happened before and after the events in the

Iliad whether they learned of them from poems that have been lost or by other means.

The earliest written reference to the *Iliad* and the *Odyssey* that survives is an inscription on a vase discovered on the island of Ischia off the coast of Naples and dated to before 700 B.C., some 2,700 years ago and 500 years after the siege of Troy. It seems to refer to the famous cup of Nestor described in the *Iliad*. Vases dated in the 670s B.C. have also been found with scenes from the *Odyssey*.

In various written works dated in the seventh century B.C., 2,700 years ago, there are epithets, phrases, and even half lines that are used frequently in Homer. The authors of these works may have been using tags common to epic poets, but it seems more likely they were familiar with the *Iliad* and the *Odyssey*.

Herodotus, who lived in fifth century B.C., 2,500 years ago, believed that Homer lived 400 years before his own time, which would put him in the ninth century B.C., 2,900 years ago or three hundred years after the siege. The great Homeric scholar Aristarchus of Alexandria (220 to 150 B.C.) believed that Homer lived 140 years after the Trojan War, about six or seven generations.

Everyone in ancient times believed that Homer was blind. Some thought he came from Chios; others thought it was Smyrna.

All these sources apparently believed that Homer recited the poems from memory. But the only person in ancient times who says specifically that he did so was Joseph Ben Matthias. Matthias was a Jew who played a prominent role in the Jewish rebellion against Rome and its bloody suppression by the Emperor Titus in the first century A.D. His history of those events became famous. There is only one reference in the *Iliad* to anything remotely like writing. This is in Book 6, in which Proteus, the king of Argos, sends a message instructing the person receiving it to kill the bearer. He "gave him tokens/ murderous signs, scratched in a folded tablet." But tokens and murderous signs do not really qualify as writing. Various primitive peoples, such as the American Indians, sent messages composed of pictographs drawn on animal skins, but such is not writing. The evidence is overwhelming that the Greeks and Trojans who fought the war had no knowledge of writing.

The Mycenaeans developed the Linear B syllabary, consisting of 87 signs for different combinations of consonants and vowels, as described in Chapter 12, but it was so complicated that only professional scribes could use it. In any case it was lost to humankind with the destruction of the Mycenaean civilization 3,200 years ago at about the same time as the siege of Troy.

The Greeks did not learn to write until much later, when they took over the Phoenician alphabet of 25 letters. This is how the word *alphabet* was derived. As we saw, the Phoenician words *aleph* and *beth* meant *ox* and *house*, but the Greek *alpha* and *beta* are simply the letters *a* and *b*, without meaning. The Phoenician alphabet had signs for consonants only, but the Greeks made some letters stand for vowels and so developed a system that had one letter for each sound, thus creating the first workable alphabet. The earliest examples of this Greek writing have been dated by their archaeological context to the last half of the eighth century B.C., 2,800 years ago, which is 500 years and about 25 generations after the siege of Troy.

The *Iliad* and the *Odyssey* were either recited or read at public affairs in Athens 2,200 years ago, 200 years after the first examples of Greek writing. Written copies with many variations were circulating throughout Greece in the fourth and fifth centuries B.C., 2,500 and 2,400 years ago. In Alexandria, a scholarly colony grew up that specialized in the two poems, editing and commenting upon them. Aristarchus was one of these commentators. It was these scholars who developed standardized editions.

When the *Iliad* and the *Odyssey* were first written down, it was on papyrus rolls, which could not be too big or they would break apart when opened. A long work would take as many as 24 rolls. Bernard Knox, in his introduction to Robert Fagles' translation of the *Odyssey* from which this account is drawn, suggests that it may well be that the 24 books of the *Iliad* were the result of dividing it into papyrus rolls.

Parchment is made of sheepskin, which had a longer life than papyrus. It replaced papyrus in the second to fifth centuries A.D. Folded quires of parchment sewn at the back, the codex form, replaced the rolls.

Before the ninth century A.D., the text was in freestanding capital letters without word division. After the ninth century copies were made on vellum in a cursive minuscule script that separated words and was complete with accents and breathings. This was the final phase of copying that went back to the ancient world.

After the end of the Roman Empire, knowledge of Greek was lost to Western Europeans for about 1,000 years. It was reintroduced from Byzantium in the fourteenth century. As Bernard Knox points out, this was just in time, since Byzantium fell to the Ottoman Turks in 1453.

The first printed edition of Homer was made in Florence in 1488 with type that imitated Greek handwriting. Before that Homer existed in Italy as handwritten books, which circulated for a hundred years or so before the printed edition.

In the early nineteenth century, Richard Porson produced an elegant handwritten text in Greek. This was the basis of the work edited by David Monro and Thomas Allen that was published in 1908 by the Oxford University Press. It was this version that Robert Fagles used in his translation, which this account has followed.

Some time in the centuries after the invention of writing, even those who accepted that Homer was blind began to assume that the great length of the epics and their consistency meant that they were composed in writing. The architecture of the poems is magnificent, as Bernard Knox points out, and this fact also supports the idea of a single author. In the eighteenth century, for example, Alexander Pope assumed that Homer composed the poems in writing, even if on occasion he recited them. However, in 1769, Robert Wood, an English traveler, suggested that Homer had been as illiterate as Achilles and Odysseus, and a German scholar elaborated his thesis. This launched decades of debate, for if Homer was illiterate, it was assumed that he could not possibly have composed poems as long and complicated as the *Iliad* and the *Odyssey*.

Still more puzzlements developed from the work of archeologists. Heinrich Schliemann digging at Troy and Mycenae and Sir Arthur Evans digging at Cnossos (or Knossos) discovered gold masks, bronze weapons, palaces, fortifications, and other things that were completely unknown to Greeks living at the time of Herodotus and Thucydides, but were described in Homer. So any objects found by archeologists that were described in the *Iliad* or the *Odyssey* could be dated, which was a great boon.

Another puzzlement that Knox believed had resulted from the work of archeologists is the following. Book 10, which the so-called analyst school thought was a late addition to the original poem, contains a description of a helmet made of leather, with the teeth of a boar stitched around it. But the only helmets that fit this description in the archeological record were found at Mycenaean sites earlier than those of Troy. So a very early boar-tusk helmet turns up in a passage full of linguistic forms that are very late!

And Bernard Knox points out a number of other inconsistencies. In the *Odyssey* people sometimes give dowries and sometimes demand payment for a daughter's hand, customs that actually existed many, many years apart. Cremation and inhumation, customs that were also separated by long periods of time, are practiced side by side. Ionic and Aeolic forms appear in the same line. Two horses draw the chariots, except in Book 8 and 11, where they are drawn by four. Horses are not ridden except in Book 10 and in similes, although this is not surprising since it was impossible to fight from the back of a horse without falling off until the invention of the stirrup, which did not appear in Europe until the battle of Tours in 732 A.D. at the beginning of the middle ages, when it made the armored knight possible.

Still another puzzlement is places in the poems where material has clearly been inserted at a later date. In the *Iliad*, Agamemnon sends three ambassadors to try to persuade Achilles to come back to the battle—Phoenix, Ajax, and Odysseus. But Phoenix was commander of one of the five regiments of Myrmidons, the troops under the command of Achilles. What was Phoenix doing with Agamemnon? As Bernard Knox says, what is even more puzzling is that this passage does not use verbal and adjectival forms that are plural, applying to three people, but dual, a special Greek termination system that indicates that only two people are involved. So the original text must have had only two ambassadors. As Knox points out, the conclusion is inescapable that the part concerning Phoenix was added later, in order to let him make the longest and most effective appeal to Achilles to come back to the fighting.

If a single author, such as Homer, added Phoenix to an earlier version, why did he fail to explain how Phoenix got into Agamemnon's camp and why didn't he amend the dual forms? Knox accepts the explanation that the Phoenix portion was added to a written copy that was regarded by later generations as authentic and sacrosanct, coming from the master himself. But this explanation is not very convincing. A possibility that Knox does not seem to have considered is that the passage concerning Phoenix was added by a generation of oral poets before they knew how to write but at a time when these verbal and adjectival forms were no longer contemporary, tacking it on to a text that they and their predecessors had long before committed to memory.

The language of the *Iliad* and the *Odyssey*, to sum up, is that of epic verse. It is full of archaisms, words and forms from different periods and from different stages of growth in the Greek language. As Knox says, no one except epic bards and oracular priests ever spoke that language, but this does not mean that only the elite knew Homer. Homer, Knox continues, was at once contemporary in content and antique in form, and the epics maintained their hold on ordinary Greeks by their literary quality, simplicity, speed and directness of the narrative, brilliance and excitement of the action, the greatness and humanity of the characters, and the ethical, political, and practical wisdom of their cultural tradition. Tradition had its influence even in such matters as the Olympic games, which the latter-day Greeks believed originated with the games that Achilles held at the time of Patroclus' funeral rites. Since Greek society believed it was important for children to be familiar with the two poems, Knox goes on to say, they were required in school to learn the meaning of long lists of words used in the two poems but nowhere else.

To sum up, the poems contain in an indissoluble amalgam that historically and linguistically spans many centuries. And they contain digressions, inconsistencies, and some weaknesses of construction as a result of oral recitation over many generations.

The language of the poems creates another problem. As Knox points out, the language had to fit the hexameter line of epic verse. This consists of six metrical units, which may be either dactyls (a long and two shorts) or a spondee (two longs) in the first four places but must with rare exceptions be a dactyl and a spondee in that order in the last two. The meter is based not on stress as in English, but on pronunciation time. Any word with three consecutive short syllables cannot be used. The bards chose freely among the many variations of pronunciation and among different dialects.

An American scholar, Milman Parry, who did his work in Paris in the 1920's, supplied the answer to all these puzzlements. The results were published in French and did not appear in English until 1971, when his son, Adam Parry, translated them. Milman Parry demonstrated that Homer was heir and master of a tradition of oral epic poetry that reached back over many generations and many centuries.

The so-called ornamental epithets were the key. These accompany almost every appearance of a hero, a place, or even something like a ship. Odysseus is "much enduring," "a man of many schemes," "clever," "shrewd," and "great-hearted." Ithaca is "rocky," "sea-girt," and "clear-skied." Ships are "hollow," "swift," and "well-benched." Achaeans are "long-haired," "strong-greaved," or "bronze-cloaked." Achilles is "brilliant," "godlike," or "swift-footed." Agamemnon is "lord of men," "wide-ruling," "son of Atreus." Hera is "white-armed."

Each one of the epithets offers a different metrical shape, and so the poet could choose the one that fit the meter of the particular line. The epithets provided a way to fit the names into the line in any of the usual grammatical forms they could assume. Parry demonstrated that the system was more extensive and highly organized than anyone had ever dreamed. Even more important, he showed that the system had been developed and used by oral poets who *improvised*. The fact that the poets improvised explained many of the puzzles.

The meter, not the context of the subject matter of the moment, determined the poets' choice. Bernard Knox gives as an example the incident when Calypso has been ordered by the gods to release Odysseus. She tells him he is free, but he suspects a trap. The line reads, "So she spoke, and he shuddered, much-enduring, brilliant Odysseus." Some time later, Calypso asks Odysseus how he can prefer his wife at home to her own, immortal charms. His answer is introduced by the formula, "and in answer he addressed her." But this, Knox says, requires something different from "much-enduring, brilliant Odysseus," so Odysseus becomes the "man of many schemes."

Milman Parry argued that such a system was the product of invention and refinement over generations and could only be the work of oral bards. Whole lines once honed to perfection became part of the work, and are especially noticeable in descriptions of sacrifice, communal eating, and drinking. These can be sung without effort, letting the bard concentrate on what is coming next.

An example of a whole line is "Once they'd put aside desire for food and drink" or "When they'd put aside desire for food and drink." It occurs over and over again. Another phrase that occurs very often is something of a puzzle—"wine-dark sea." What does a "wine-dark sea" look like? Is it red? Seas may be gray, green, or blue, but who has ever seen a sea that was red?

In Paris, Parry met scholars who had studied bards still living in Yugoslavia who were illiterate and who improvised. So he made a trip there to study them first-hand. Interestingly, none of the people puzzling over the possibility of illiterate bards reciting from memory mention what Henry Creswicke Rawlinson had to say on the subject in 1786. As we saw in Chapter 14, he noted that the Sanscrit Vedic hymns had been committed to writing very early but that countless generations of illiterate Brahmin monks continued to recite them monotonously for 25 centuries with remarkable accuracy, long after Sanscrit had died as a spoken tongue. Rawlinson speculated that towards the end the Brahmin monks probably did not understand very much of what they were reciting.

So the epithets were created to meet the demands of dactylic hexameter, to give the improvising bard different ways of fitting the god, hero, or whatever into the hexameter line. When strong-greaved Achaeans doesn't fit, they become long-haired Achaeans. In the genitive case, they have to be "bronze-cloaked." The system was the product of refinement, invention, and elimination of superfluities over generations of oral bards.

But the most important point of Parry's work was that the poet did not have to recite these long, long passages from memory. He improvised along known lines, relying on a huge stock of formulaic phrases, lines, and even whole scenes, especially those dealing with eating and with arming before going into battle. The outline remains the same, but every time the bard does it, he does it differently. The poem is new every time it is performed.

So Homer's poetry is the culmination of a long tradition of oral composition. Formulas are retained or rejected for their usefulness in improvisation. Small wonder that Aeolic and Ionic forms appear in the same line, that a Mycenaean boar-tusk helmet can turn up in a passage of very late linguistic forms, that people sometimes give dowries and sometimes demand payment for their daughter's hand, that cremation and inhumation occur not centuries apart as the custom changes but side by side. If the singer improvised it is no accident that reflections on reality contemporary to the singer also creep into the text, especially in the similes. The result is the unhistorical amalgam of customs, objects, and linguistic forms that are found in the Homeric text.

Although Homer was the heir to an oral tradition and although there was no writing in his lifetime, writing occurred soon after. But even if writing did overlap somewhat, the early writing was too cumbersome to permit dictation. Writing in Greece in the early days was free-standing capitals, crudely and laboriously formed, written from right to left on one line and from left to right on the next. Scribes could hardly have taken dictation. As Knox said, one critic conjured up a picture of Homer dictating the first half line of the *Iliad*, "*Mênin aeide thea.* You got that?"

The most logical conclusion is that Homer inherited an oral tradition, that he reworked it with his genius, that his version was admired and imitated, and that within a relatively few generations after he lived the poems were written down much as he had sung them.

There are also a few other points that should be clarified. One is that both the *Iliad* and the *Odyssey* are full of vivid descriptions of bloodshed. "Menelaus hacked Pisander between the eyes, the bridge of the nose, and bone cracked, blood sprayed and both eyes dropped at his feet to mix in the dust—he curled and crashed. Digging a heel into his chest Menelaus stripped his gear." And in another place, "speared him between the genitals and the navel—hideous wound, the worst the god of battles deals to wretched men." But the generations of Greeks who enjoyed the two poems were clearly not put off by the vivid descriptions of bloodshed, but seemed to enjoy them.

Another interesting matter is the references to iron. The Iron Age is reckoned to have begun about 2,700 years ago, some 500 years after the siege of Troy, but iron was known at the time of Troy and was available in small quantities. In the *Iliad* and the *Odyssey*, it is mentioned several times in similes, such as "heart of iron." One of the arrows that the Trojan archer, Pandarus, used had an iron arrowhead. In the games that Achilles held after the death of Patroclus, he offered a bar of iron as the prize for weight throwing. Some of the battle-axes that were lined up in the test to see if the suitors could use Odysseus' bow were iron. And earlier in the *Odyssey* Athena posed as a friend of Odysseus who had stopped at Ithaca to visit on his way to exchange a "cargo" of iron for bronze. But iron was not plentiful, and "cargo" does not mean a shipload. When iron is mentioned in the *Iliad* and the *Odyssey*, it is as a precious metal—e.g., "gleaming."

Iron is not suitable for weapons. Cast iron is brittle and apt to shatter, so it is useless as a sword or spear. Wrought or worked iron does not shatter, but since it cannot hold an edge anywhere near as well as bronze, it is equally unsuited for swords and spears. Just what its utility was as a battle-axe is a matter of speculation. Combining iron with carbon to make a form of steel that would hold an edge was not yet known, and it was only when the technique was developed of adding carbon to iron that iron in the form of steel replaced bronze for weapons.

Another interesting aspect is hospitality in the Greek world. The Greeks at the time of the *Iliad* and the *Odyssey* put a high value on hospitality. Menelaus and Helen welcomed Paris. After the war when the two were back in Sparta, they also welcomed Telemachus. Almost everywhere that Odysseus went he was welcomed. So the exceptions were all the more horrible, like the one-eyed, giant Cyclops who seized and ate several of Odysseus's men and the huge, ugly queen of Laestrygonia, whose husband seized and ate another. Hospitality was part of the culture, and it was in everyone's self interest. Otherwise, no one in those dangerous times would have dared travel. Also, little news of the outside world came into their isolated communities and those communities provided rather meager entertainment. A guest brought both news and entertainment. It is understandable that so many hosts kept their guests longer than the guests wanted to stay. The Greek aphorism "Welcome the coming, and speed the parting guest" was not universally honored.

Still another point that needs clarifying is the attitude of later Greeks towards the old myths. Edith Hamilton, the great translator of Greek myths, says that by the last part of the fifth century B.C., 2,500 years ago, the old myths had begun to lose their hold on people's minds. To illustrate she tells the story of Socrates on a stroll with Phaedrus near the spot where the myths relate that the North Wind had carried away a girl with whom the North Wind had fallen in love. Phaedrus asks Socrates if he believed the story, and Socrates replies that the wise were doubtful and "I should not be singular if I too doubted."

The inconsistency of Zeus, the protector of strangers, in suggesting to Poseidon that he turn the Phaeacian ship and its crew to stone along with blocking the harbor with a mountain apparently bothered a number of the ancients. Aristophanes changed three letters in the Greek to make Zeus say, "Do *not pile* a mountain." There is no record that says anything about Aristophanes' motive in any of the changes he made, except that he was a stickler for decorum on the part of royalty. He changed the text so that Nausicaa had the maids bring the laundry to the wagon, not herself. Princesses do not carry their own laundry.

Chapter 31

With a Bang or a Whimper?

How does it all end? With a bang or a whimper? The universe may continue the expansion that began with the Big Bang for as long as humankind can see ahead. Or it may reverse itself and contract, although this is uncertain and probably not true. Humankind has existed for only 50,000 years; the Earth has existed for 4.6 billion years and life began on it 3.8 billion years ago. The universe has existed for about 14 billion years.

In either case, time will not be a problem. Two things have changed very recently that have made an enormous difference in our capacity to analyze. One, as noted earlier, is the invention of the electronic computer. It has vastly changed the way people work and the results of their work. It can perform calculations in less than a second that would take more than 10,000 lifetimes of human calculation.

The other is DNA. Also, as noted earlier, DNA is unique to each individual. If a drop of blood is left at the scene of a crime, the criminal will be identified without any shadow of a doubt.

Smallpox has been eliminated completely, although criminal elements may succeed in stealing some from the tiny stores maintained in Russia and the United States. So has infantile paralysis. Leprosy and tuberculosis can now be treated without isolating the patient. Soon we can eliminate all the diseases that are caused by some faulty organ or one that has been damaged—a liver, a lung, or a gut. Even now, all four arteries to the heart are being replaced with a piece of vein from the leg. More than that, a whole heart has been replaced with counterfeit material. Breasts can be removed. Diabetes can be fantastically reduced by modest changes—eating a low-fat diet, 150 minutes of moderate exercise, and reducing weight by about 15 pounds. Measles and influenza are not the terrors they were. In the face of modern drugs, bubonic plague, typhus, diphtheria, cholera, and scarlet fever have all become relatively subdued. Cancer is more complicated, but even it is becoming more controllable. AIDS and a few other diseases are still puzzles, but in the not too distant future, these, too, will be conquered.

Humankind may snuff out its life before seeing the end of some essential element. Or it may see the end of that element, and be unable to do anything about it. An example might be ozone. Ultra-violet light, which is emitted from the Sun in great quantities, is hostile to life. However, although oxygen atoms are normally found in pairs (O_2), some exist in threes (O_3) to form ozone, and ozone serves as a shield that protects the Earth's surface from most ultra-violet light.

A huge comet that humankind has not yet learned to divert might collide with the Earth. Humankind might so pollute the Earth that it becomes uninhabitable. A volcanic eruption can occur that will wipe out a large proportion of humanity.

At a certain stage, some four billion years from now, the Sun will reach the end of its seemingly vast array of hydrogen. It will greatly expand in size, covering the Earth and killing all living things. Then it will contract to become a neutron star, occupying only a tiny fraction of the space it did before. As already mentioned, a neutron star is very dense. Its gravity is 10^{12} times that of the Earth.

In the meantime, humans with computers should be able to manipulate the environment almost in any way they wish. The discovery of clones and with them ways to manipulate life itself boggles the mind. Humankind might be able to develop some new forms of life.

In our galaxy, the Milky Way, life will take every form that it has in our own little world—from dinosaurs to birds—and many other forms. Any one of these may develop intelligence, so intelligent life can take many forms. It could develop from some form of insect. It is very unlikely that intelligent life will look anything like us.

What will happen after humankind learns how to change itself? Humankind will learn how to do this, of course. Some humans will even be content with being a brain, with no way to get from one place to another. In any case, the form that humans will take will vary enormously.

There is another possibility. We are now on the verge of being able to manipulate the human form. There are now some 30,000 to 40,000 genes that produce human traits and a number of others that are merely along for the ride. Once we determine which are which we can begin to manipulate them.

Sports are one field that could be affected by such manipulation. We may be able to produce fantastically better football, baseball, and basketball players. But that gives us pause. What will play be like when the football players are all 500 beautiful pounds, the baseball players are all marvelous hitters, and the basketball players are all 12 feet tall? Sports as we know them are likely to disappear.

What about music? This is more difficult. It is no accident that the greatest works were composed in the sixteenth, seventeenth, and eighteenth centuries and that centuries that followed saw fewer of these great works. It may be that the athletes are more talented, bred to the task, while the composers are limited by the nature of music.

What about art? It may be that artists will develop ever more abstract forms of art, Picasso-like, that deal more and more with imaginary forms. It will be difficult to tell a true abstraction from a fake.

What about science? Humankind could learn about how to do almost anything that would be supported by the nature of the world. Such knowledge would permit humankind to do fantastic things. But they would still be limited by the nature of the world. A human being could not send a message faster than the speed of light.

What about sex? It, too, could be improved. A climax could last longer. It could be more intense.

Remember, *Homo sapiens sapiens* are a very recent development—nine percent of all humans are alive today.

Humankind could migrate to a suitable planet orbiting some relatively nearby star. It is simply not conceivable that humankind could even dream of reaching any place in another universe. It will be extraordinarily difficult to reach another planet in our own universe. Living space would be needed for at least fifty couples. A dozen or so nearby planets would be picked. It would still take about 50 generations to reach the nearest of these.

The groups would have to be prepared to fight a less well-organized group, but it is extremely doubtful if a society would be encountered that would be capable of fighting or even willing to fight. More likely the society would be grossly inferior or grossly superior. The incoming group would find itself like the Polynesians among the Moa in New Zealand, able to come up to a native and be regarded with no more than curiosity. Or the newcomers would be welcomed as an inferior race that could be communicated with and regarded as a new, remarkable, and delightful addition to life.

Among astronomers there is a growing belief that our universe abounds in stars with planetary systems like ours. One scientist, Dr. Debra Fisher, says that recent discoveries imply "that planets can form more easily than we ever imagined and that our Milky Way is teeming with planetary systems."

A space ship designed to find new planets could find about 2,400 new ones, including perhaps 100 that might have a size and solid surface like Earth's. But the point to be remembered is sobering. Humankind is a fleeting phenomenon. It has existed for only 50 generations. Why would anyone want to engage in a project that would mean confinement for 49 generations on the off chance that the fiftieth might find something at the end? It is but a tiny fraction of the multitude of life forms possible. The number of planets suitable for life forms of all kinds in all the universes has been estimated at 100,000,000,000,000,000,000. For example, Abel 881 examined a cluster 73 galaxies each containing 200 billion stars, and all of them fit into no more than one quarter of diameter of the moon.

The Milky Way, our own galaxy, has been estimated to have about 100 billion stars. Planets may be lurking around about half of these. The number seems huge. But it is no more than a very, very small accident in the vastness of our universe alone. Even when we solve the problems of sending a space ship the vast distance even within our own galaxy, it might take 50 generations to reach another "Earth." This is as long as human beings have existed. Even if some group decided on the project, in 50 generations one generation at least would decide on something different.

The most that can be hoped for is that a message can be received confirming the existence of another race. But nothing more.

Index

A

Aborigines 146-7
Aborigines, Australian 218
Accelerator mass spectrometry 98
Achaeans 328
Acheulean tools 122
Achilles 312, 314–5, 319–20, 321–4, 336, 344, 348–9
Achilles heel 314
Aeneas 318, 324
Afro-Asiatic. 129
Agamemnon 312, 314–20, 322, 325–6, 330, 335, 344, 348–9
Agassiz, Louis 233
Aguinaldo, Emilio 231–2
AIDS 91
Ajax 322, 330
Akbar 165, 166
Akkadian 129, 139
Alfred, King 265, 273
Algonquin 191, 198
Kober, Alice 139
Allen, Thomas 347
Alphabet Writing 141
alphabetic writing 142
Altaic 130
Alvarez, Luis 75
Alvarez, Walter 75
American Indians 187, 189-90
    alcohol and 195; diseases of 194;
    female infanticide among 196
American Revolution 209
Amerind 131
An Lu-shan 183
Ancient Egyptian 129
anthropoids 98
Aomori site 248
Apaches 205
Aphrodite 313, 317, 318, 319, 324, 325
apocryphal Gospels 309

Apollo 315–6, 321, 333, 337, 339
Arabic 129
Arago Man 112
Aramaic 129
Aramaic alphabet 141
Arawak Indians 194
Archaic Homo sapiens 111
Archbishop of Canterbury 273
Ardipithecus 99
Ardipithecus ramidus kadabba 99
argon-argon 98
Ariadne 335
Aristarchus of Alexandria 345–6
Aristarchus of Samos 23
Arjuna, Prince 301
Ark, Noah's 233–4
Aryan 158, 292, 294, 303
asthenosphere 73
Athelstan 265
Athena 316, 318–9, 321, 324–5, 327–9, 331, 336, 338, 340, 342, 352
atl atl 119
Atreus 325, 326
Aubrey Holes 286, 287, 291
au-neutrino 30
Aurangzeb 166
Australian 130
Australoid 145
Australopithecines 99, 102, 105, 107, 113, 125–6
Australopithecus 99, 106
Australopithecus (Paranthropus) aethiopicus 107, 108
Australopithecus (Paranthropus) boisei 105, 107, 108
Australopithecus (Paranthropus) robustus 105, 107, 108
Australopithecus afarensis 106–8, 110
Australopithecus africanus 105, 108
Australopithecus anamensis 99

E

E = M C² 34, 38, 39, 43
Earl of Mercia 271
Earl of Northumberland 271
Earl of Northumbria 271
Earl of Wessex 271
Neolithic 133
East India Company 168, 169
economic feudal system 281
Edgar the Atheling 270, 279
Edward the Confessor 269, 270-1
Edwin 271
Einar 93
Einstein, Albert 11-3, 18, 19, 20, 33, 36,
    37, 41, 46, 48, 52, 53, 54, 57, 61;
    theory of special relativity 18, 40;
    theory of general relativity 35, 49
elativistic quantum field theory 40
electromagnetic force 31
electromagnetic wave 37
electromagnetism 33
electron-neutrino 30
electrons 21, 28
Ella of Northumbria, King 264
Ellis, Richard 60
Emma 269, 270, 271
Eosimias 98
equivalence principle 17, 35
Erastothenes 16
Erik the Red 267
Erikson, Leif 267
Escale 122
Eskimo-Aleut 130, 131, 151, 187
Eskimos 149, 174, 186, 188, 198
Española 194
etak 227
Ethelred 270
Ethelred the Unready 269
ether 17
Etruscan 135
Euclid 16
eukaryotes 84, 89
Europa 85, 88
Eustace of Boulogne 277-9
Evans, Sir Arthur 138, 139, 140, 347
Ewing, Maurice 70
extinction, role of human beings in 189

F

Fagles, Robert 315, 346-7
Faroes 266
Felderhof Cave 117
Fermi National Laboratory 26
fermions 46-8
Fertile Crescent 239, 241, 242, 243, 250
Filipinos 216
Finnegan's Wake 29
fire, first use of 122
Fisher, Debra 357
Fitch, Val 60
Five Dynasties period 183
Flood, The 234, 243
Folsom point 187
Fosna folk 249
Freedman, Wendy L. 20
Friedman, Alexander 54
Frolov, Boris A. 132
Fyrd 273, 274, 276, 281

G

Galen 16
Galileo, Galilei 17, 69
Gamow, George 21
Gandhi, Mohandas K. 172-3
Ganesh 293, 295, 296, 302
Garraty, John A. 162
gauge bosons 46
Gauls 256
Gay, Peter 162
Genome project, The 91
genus Homo, 106
George Gamow 21
Germer, Lester 38
Ghuri, Muhammad 164
Gibraltar 80
Gibson, Kathleen 127
Gilgamesh 236
Glob, P. V. 255
gluon 31, 40, 43, 46
gluon field 29
Godwin of Essex 270, 280
Godwinson, Harold 271
Gokstad ship 259, 260, 261, 262
Golden Fleece 234
gorillas 99
Gould, Stephen Jay 88, 98
Gratian, Emperor 307

Y

Z